NAR *The emphasis of NAR #4 is on American politics. This is occasioned, in part, by the election season, though our material does not deal directly with the candidates, campaign issues, and so forth. The purpose of NAR is not to tell and foretell the political news, but, instead, to carry on what one reviewer called the "dialogue between public concern and private imagination." It requires no partisan position to recognize that the mood of this dialogue today is likely to be grim, if not desperate. The business-as-usual mentality that seems likely now to prevail in both major parties (this is being written shortly after the assassination of Senator Kennedy) may mask this mood but cannot dismiss it. For politics is not only what the politicians, columnists, and pollsters tell us it is; that is only the surface, and often one of manipulated illusions. Politics is also the spreading shadow that lies athwart intelligent consciousness, heart, and conscience: this is what our writers tend to see and it is no more illusory or dismissable than the shadow in a chest X ray.*

There is, first of all, Robert Coover's extraordinary fantasy, "The Cat in the Hat for President," which conveys the ominous drift of the electoral process toward the brink of absurdity. The tactics and antics of the Cat as a runaway Presidential candidate go well beyond being another spoof of the hoopla that attends the choice of our national leader. The career of the Cat, with his mystical platform of "Voom!" reveals a society poised precariously between malaise and apocalypse, its show-biz politics merely another symptom of the malady produced by the national diet of hypocrisy seasoned with fantasy. Supplementing Mr. Coover's story is Conor Cruise O'Brien's essay, "Politics as Drama as Politics," which describes the natural connections between statecraft and stagecraft and then forcefully points out how the excessive use of dramatic means to mold public opinion and support is turning the American republic into what Ruskin called "a certain polluted theatrocracy."

Such politics breed "alienation"—a term that had a few years ago grown empty of content but that is now filling again with fresh meaning and experience. In his essay, "The Night Is Dark and I Am Far from Home," Eric Bentley restates the historical implications of the term in religious and literary, as well as political, contexts; he then goes on to explore the dangers and opportunities confronting the diverse legions of Americans who are presently seeking "a home from home." The private life of two such young people is the theme of Alan Lelchuk's long story, "Of Our Time": a finely observed study of an affair between an unsolid citizen of the academy and a "freaked-out" mother of two. Several other stories such as George Stiles' poignant letter from a Negro girl who has drifted into jail, Russell Banks' "The Drive Home," a subtle study of an intellectual's anomie and cruelty, Alan Distler's hard-edged sketch of a fragmented family—all speak to the general mood of randomness and contactlessness, to the kind of psychic underground of a society that is increasingly more complex, empty, and prone to violence. Much the same can be said of David Henderson's two poems from the streets of Harlem, of Charles Wright's "Bayonet Training," of Marilyn Coffey's "Wordlessly," among other poems.

This is not to say that opposition, cynicism, drift, and brutality furnish the only themes of contemporary writing, or that contemporary politics and the consciousness thereof provide their only motive. There is plenty of evidence from all sides that the verities and velleities of liberal humanism have commanded little interest or trust for sometime now. One of the revelations of Mordecai Richler's memoir of Paris in the early fifties is that of the casual but almost inevitable way in which the exuberant nihilism of these young writers, bred on the pop culture of the thirties and forties and enamored of Céline, formed the basis for the black humour of the sixties. Amy Goldin's essay on "Deep Art and Shallow Art" provides a closely reasoned analysis of the shrinkage of the extremes between the two by the interposing of a style that refuses to moralize experience. Richard Gilman's "The True and Only Crisis of the Theater" takes up still another chapter in the natural history of post-bourgeois and post-humanistic sensibility.

There is other material in NAR #4 which is related only marginally, if at all, to this general perspective. The "private imagination" still has its own imperatives and options. But the overall tone of crisis in the "dialogue" is unmistakable and—given the grounds of "public concern" today—virtually inescapable.   TS

NUMBER 4

New American Review

PUBLISHED BY THE NEW AMERICAN LIBRARY
NEW YORK AND TORONTO · THE NEW ENGLISH
LIBRARY LIMITED, LONDON

NEW AMERICAN REVIEW

EDITOR: THEODORE SOLOTAROFF
POETRY EDITOR: STANLEY MOSS
ASSISTANT EDITOR: NANCY HARDIN

EDITORIAL COMMITTEE:
Edward T. Chase, Mary Corey, Nina Finkelstein, Robert Gut-
willig, Robert Haynie, Katharine Kidde, Thomas McCormack,
Patrick O'Connor, Jean Read, Marcia Seligson, James Trupin

Art Director: William Gregory
Editorial Assistant: Michael Seidman
Production Associates: Irene Kask, Terence McCabe

First Printing, August, 1968

Library of Congress Catalog Card Number: 67–27377

NEW AMERICAN REVIEW is published in the United
States by The New American Library, Inc., 1301 Avenue of the
Americas, New York, New York 10019; in Canada by The New
American Library of Canada Limited, 295 King Street East, To-
ronto 2, Ontario; in the United Kingdom by The New English
Library Limited, Barnard's Inn, Holborn, London, E.C. 1, Eng-
land · Copyright © 1968 by The New American Library, Inc.
· All rights reserved · Printed in the United States of America ·

The editors invite submissions. Manuscripts will not be returned
unless accompanied by stamped, self-addressed envelope.

CONTENTS

The Cat in the Hat
for President

Robert Coover

Wнy do you sit there like that?" asked the Cat in the Hat.

We stared back at him. The sonuvabitch was unconscious.

> "Lift your chin
> Out of your shoes!
> We will win
> And they will lose!"

Ned held the phone receiver like a club, glared at the Cat, his temples throbbing. What in August and September had looked like the political upset of the century, had by mid-October become a total disaster, not only for our party, but for the nation as well.

> "Some news is glad,
> Some news is sad,
> I do not think—"

"Shove it," snapped Joe. Ned dropped the phone receiver to its cradle with a bang. Our party's moderates and liberals, so-called, my men Riley and Boone among them, had just pulled out, leaving us stranded, to form a rump group in support of the Opponent. It was a move almost unprecedented in the history of American politics. So was the more serious threat that lay behind it.

Sam, pacing, paused to clap one hand to the Cat's shoulder and suggest quietly that he go for a walk or take a nap or something. But the Cat remained, grinning foolishly. Sam shrugged, resumed his pacing.

I watched Clark. Clark watched us. Benignly, hugely, over thin hands folded just under his eyes. He more than anyone had brought us to this strange crisis. Yet he betrayed no surprise, no solutions, no remorse.

Joe took a hard drag on his cigarette, ground it out savagely in an ashtray. "Well, we've gotta think of something and damn quick," he snapped.

The Cat doffed his Hat and out popped a Something that commenced to dash preposterously around the room. Infuriated, Ned leaped up and stomped on it. *"Get your silly ass outa here!"* he screamed at the Cat, and kicked him out the door. Ned was an affable guy, circumspect and deferential. His reckless boot in the butt of our party's nominee for the next President of the United States of America only showed how bad things really were.

I could have said, I told you so, but it was no time for that either. Nor for that matter was it necessary. It was clear they all remembered my early opposition—an opposition that had nearly cost me my job—remembered it and now counted it as wisdom, for much of the decision-making was falling on my shoulders again. "Your ball, Sooth," Joe said. Given the nature of the decisions that lay ahead, I can't say I was all that happy about it.

In truth, my original objections to the Cat in the Hat had been of a merely practical sort. I'd been convinced from the outset of the impossibility of unseating the incumbent party this year: a war was on and the nation was prosperous. As I saw it, our job was to build for the elections four years hence, and I accepted the National Chairmanship of the party in that spirit. I was convinced we had to strengthen and enlarge the center to win, and therefore sought the nomination of a solid middle-of-the-roader with an uncontroversial record, a man whose carefully controlled candidacy this year would lay the groundwork for his election four years later.

Moreover, even had we, not they, been the party in power, the Opponent would have been a tough man to beat. Born in a small Midwestern town of middle-class parents, reared and educated in the Southwest, known to have considerable holdings and influence in the Eastern Establishment, a poker buddy of several Southern Senators, progressive and city-oriented yet bluntly individualistic and rural in manner, rugged, shrewd, folksy, taciturn yet gregarious, a member of everything from SANE and the NAACP to the American Legion, Southern Baptists, and the National Association of Manufacturers, a chameleon personality who could project the faces of Chairman of the Board, Sheriff, Sunday Duffer, Private Eye, Young Man on the Go, Cracker-barrel Philosopher, Lion-tamer, Dad, Quarterback, Country Gentleman, City Lawyer, Good Sport, Field General, Swinger, and the Guy Next Door, all in one three-minute TV sequence, the Opponent was, in short, a natural. Of course, as Clark was to point out and the Cat to demonstrate, he was not without serious failings, what man is? But when I took over in early spring as the minority party's National Chairman, it was generally conceded he was a shoo-in. Later, at their Convention, a young soft-spoken Harvard-educated New York Congressman was chosen as his running mate. Beautiful. Christ, how I envied them!

There are risk-takers in politics, bold men who wait their chance, then go for broke, latent Hotspurs suddenly gunning for immortality with the intensity and single-mindedness of an assassin or a saint. I'm proud to say I'm not one of them. My life in business and politics has been long, successful, and colorless. I have been, among other things, a state senator and treasurer, a U.S. Congressman, an undersecretary in the Department of Commerce, and Ambassador to Costa Rica, but most of my political life has been spent —in and around business—working quietly for the party. I could no longer count the number of ad hoc committees I've chaired, closed sessions swayed, anonymous tasks performed. Without headlines, without glory—though not without honor. It was a tribute to my effectiveness that the press, upon receiving news of my appointment, merely took it for granted. MR. BROWN NAMED PARTY HEAD.

Theoretically, politics is all issues: the word used to describe the conflicts arising in men's efforts to suffer one another. But practically, of course, there are no issues in politics at all. Not even ideological species. "Liberal," "conservative," "left," "right," these are mere fictions of the press, metaphoric conventions to which politicians sooner or later and in varying ways adapt. Politics in a republic is a complex pattern of vectors, some fixed and explicable, some random, some bullish, some inchoate and permutable, some hidden and dynamic, others celebrated though flagging, usually collective, sometimes even cosmic—and a politician's job is to know them and ride them. So instinctive has my perception of the kinetics of politics been, so accurate my forecasts of election outcomes, I have come to be known jocularly as Soothsayer Brown among my colleagues, or, more spitefully, Gypsy.

I even foresaw, many campaigns ago, what most men cannot: my own electoral defeat—foresaw it, accepted it, and then willingly took on the scapegoat's role by espousing a number of unpopular minority views to help broaden the party's base. I've been called a "liberal" in the media ever since: I! who own twenty suits, all in obscure shades of brown, and who in over forty years of eating in restaurants of every category and cuisine have yet to order anything except hamburger steak, charred to a crisp. You see, I am blessed—or damned, as you will—with puffy pink lips. They helped me to win my seat in the House of Representatives, just as later they helped me to lose it. My short stature, round belly, smooth pink scalp, anonymous name, and occasionally irascible temper no doubt contributed, but mainly it was the fat lips. By thrusting the lower one forward, I was able to project a marvelous complexion of self-righteous anger, a kind of holy Bible-belting zeal for judgment, which complemented nicely the central issue, so-called, of my winning campaign: an attack on my incumbent opponent's corruption. That wonderful pout did me little service, however, in defending myself against the same attacks two years later. Of course, there were many factors, many vectors, but the fat lips were decisive. "Greatness" in American politics has always been associated with thin lips—some obscure racial or iconic bias, no doubt—and there was nothing I could do about it. I predicted my young tight-lipped challenger would take 56 percent of the vote; he won 56.4 percent.

And so, many years, many engagements, many auguries later, now chairmaning my party and confronting an apparently invincible Opponent, publically proclaiming an upset victory in November, whoever our candidate might be, but privately seeking a candidate to fit the probable vectors of the campaign four years hence, I could only react with bitterness and frustration to the Convention-floor move by a clutch of zany young turks to nominate the Cat in the Hat.

Every man has his weakness and I have mine: my own failing, as perhaps you've already noticed, is a limited sense of humor. It has flawed my campaigns, curtailed my diplomatic career, been the blind spot in my perception of political dynamics. Rationally, I accept the idea that life is at best a game, yet my nature is serious and fiercely competitive: I fight to win and couldn't help it if I would. The Cat in the Hat campaign buttons appeared the second day of the National Convention, provoking a general merriment. As the laughter mounted, I grew uneasy, then irritable, finally incensed. Not until the Convention was nearly over —and then only thanks to Clark—did I discover the significance of that laughter. Soothsayer or no, I was the last to embrace the Cat and wear the badge.

Not only, you see, had I succeeded in finding the ideal candidate for my long-range plans, I had found two: a spirited Irish Protestant from Boston named Riley, and a tall lantern-jawed Westerner named Boone, direct descendant of the romantic frontiersman. I delight in the illusion of democracy in action, not only because it wins votes, but also for its own sake. An open contest between two well-chosen candidates is a great entertainment, an exciting relaxation from the real work of politics. There are risks, of course, especially in intraparty matches such as the one I was arranging. A deadlock could occur, for example, bringing about the nomination of a dark horse—or a dark cat, to speak to our case. But, given the virtual inevitability of losing the elections this year, even that possibility did not seem entirely undesirable: Riley and Boone would get all the pre-Convention publicity, one of them would probably be the Vice-Presidential candidate, the dark-horse Presidential contestant would bear the onus of defeat, and my two men would again be going for the top spot four years later, then as seasoned and respected veterans. So I organized support teams for them in all fifty states, secured sizable campaign funds for each, through friendly media outlets elevated them from anonymity to world fame almost overnight, encouraged and directed their participation in selected state primaries, brought them onto the Convention floor in a final rush of electoral fever, drama, and glory— and all for nothing. Once the Cat took over, they somehow looked like fools.

"I CAN LEAD IT ALL BY MYSELF" was the legend on the Cat's campaign buttons. His button portrait was the familiar one: tall floppy red-and-white striped hat, red bow tie, white-gloved hands clasped decorously over his chest, thumbs pressed together, grinning that idiot grin (though thin-lipped, I had to admit). The Cat in the Hat himself did not at first appear. His madcap explosion on the scene was engineered—apparently at least—by Joe and Ned, a couple of maverick Midwesterners whose techniques were as fresh as they were amateurish. Only several hysterical hours later was I to meet the real spirit behind the coup: a luminous ingenious pear-shaped mass named Clark.

The first day went as I'd planned, with plenty of fanfare, good food and drink, back-slapping and vote-trading, stirring speeches, the usual Convention hoopla—though admittedly it was all a little hollow, beclouded with the factuality of being the party out of power and little or no hope of getting in. The only hint of something out of order was the slogan that appeared on toilet walls and crept oddly into conversations: "Let's make the White House a Cat House." But the next morning, into the hotel breakfast rooms throughout the city, Joe and Ned, dressed like the Cat in striped hat, bow tie, and gloves, came shuffling, doing a soft-shoe to their "Cat in the Hat Campaign Song":

It is no time for no, it is time for yes!
It is time to elect our candidate!
Here is the Cat who will clean up the mess:
The Cat in the Hat for the Head of State!

So go to bat for the Cat in the Hat!
He's the Cat who knows where it's at!
With Tricks and Voom and Things like that!
Go! Go! The Cat in the Hat!

It is no time to fear, it is time to cheer!
It is time to play on your instrument!
The New Day is near, the New Way is here!
The Cat in the Hat for President!

So go to bat for the Cat in the Hat!
He's the Cat who knows where it's at!
With Tricks and Voom and Things like that!
Go! Go! The Cat in the Hat!

They passed out buttons, introduced the Cat-Call (*Me-You!*), and yak-yakked their way through a cornball vaudeville routine with such awful gags as:

NED: Hello!

JOE: Hello!

NED: I called you up to say hello!

JOE: Hello!

NED: I said hello! Can you hear me, Joe?

JOE: (*aside*): My God! And this is what they call the hot line!

NED: Hello?

JOE (*aside*): The balloon going up, nuclear missiles on the launching pads, aimed at all the major capitals of the world, sirens screaming, and the President gets a wrong number . . .

NED: Hello, HELLO!

JOE (*aside*): Or a party line . . .

NED: Yes, that's what I'm calling about, Mr. Joe!

JOE: What, bad numbers?

NED: No, that's the *other* party, Mr. Joe! I'm talking about *our* new party line!

JOE: What line is that, Mr. Ned?

NED: Why, a *Fe*-line, Mr. Joe! I'm talking about the next President of the United States!

JOE: The next President! Who's that, Mr. Ned?

NED: Why, it's the Cat in the Hat!

JOE: I'm sorry, Mr. Ned, I didn't get your predicate . . . ?

NED: A pretty cat? Well, no, he ain't so pretty, Mr. Joe, but he's got a lotta *pussy-nality!*

Or:

NED: Say, Mr. Joe, our nation has got *cat* problems!

JOE: How do you mean, *cat* problems, Mr. Ned? Can you make me a list?

NED: Make you a *list?* Why, Mr. Joe, I'll make you a *catty*-log!

JOE *smiles at the audience guffaws and issues the Cat-Call.*

NED: I mean, things is catty-clysmic, Mr. Joe. They are catty-plectic, catty-strophic, and all cattywamptious!

JOE: That bad, hunh? Well, what're we gonna do about it, Mr. Ned?

NED: Well, Mr. Joe, I say you gotta send a cat in to do a cat's job.

JOE: Send a cat in to do a cat's job? How do you mean, Mr. Ned?

NED: Well, Mr. Joe, supposing *your* house was full of rats, what would *you* do?

JOE: Unh-hunh, I think I see what you mean, Mr. Ned! The Cat in the Hat for President sounds like a good idea . . .

NED: It's not just a good idea, Mr. Joe—it's a *catty-gorical im-purr-ative!*

JOE *and* NED *sing the "Cat in the Hat Campaign Song" while passing out buttons, then soft-shoe out.*

By evening my beautifully planned Convention had turned into something of a circus. Regardless of political commitments, nearly everyone had taken to singing the Cat in the Hat song and, even alongside their other pins, to wearing the Cat button—I even caught my man Riley with one of the damned things on. On the toilet walls: "What This Nation Needs Is More Pussy!" And sure enough, at the banquet that night, in pranced a hundred gorgeous milk-fed Midwestern co-eds, dressed in tight elastic catskins, wearing the goofy hat, bow tie, and gloves, leaping in and out of laps and licking faces, sending up a delicious caterwaul of *Me-You's.* The new gimmick of the night was a miniature replica of the Cat's Hat with an elastic band for fastening under the chin—when you squeezed the Hat, it emitted the Cat-Call. "Keep it under your Hat!" the girls purred as they passed them out, then whisked away, twirling their tails. For some reason, everyone kept grinning at me, apparently conjecturing that I'd arranged the whole gag, and since I still wasn't sure just what was up, I grinned along with them, returned their winks, even —though only one time—squeezed the silly Hat.

The Cat in the Hat himself appeared a day later right in the middle of my man Boone's big parade and rally, breaking it up. It's against tradition for a candidate to appear on the Convention floor before his final nomination. It's against all propriety to intrude on another candidate's rally. And the Cat's performance itself was against every standard of Convention-floor behavior, not to say all probability. But that damned Cat couldn't care less—in fact, this balmy flaunting of the rules of the game was to become the pattern, if not in fact the message, of his whole Presidential campaign.

Boone, a Californian, had been nominated by the Governor of Kentucky, with handsome seconds from Alaska, Virginia, California, and Idaho. I was delighted. His symbols were coonskin caps (Boone-skins, his supporters were calling them) and b'ar guns (in fact, before politics, he'd been a chemist and later vice-president of one of the nation's largest pharmaceutical companies, had never had any kind of gun in his hands before in his life); his slogans: "Explore the moon with Boone!" and "We want Boone *soon!*" A thousand frenetic, hollering, coonskin-capped, placard- and flag-waggling, bull-roaring, Madison Avenue b'ar-gun-toting demonstrators had piled in, pushed wildly to the front, seized the microphones to broadcast their chants, looking like they might decide to take the Convention by force, when the Cat in the Hat turned up. Clinking and clanking in on that goofy clean-up machine of his, the machine now bearing in red-white-and-blue letters his famous line: "HAVE NO FEAR OF THIS MESS!"

Maybe the Boone people thought the Cat was one of their own—certainly he was lugging a rusty old b'ar gun over what he had of a shoulder. At any rate, they went suddenly silent, quick as it takes to snap off the TV, and turned expectantly to the Cat, who said:

> "Hello! hello!
> How are you?
> Can you do
> What I can do?"

Arms reached out from the clean-up machine, snatching Boone posters. The Cat shuffled them, passed them out again. Now they read: "Eat a prune at noon with Boone!"

Another mechanical arm stretched forth and from the crowd plucked, by the seat of his honorable pants, Boone's nominator, the Governor of the State of Kentucky, by image a rotund dignified Southern gentleman, already looking a little out of character in his Boone-skin cap, much more so now dangling, rump-high, over the Convention floor, the tail of his cap down between his eyes. The Cat in the Hat lowered him to the platform, whisked off his coonskin cap. Under it was another, oddly a bit larger than the first. The Cat pulled this one off, revealing yet another, larger still. The next coonskin lay on the Governor's ears, the next flopped down over his eyes. As the Cat whisked off caps, the Governor gradually disappeared beneath them. Soon he was wearing a cap that covered his head and rested on his shoulders, then one that flopped down his shirt front, others that lay on his plump belly, reached to his knees, his shoes, until finally there was only one huge coonskin cap on the platform. The Cat lifted the cap: no Governor! Shouts of amazement, even fright, from the Convention floor. The Cat, though smiling still, looked perplexed. Silence fell. The Cat doffed his own Hat, and there, on his head, in the lotus position, sat the Governor of Kentucky. *"Me-You!"* the Governor said, then clapped a pudgy hand over his mouth, gazed sheepishly at the now wildly cheering, wildly hooting crowd.

The Cat fired his b'ar gun suddenly, tremendous explosion and cloud of smoke: when it cleared, all the Booneskins had turned into live raccoons which were scampering wildly about, sending the girls shrieking up onto chairs with lifted skirts. Sure enough, under most of the Boone-skins, the delegates had been wearing the miniature Cat Hats, which they now merrily squeezed, raising a din of happy Cat-Calls. Some of the coons balanced balls on their noses, some rolled and tumbled, but most of them started humping each other. The whole nationally televised Convention floor was a mad melee of shrieking laughing girls, Cat-Hat-squeezing delegates, and copulating coons. I fainted dead away. Later, they told me that the Cat fired one final salvo on his b'ar gun, and a little flag popped out that said:

> "Come along!
> Follow me!
> Don't be afraid!
> There are many more games
> That we haven't yet played!"

And then he'd clinkclanked out of the hall in his clean-up machine, the Governor of Kentucky squeezed, wide-eyed and jolly, in beside him, most of the delegates deliriously *Me-Youing* along in his wake.

Riley never even got nominated. It took hours to clear

the hall of coons—in fact, as far as I know, they've got the run of the place yet—and anyway the delegates never came back. In the media nothing but the Cat in the Hat: he was a national sensation, though the media people themselves, infected by it all, were filing haphazard and even outrageous stories. The Cat, though in great demand, slipped out of sight, but his disruptive spirit lingered on. The delegates were completely out of hand, and the banquets that night were slapstick table-dumping pie-throwing affairs. Only one of my scheduled speakers had the nerve to carry on—someone rigged his mike through a tape recorder so that everything came out backwards; when he paused, his scrambled voice carried on and when he spoke the speakers went silent. "What's happening?" he cried and sat down abruptly—on a miniature Cat Hat someone had planted in his chair, issuing a lusty *ME-YOU!*—had a heart attack, and nearly died. Things were that serious. And through it all shuffled Ned and Joe with their lame-brain hayseed routines:

JOE: Say now, Mr. Ned, I hear we got us a Cat who's a real vote-getter!

NED: Yessir, that's right, Mr. Joe! He's very big at the polls!

JOE: Big at the polls, you say?

NED: Yeah, you might say he was a real *poll*-cat!

JOE: Haw haw! That's a good one, Mr. Ned! But tell me, did you ever bump into a *pole* cat?

NED: No, Mr. Joe, I've never bumped into a *pole* cat, but I've stood on a catty-*pillar!*

As I knew sooner or later they would, they cornered me. Intermediaries arranged it. In a locked hotel room. Darkened, shades pulled. Forty-buck fifth of whiskey between us. With them, to my astonishment, was my old friend Sam, popular governor of a Northwestern state and a Favorite Son candidate for the Presidential nomination, one of the men I'd counted on to break any possible deadlock between Riley and Boone. All three tense and serious, no comedy now.

At a late-afternoon press conference, I'd issued some pretty harsh statements about the Cat. His forces, most vocally Ned and Joe, had countered with accusations of king-making and obstructionism and even senility. Attempting that evening to put my Convention back together again, I'd discovered a terrible foolishness, a vast derision, a widespread breakdown of all I'd considered solid and meaningful in American politics. As far as I could tell, Riley and Boone were not so much running neck and neck as skidding rump and rump. In a desperate gesture, I'd pressured Boone into agreeing to throw his support to Riley upon the latter's expected nomination the next day, but it was no longer certain Boone *had* any support. I'd sought out the Favorite Sons, but most of them were wearing those silly little Cat Hats and chasing drunkenly after the cat-skinned co-eds. The sane ones left had seemed to be clustering around my friend Sam, as I'd hoped, but Sam was nowhere to be found. When I encountered him at last, in the locked hotel room, cheek by jowl with Joe and Ned, I knew that all was lost. The laws in Sam's state forbade his running for reelection and he had no chance for the Senate. I knew that, more than anything else, he wanted to be Secretary of State, and I figured he'd made his deal. But I hadn't made mine, and I wasn't about to.

In spite of their attacks and the reported rumors I was soon to be dumped, I knew they needed me—needed my long experience, my innumerable contacts, the accumulation of favors owed me, my weight with party regulars, my notorious capacity for political prophecy. As for my part, I didn't need them so much as I needed their absence. But I respected their sudden power and knew I'd have to negotiate. I was trying my damnedest to see Joe as a Vice-President, Ned as Secretary of Agriculture or something. As a result, we never really got on the same circuit. As we drank, Joe was talking about air power and the Red menace, Ned about technology and history, and I was trying to pry out of them what they wanted for themselves. Finally, I turned to Sam. "What are you doing here?" I asked him.

"Well, as you know, Sooth," said Sam, who was, almost ineluctably, to get tagged Sam-I-Am by the media in the campaign to come, "I live existentially. I'm not as confident as these fellows are that the Cat is going to be our next President, but I do believe nobody else is going to get nominated by our party. For good or bad, Sooth, we've got to accept the Cat's success and timing."

I grunted depreciatively. I knew he was right. But I was too disgusted to admit it.

"Besides, as I've learned, the Cat has many virtues. He's fresh and original, and famous, too. A whole new generation of voters, Sooth, has grown up on his tales. He's a living legend."

"So is Woody Woodpecker," I said grumpily.

Sam smiled. "Well, okay, he's something of a nut, it's true, or at least that's the way he chooses to come on. Yet it's a charismatic kind of zaniness, Sooth. He's funny. He's captivating. And ultimately I think he's sane. Did you see what he did to that Convention today?"

"Are you kidding?" I'd seen the replay of my swoon on the six o'clock newscast, and I supposed that Sam had, too. Stuffy, they called me. CAT SHATTERS BROWN'S BORE, said the press. "But, damn it, Sam, what are we running here, a political party or a carnival freak show? You want a deal, I'll make you one. But I won't see my party given over to a bunch of short-sighted crackpots without a fight!"

Sam winced; the others seemed offended. They leaned back. "Let's let him talk to Clark," Joe said.

And so that was how and when I met Clark. Large. Pale. Soft. He emerged from the obscurity of the room like an apparition. He was ugly, stark, nearly expressionless, spoke in a monotone—yet so charged the space around him as to seemingly snuff out the rest of the world. Joe, Sam, and Ned were surely there all the while, but I didn't see them. I recognized my new antagonist intuitively: the political visionary. Suddenly, though still indistinctly, the Cat in the Hat movement took on a new dimension. For one blinding instant, I glimpsed beyond the Cat's antics toward something new and extraordinary, beyond the disruption of National Conventions toward a vast reconstruction of human life. And then, as instantly, it faded. I resent, instinctively, such illusions. "Mr. Brown," he said with a slight nod of his head, but without extending his hand, "they call me Clark."

He sat, or perhaps he was sitting all the time. There was nothing, directly, to fear from him. Yet I was afraid. My own lucid perception of the vectors of politics was fast dissolving. In self-defense, I got right to the point: "What do you want?"

"A new world, Mr. Brown."

"Full of rutting raccoons," I said derisively.

"We had to work with what you gave us."

"What does a hall full of fucking coons got to do with government?" I asked angrily.

"What does grown twentieth-century men wearing their skins on their heads have to do with government?" he countered.

"It's a metaphor, Clark. That's politics."

"Exactly." A brief smile seemed to flick over his face. "You have a reputation, Mr. Brown, for phenomenally accurate political analysis. Yet not only do you seem unable to understand *why* your metaphor failed and ours worked, you seem unable to accept the simple *fact* that this is what has happened."

"All right," I admitted, "it worked today. Maybe. But tomorrow the building employees will probably be out on strike, refusing to clean up all the coon shit. Then what?"

"If it were necessary, the Cat would have them wallowing in it up to their ears and loving it," said Clark calmly. "Though of course it won't be necessary."

"Okay, okay, I accept the fact. Now what?"

"No, Mr. Brown, I'm afraid you don't. You came here hoping to make a deal. You still hope to make a deal. But the revolution has begun, Mr. Brown. There are no deals to be made."

Something whistled through me like a cold damp wind. With difficulty, I put it down. "But what's the Cat in the Hat got to do with your so-called revolution?" I asked with what little sarcasm I could still muster.

"Most immediately, Mr. Brown, the Cat is funny. And dramatic. We have a terrible need for the extraordinary. We are weary of war, weary of the misery under our supposed prosperity, weary of dullness and routine, weary of all the old ideas, weary of all the masks we wear, the roles we play, the foolish games we sustain. The Cat cuts through all this. We laugh. For a moment, we are free."

"Maybe," I said, "but clowns never win elections."

"I see you are still resisting," said Clark. "In your adoration of the past, Mr. Brown, you have isolated yourself from the actual and the possible. It is the great Western disease."

"What? Freedom from illusions?" I asked drily.

"No, history." Clark was utterly imperturbable. Or else

he had a worse sense of humor even than I did. "The mystification of history produced by our irrational terror of reality. If you'll pardon the pun, Mr. Brown, we need to perform a kind of racial historectomy on all humankind."

I smiled politely, though Clark did not return it. "So your Cat is going to wield the surgical blade," I said, the smile having soured. "With Tricks and Voom and Things like that." Still, I knew what a random business being was, what a hoax, what a hobble, history could be. Hadn't I been thumbing my nose at it all my life with my practiced anonymity? Clark had got to me there.

"He's the first step, Mr. Brown, that's all. Remember, I speak of a total revolution, not merely this election."

"Now you're resisting, Clark. There's still the election to be won. Otherwise, your would-be revolution doesn't get off the ground."

"Perhaps." Clark paused, almost as though he hadn't considered my objection before. "As a famous political analyst, Mr. Brown, what would you say was a politician's greatest asset?"

I paused. In my perception of a field of charged vectors, I tend to deny hierarchies of power. "I don't know," I said finally. "Ambiguity, I guess. Meaningful or potent ambiguity."

"Wonderful!" said Clark, and again that glimmer of a smile flickered for an instant on his pale face. "And what do we know about the Cat in the Hat?"

It had been some time since I'd read the stories to my grandkids. "Two hundred twenty-three different words," I said. It was the kind of thing I'd be apt to remember. Clark said nothing and I didn't like the silence, so I added: "There were these two kids by the window. And the Cat let these two Things out of a box and they flew some kites around in the house making one helluva mess." My grandkids had got a big charge out of that. "The Cat cleaned it up with that machine he used today." When my grandkids tried the kite act, we didn't have a machine. If they'd been my kids, I would've tanned their fannies, but what can a grandfather do? "Then, in the second one, he eats a cake in the bathtub and leaves a pink ring." My grandkids wanted to know why you couldn't see the Cat's peenie while he was standing in the tub. They didn't ask that about any of the other pictures. "Before he's done, everything in sight is pink."

"That's very good, Mr. Brown," said Clark. A pun on catechism occurred to me, but I swallowed it down. "And this time his solution, after running through an alphabet of cats all residing in his own hat, is—"

"Voom."

"Voom indeed!"

"The Bomb, as Joe has it."

"Yes, it's true," said Clark. "For Joe, the two stories are parables of the foibles of diplomacy, the first being about the effectiveness of air power, followed by technological recovery, the second about the eradication of the, uh, Red menace by atomic power."

"This is what you call freeing the mind."

Again that flicker. Clark's moods were subtle, but I was beginning to appreciate them. "Any dramatic change of the rules of the game, Mr. Brown, is by definition a radical action, and so attracts radicals of all stripes. At any rate, we are speaking as practical politicians now, Mr. Brown, and my purpose is merely to demonstrate the Cat's essential ambiguity, and thus his electoral power."

It was my turn to smile. "And Ned?" Not the question I wanted to ask, of course, but I knew he'd give me his own version willy-nilly, and I had but to wait.

"He's not a reader. He probably has the stories by hearsay only. I think he was surprised to discover this is a real cat. The technological solutions impress him. He doesn't believe in the Cat's magic, just a lot of clever hocus-pocus as far as he's concerned, but he's a pragmatist and understands the appeal magic has on the populace. If nothing else, it's entertaining. He sees the Cat as an exciting personality and believes the Cat can win. He's politically inexperienced, he hasn't done anything except sell shoes in St. Louis until now, but he's therefore free of all the myths and pseudo-realities of politics. He thinks the Cat is about to make history and he wants to be in on it."

"I thought history was done for."

"All of us have much to learn, Mr. Brown. Step at a time, please. Already Ned is approaching the idea of the Cat as agent of the absurd. Do you know what he said to me this evening? He said, 'You know, Clark, if you can accept that damned Cat, you can accept almost anything . . . even the universe.' Even the *universe*, Mr. Brown!"

"While it lasts. Voom!"

"Ah, that troubles you still! But remember, Mr. Brown: ambiguity! *Ambiguity!* Why must it be nuclear power? All the Cat says about it is that it is too small to see, yet enormously effective. Why not Reason? Or Love? God? Perception of Infinity and Zero, or the Void? It rhymes with Womb and Tomb: Being and Nonbeing. It suggests Doom or Bloom, Vow or—"

"Vomit," I suggested. "Maybe it's a great emetic."

Clark never batted an eye. "True," he replied in all seriousness. "Or simply OM, the final linguistic reduction of the universe. And then again, it may only suggest some hidden latent power. Beyond the alphabet, but in his Hat. An accent on Inner Space, Mr. Brown, a return to racial sanity. Voom may simply be the reality principle!"

"Well, all that's very cute, Clark," I said, "but there's a lot of destructiveness in those Cat stories. Think of those—"

"But what does it *matter* that there's destructiveness, Mr. Brown? The question is rather: *what* is being destroyed? The Cat breaks the rules of the house, even the laws of probability, but what is destroyed except nay-saying itself, authority, social habit, the law of the mother, who, through violence in the name of love, keeps order in this world, this household? Ah, no, mess-making is a prerequisite to creation, Mr. Brown. All new worlds are built upon the ruins of the old."

"Bump, thump," I said, recalling some of the lines. My opposition, nevertheless, was waning.

"And *jump*, Mr. Brown! The leap into the future! *Jump!*"

I sighed. "I'm too old to jump, Clark. Or should I say, too plump in the rump? But I'm not young enough to stop you all by myself either. What are your terms?"

"You're not listening, Mr. Brown. *There are no terms.* Take, if you like, the existential perspective of your friend Governor Sam. It is *happening*, Mr. Brown. Are you with us or not?"

Revolt, derring-do, mess-making are not my way. I liked my mother. But Clark was right; I saw all the vectors again: it was indeed happening. And anyway, the Cat, I recalled, always cleaned up his own messes. After the liberating infractions, the old rules were restored—reinforced, in fact. Appreciated. "Okay," I said, and poured a long one. I needed it badly. "Here's to the Cat who knows where it's at," I proposed, meaning whomever you please.

The Cat in the Hat was nominated by acclamation before the completion of the first ballot the next day as our party's candidate for the next President of the United States of America. There was some prior debate about the Vice-Presidency. It seemed that the Cat's supporters were prepared to let me have my way in the matter. But I discouraged Riley and Boone from getting mixed up in it—to tell the truth, they'd both started to get a little whacky themselves, and broke into wild laughter every time I mentioned the Presidency, but they willingly went along with me, backed the Cat and withdrew from the game. Finally, we settled on Sam. The way things turned out, I wish I'd talked him out of it, too, but at the time he was too obviously the right choice.

Actually, the nomination and balloting procedures that final day were orderly, just about like any other National Convention, and in spite of the coon odor, I was even beginning to feel at home in the hall again, but then the Cat came on to accept the nomination. He arrived on roller skates, holding up a cake on a rake. On, or in, the cake sat a goat wearing a coat, an umbrella balanced on its nose. On the tip of the umbrella wobbled a fishbowl, with a fish inside that was crying:

> "Stop it! Stop it!
> I will fall!
> I do not like this!
> Not at all!"

The delegates cheered madly. I shuddered, expecting the worst. Though admittedly, the worst could not be as bad as it would have been before my capitulation to Clark. I shuddered, that is to say, and giggled a bit at the same time. Certainly, we had one helluva candidate.

The Cat was now doing a handstand on the skates, balancing the whole assemblage on his toes. He lifted one hand. Then he lifted the other. Down with a crash came Cat, Hat, rake, cake, goat, coat, umbrella, and bowl. The fishbowl hit the platform like a tidal wave. Suddenly the entire hall was engulfed. I was swimming for my life, far below the surface. Which was a miracle in itself, since I don't know how to swim. I don't even take deep baths. People floated by, some struggling, some laughing, some waving, some weeping, some winking, all making little bubbles that turtles, eels, and schools of peculiar fish swam through. Chairs passed. On one sat a little old lady delegate from New Hampshire, knitting as always. She glanced up, scowled at me over her spectacles. Placards. TV cameras. Ned, upside down, tangled in phone cords. Raccoons. Little Cat Hats. Riley passed, astride a catskinned co-ed: he tipped his hat politely and gave the victory sign.

I surfaced, gasping for breath. The goat bobbed by, riding his cake. I grabbed for the cake to save myself, got only a fistful of soggy frosting. I was going under again. My entire life passed, in melodramatic accord with that old wives' tale, before my eyes. It was full of brown suits, charred hamburger, political polls, income tax forms, exchanged gratuities, and unreadable newspapers: so dull, so insane. I spluttered, "I consider it a great honor!" and sank away. At which point, the fish, now grown to Leviathan size, appeared and swallowed me up.

I was not alone in the belly of the fish. The whole damned National Convention was in there. Except the Cat and Clark. I was looking for Clark. This was too god-damned much. I'd nearly died. I was soaked, nauseous, exhausted, terrorized, enraged. "Clark!" I screamed. "Where the hell are you?" That vicious bastard. "Get us outa here, Clark!" My voice echoed and resounded in the fish's belly, mingling with the moans and cries of others.

A catskinned co-ed, hair dribbling down her face and cattail adroop, fell on my shoulder weeping. "There, there," I said. I patted her wet bottom. I began to feel a little better.

"Maybe he's Jesus," she whimpered.

"Now, now," I said, "we'll be all right."

All of us, even the raccoons, stayed huddled close together, grateful for each other's presence. A soft lamentation went up: what to do? who can save us? Sam remembered that in the morning TV cartoons they always used pepper. But nobody had any pepper. Then I recalled my crack about the great emetic. "Hey, Voom!" I said. "Voom!"

They all picked it up. "Voom!" they shouted. "Voom! VOOM!" The gates opened and we spewed forth.

I was rushing through the water at a tremendous speed. Luckily, we were all expelled outward in diverging directions: collision would have been fatal. I slowed, breathless, knocked up against a glass wall. I'd been clinging to my catskinned co-ed all the while, frantically patting her bottom to reassure myself. Or at least I'd thought it was hers—I was distressed to discover that in reality it belonged to my candidate Riley. I apologized confusedly. He tipped his straw politely and bobbed away.

I stared out through the glass wall. We seemed to be in the Convention hall, which was now enormously expanded —some trick, maybe, of the glass wall. Certainly, unless my eyes deceived me, it was concave. We seemed high up. I tried to make out what was just below us. It looked for all the world like a huge umbrella. And beneath that: the face of the Cat in the Hat grinning up at us. Swimmingly, monstrously distorted. We were, I realized, in the fishbowl. "Hang on!" I shouted to myself and held my nose. And, sure enough, we fell.

We washed up on our own Convention hall benches. I seemed to hear the Cat's voice behind me the while:

> "Now you see
> What I can do!
> I can give you
> Something new!
> Something true
> And impromptu!
> I can give you
> A new view!"

"Up yours," said I, as I collapsed, gasping, into my chair. Phoo! Another round of that and I'm done for. It was about then I began thinking of getting out of politics. It wasn't the last time I was to have such thoughts. I felt my clothes; they were dry. I glanced around at the others. Everyone in a state of bug-eyed shock. That old New Hampshire grandmother was still knitting away, but she'd lost her yarn. Click, click. There was a moment of general recognition, a Convention-wide blink. Faint foolish smiles. When, now warily, we turned once more toward the Cat in the Hat, he was exiting, balanced on a ball, juggling hopelessly infatuated catskinned co-eds. Ned and Joe led us in singing "The Cat in the Hat Campaign Song" and "The Star-Spangled Banner." We had our candidates. The campaign was on.

That night, I found a fish in my pocket. Dead, I think. Anyway, I flushed it down the toilet. I was not just a little bit disgruntled, nor was I the only one. The Cat's contemptuous travesty of an acceptance of a Presidential nomination by one of the nation's two major political parties had shocked us all, even his wildest supporters. Oh, we were quick to rationalize it, give the world at large a happy line, and all the old Jonah jokes got revived, but there was the gloomy cautionary stink of seaweed in the air. The Cat was entertaining maybe, exciting, liberating, even prodigious—but he was also, obscurely, a threat. Dangerous, yes, he was. He seemed to be in control of himself, but who could follow him without great personal peril? A whole nation in a fish's belly? No, we were in trouble. We all squeezed the *Me-You!* hats merrily and, with enthusiasm and the stirring sense of a great impending drama, went to bat for the Cat in the Hat, but, alone, we'd all found dead fish in our pockets and handbags.

I explained this that night to Clark. "Any great liberation is always accompanied by a vague sense of loss," he replied. "The structures we build to protect us from reality are insane, Mr. Brown, but they are also comforting. A false comfort, to be sure, but their loss is momentarily frightening."

"It's not going to get a lot of votes, Clark."

"You're still concerned about the elections, Mr. Brown."

"Hell, yes! Aren't you?"

Clark stared at me. I grew uneasy. "I believe, simply, that we live in an age of darkness, that humanity, with all efficiency and presumed purpose, has gone mad. What we must do, Mr. Brown, is help all men once more to experience reality concretely, fully, wholly, without mystification, free from mirages, unencumbered by pseudo-systems. If we succeed at that, don't you see, elections may no longer be relevant."

"That's what the goddamn fish's belly was all about, hunh?"

"Extremity is often a great catalyst, Mr. Brown. As a practicing politician, you must know that better than I."

I remembered the catskinned co-ed's sleek wet bottom, her warm tears, the sense of emptiness and community, the cavernous hollow of the fish's innards. A la Walt Disney, I realized, having cleaned a few fish in my time. Also, now that I thought about it, there was light in there. Where did it come from? Well, it didn't matter, it was a great show, I had to admit it, I'd never see things the same way again, find your soul in the Cat's fishbowl, and briefly, before I remembered its sliminess, I even appreciated the dead fish I'd found in my pocket. Then I recalled that old lady clicking her empty knitting needles. "It's a pipe dream, Clark. People aren't built for it. Call it insanity, if you like. I call it survival."

"But who is surviving, Mr. Brown? We are engaged in brutal wars, we live in the shadow of thermonuclear world-death, we continue to exist by virtue of dead forms, cut off from all life, from all being, as much murderers as survivors . . . and then we all die anyway."

I stared at Clark. He was intense, assertive, ugly. He radiated concern and engagement. And he knew too much about loneliness. "Say, listen, Clark, tell me: do you have a single goddamn friend in the world?"

"Certainly, Mr. Brown. You." I was sorry I had asked. "You're not quitting are you?"

I sighed. I was close to it that night. "No, but, nutty or not, I'd sure as hell like to win this election."

"Who says we won't?"

"Well, I tell you, it'd sure help if you could get the Cat to act just a little more . . . well . . . normal."

That incipient smile flickered over Clark's face. I grinned openly in return, went out for a couple platesful of hamburger steak, done to a bloodless crisp. I was starved.

The Cat was a phenomenal campaigner . . . if that was what he was doing. Tireless, astounding, unpredictable, he was literally everywhere at once, plummeting out of airplanes, umbrella for a parachute, over Butte and Baltimore, popping up out of sewers in Hyannis and Williamsburg, whistle-stopping from Cucamonga to Santa Monica, flying kites in Houston and dropping confetti on Bedford-Stuyvesant, setting up a freak show in the valleys at Gettysburg,

bathing in the Chicago River and brushing his teeth in
Hot Springs, peddling boxes and foxes to passersby in Old
Rampart, Alaska, giving away life insurance in San Fran-
cisco, eating grits in Spokane and knishes in Biloxi. He
juggled live bears in Yellowstone, spaceships in Florida,
dialects in New York. He fell off Pike's Peak, doing a handstand on a cane and a vane, and washed up on a door with
an oar off Kailua Bay, singing his Happy Birthday songs.

But if he was unpredictable, he was also unmanageable.
I made the mistake the first couple weeks of arranging
speaking engagements for him—the Cat missed them all,
popping up at the Opponent's rallies instead. The Opponent, political genius and campaign veteran though he
was, was at as much of a loss as Boone or I had been at
our Convention. I admit I was secretly pleased to see the
sonuvabitch discomfited, but I couldn't go along with
Clark's claim that the Cat's goofy gambits were exposing
the madness of normalcy. Okay, I realize the Opponent—
Mr. America, his party's buttons and posters called him—
was guilty of all the old clichés about "free enterprise" and
"government of the people, by the people, and for the
people," and "unalienable rights" and "the American Way
of Life" and "defense of freedom" and "government is a
business and should be run like one," all the usual crap, but
what the hell, that's pragmatic politics, that's winning elections, that's talking the tribal language, and it's not what
Clark liked to call "our national depravity." And sure, the
Cat's playback of these old saws in his singsong ditties did
make them sound pretty nutty. "This Wee of Life is rife
with strife!" he'd singalong. And:

> "Some laws are no!
> Some laws are yes!
> All flaws are good
> For bus-i-ness!
>
> Some laws are may!
> Some laws are must!
> The Mannikin Way:
> In God we rust!"

Or he'd carry that "government of the people" jazz out to
"until the people, down the people, between the people,
across the people, past the people, into the people, round

the people, beyond the people, since the people," and so on to "government up the people." That always brought the house down, but I wonder if the Cat ever knew why. I mean, he just didn't seem to have that kind of mind. If he had any mind at all.

Clark was convinced the Opponent was mad. And therefore his party was mad. And in fact any nation that could seriously consider for President a man who, for example, in Paterson and Cleveland promised vast federal programs "to liberate our great cities, once and for all, from misery, suffering, and despair," and in Phoenix and Mobile championed states' rights and reduced taxes, and embraced the local governors, was ipso facto a crazed and stricken society. His pet phrase was "biologically dysfunctional." As far as I was concerned, it only showed Clark knew a lot less about people and politics than he liked to think. It even bothered him that the Opponent was a Mason, kept dogs, went to baseball games, taught Sunday School, watched TV, and played golf, especially when he learned that the Opponent didn't especially *like* to play golf.

It's true, the Opponent made a pretty bad showing against the Cat, even blew his wig a couple times, but what would you do if you stood to address your fellow party members at a five-hundred-dollar-a-plate dinner, and discovered it was nothing but a stable full of braying polka-dotted donkeys wearing Cat Hats? What would you do if you got into a nationally televised VIP Golf Tournament and found yourself up against a silly Cat in a floppy Hat who swished eight-foot-long rubbery clubs at skittery golf balls with eyes and noses and got holes-in-one, while your own clubs oddly weighed a ton all of a sudden and kept sticking into the ground and taking root? What would your comeback be if, while addressing a national convention of the American Legion on the primacy of patriotism, your clothes suddenly fell off you ("defoliation," my friend Sam quipped in a speech in Minneapolis), leaving you diapered in Old Glory, noticeably soiled? What the Opponent said was: "This is an outrage!" And indeed it was.

The Cat's first encounter with the Opponent set the pace for the entire campaign, as long as the Opponent lasted anyway. The Opponent's party had selected the American eagle as its election-year symbol to go along with the Mr.

America idea, and the Cat arrived flapping in on one, a huge, shaggy, cross-eyed, baldheaded beast, surely the dumbest bird I've ever seen. The Opponent had just finished lifting his right hand and saying, "With God's help and yours . . ." when the whole apparition descended upon him. The bird, clutching a popgun and a jar of olives in its claws, landed square on its face, tumbling pell-mell across the stage with the Cat in the Hat, knocking over the lectern, upending lights and cameras, smearing the Opponent's TV makeup, shitting frantically on everything and everybody, and sending olives bounding around the place like pinballs. The bird stumbled clumsily to its feet in a tangle of wires, yuk-yukking giddily, shot itself in the eye with the popgun, and staggered around the stage, trampling right over the bewildered Opponent. The Cat leaped up to conduct the orchestra in playing the National Anthem backwards, the stupid eagle clucking raucously like an old hen through the whole performance and holding up a sign that read: MAKE AMERICA SAFE FOR DEMOCRACY! The Opponent, besmeared, trampled, splattered with eagle shit, staggered desperately to the microphone to call a halt to the travesty, but when he grabbed hold of it, it turned into Ned dressed up like Liberty. "*RAPE!*" he/she shrieked, and four burly cops rushed onstage to haul off, kicking and bawling like a baby, Mr. America.

Needless to say, the Opponent's poll ratings fell off pretty sharply after that. Under his picture in the papers the next day: *Can't Cat-chup!* The press was having a field day and the Cat seemed to have the election in the bag. The Feline in the Felt, they called him, Tom in the Tam, the Magic Mouser, King Kitten, the Tabby in the Topper, the Peerless Puss, the Magnifi-Cat, the Chief Exekitty. They loved him, couldn't get enough, ran whole special editions on the trips he took them on. A lot of it was due simply to the power of sensationalism—who'd ever done what he was doing?—but also I had to admit it, we were all hungry for some good fun, tired of war and all our private miseries, sick of the old clichés, the bomb scare and the no exits, in the mood for extravagance and whimsy ("Tom-foolery," the press labeled it); there was a long-repressed belly-laugh rumbling deep in the collective gut, and the Cat was loosing it. Clark called it a kind of exorcism, and I had to agree.

"We'll rid you yet, Mr. Brown, of all those troublesome 'vectors,' " he added, and since against all logic and my own instincts, we were winning, I only grinned and supposed it might be so.

Frankly, I still couldn't grasp the Cat's success, and my acceptance of it was something like a leap of faith. I'd watched the American people vote for several decades, and though I was beginning to get a feel of their almost hysterical delight in what Clark called "freedom," I still couldn't see them soberly pulling that lever for the Cat in the Hat, come November. Nevertheless, I had come along some since the Convention. I'd even bought myself a red-and-white striped tie. The middle of a frenetic Convention hall floor is an awkward place from which to look out on the world, which is probably why, from there, I was sure we were making a big mistake. I just couldn't imagine those people out there getting excited about that zany Cat. A Convention hall is like a lot of mirrors: you're looking at yourself looking out at them looking in at you looking at yourself, and so on, until finally there aren't any lookers or objects, just looking itself, which is to say, nothing at all. "Our catechumen in catoptrics," Clark once jokingly called me, and he had his point. Then, once the campaign had actually begun, I began to pick up new sounds, new signs, new motions. Yes, the Cat was touching something, some forgotten nerve, and something was happening. Testimonials were coming in. Not just from nuts, but also from plain Americans—grocers, housewives, doctors, carpenters. They liked the Cat. They were going to bat for him. They believed in him. They wanted him to go to Russia and China as soon as he was elected and talk to the people there. Where could you buy a set of those rubbery golf clubs? Was the clean-up machine patented?

"Be careful, Mr. Brown," Clark cautioned me when I talked about the testimonials. "There are no plain Americans. And there's much more yet to happen."

"Listen, Clark, don't screw things up now. I mean it. This can be something great, but we're not there yet."

"No, that's true, Mr. Brown. And neither are you."

I let it pass. I was feeling too good. An election I couldn't win, and somehow we were winning it. In fact, I got a lot of compliments about it. I came to understand that the whole nation was in a defeatist mood, just like our party, so that our Convention was like a microcosmic image, a preview, of what was now happening across the country. As for the magic, well, an age of wild scientific leaps is well-conditioned to accept amazements. I'm sure everybody, just like me, expected to find out later how it was all done. Some new formula, no doubt, that nobody would understand but everybody could accept.

Though not as funny maybe, the Cat's most devastating act came during his and the Opponent's first—and last—nationally televised debate. The Opponent appeared wearing his familiar small-town brown fedora, and began to speak of his pioneer grandfathers, one a blacksmith, the other a prairie preacher. The Cat suddenly interrupted: "Off with your hat, please!" The hat flew off, and under it was found to be a banker's bowler. The Opponent, as though unaware of what was happening, continued his speech without a pause, but now he was talking about investment credits, the threat of peace and depression, and "dynamic" solutions to "the problems of inventory." "Off with your hat, please!" said the Cat in the Hat. The bowler flew off and there was a biretta. Now it was "soldiers of Christ" and "the Prince of Peace" and the menace of "atheistic materialism" and "families that pray together—" which got interrupted again by the Cat's command. Off flew the biretta, revealing a wide-banded golfer's straw, and the Opponent switched abruptly from Christian pieties to locker-room banter and a really awful story about a guy with piles. This was followed by a miner's helmet, a fraternity pledge cap, a periwig, a pith hat, a *yarmulke*, a football helmet, beret, ten-gallon hat, mortarboard, earmuffs, Marine general's cap, nightcap, morion, a half-collapsed beaver, a black billycock, a cowl, a crown, a feather, a flower. The Opponent rattled on insanely, now a jungle fighter, now a hippie, next a cop hollering for law and order, then a farmer shooting pigs, a sociologist discussing the "territorial imperative," a dry-goods salesman trying to make out in the big city. At last it was all running together in one mad gibberish of sound, hats flying off his head like a string of rockets, until—suddenly—he seemed to swallow his tongue; off flew the last hat, a dunce cap, revealing: the Cat's Hat, of course. In the sudden silence, he reached up and pinched it. *ME-YOU!* It convulsed the house, ended the debate, all but ended the campaign. The Opponent sat there in the Hat, giggling idiotically, squeezing it spasmodically. There was, in fact, talk afterwards about committing him to an institution, which would have caused a terrific international scandal, but the Cat generously undertook his reconstruction, beginning all over with the ABC's and a bunch of other letters the Cat had thought up. The Opponent, in turn, simply retired from the public scene. This was about the end of September. A poll then revealed the Cat was assured of roughly 87 percent of the vote. The other 13 percent was uncommitted. It looked to be an electoral college whitewash.

In retrospect, I realize that, although the Opponent got shot down mainly by the Cat, the Cat's own complementary rise was mainly the work of people like Sam and Ned and Joe. And myself, if you don't mind. Not only did the Cat's acts insist on a lot of interpreting ("Well, what the Cat's trying to say, you see, is that things aren't always what they seem, life is unpredictable, and so to thine own self be true, because you can fool all of the people some of the time and some of the people all of the time, but not . . . yes, that's right, now you're getting it . . ."), but after suffering through a couple of his spectacles, people simply needed the reassurance of other normal human beings around them, even if Clark was right, and we were *all* really out of our minds. Ned and Joe, in fact, virtually ignored the Cat after the Convention, running their own show quite apart from him, at least as much as they could; you couldn't always depend on the Cat staying away. I sometimes wondered if those two guys really had the faintest idea who or what their candidate was, but I have to admit, I needed the familiar as much as anyone else, and so found comfort in their traditional barnstorm tactics. Ned operated mainly in the Midwest, Joe in the South and Southwest, though they often reenacted their Convention soft-shoe routines together.

My job, as I saw it, was to keep the party regulars in line, and given the Cat's irreverent antics, they were pretty nervous, so it was a full-time job. He projected all our Chicago ward bosses right through the Planetarium dome one evening, for example, and kept them in orbit for seven days, before soft-landing them in a Zen Buddhist monastery in the Sierra Nevada, where, every time they asked how to get to Chicago, a Zen master would slap their faces or dump bowls of porridge on their heads. Two of them came back with flowers in their hair, but the rest of them, quite naturally, wanted to quit. I reminded them that the Cat was sweeping the country, that that very stunt in fact had added another three percent to the Cat's advantage, that this was no time to get off the winning team, and I even, with great difficulty, managed to get Honorary Astronaut medals for them. They stayed.

But it was Sam, more than any of us, who carried Clark's special message to the world—deflected, of course, through a professional politician's caution, but for that, the easier to swallow. While Clark argued that our national inertia was the impermissible product of praxis, for example, Sam merely suggested that we needn't suppose the status quo was necessarily either natural or ordained by God, but, since we were free men, we could try to make life into something fresh and new and beautiful. Clark wanted an immediate total-population recognition of the full spectrum of personal and social options; Sam indicated ways we might improve things on earth by working together. He did well, especially in the East and Northwest, and on college campuses. I began to see him as our Presidential candidate four years from now. I was still thinking in those terms. In fact, I confess, I found myself wishing more than once that he was our candidate right now, and not merely running for the Vice-Presidency.

One night, between stops in an airport bar in Albuquerque, Sam going one way and me the other, I asked him: "Well, how's it gonna feel to be Vice-President?"

"What?"

"Vice-President. You're running for Vice-President, you know."

He smiled. "I don't know if I'm running *for anything*, Sooth. Sometimes it seems like what it's all about is the running itself."

"I know what you mean. The trouble with the democratic process is that the campaigns are too much fun, the jobs themselves too goddamn boring. Those two years I spent in Congress were the worst years of my life."

"That's not exactly what I meant. I mean, I think the Cat is carrying us out past ordinary space-time notions, out to something new where these old ways of identifying ourselves will seem sad and empty."

"I've had that feeling, too, Sam. Sometimes I think there aren't going to be any actual elections in November, that instead this goddamn thing is going to just keep on expanding and expanding, until taking an actual vote is going to be about as meaningful as pausing to pick a flower in a stampede."

"Are you worried about it, Sooth?"

"Goddamn right. It scares the hell out of me to think of no elections four years from now and eight years from now, just like I'm scared to die. I'm a coward, Sam. Pussy-laminous Brown. There's one for your fucking Cat."

Sam laughed. "Sooth, you're still holding back, you're still not with us. Come on, jump in, something's happening, something great!"

"I wonder if the Opponent would agree with you there."

"Sure he would! He does!"

"His wife doesn't."

"Sooth, it hurts to heal. Give her time. We've been living in a shutdown world. We're opening it up. It's worth it."

"You've been hanging around old Clark too much. Listen, he's a bright boy, but he's all mixed up about the psyche. He thinks you can do anything with it, that it's essentially empty and formless, you just have to realize it and presto! a new world. Well, people with psyches like that aren't the people I know. I don't even know newborn babies like that. I'll tell you what the human constant is, Sam, and you should know it as well as I, it's that big fat immovable mass, the old muddle-of-the-roaders, most of them programmed the wrong way from birth, all of them stuck to the earth with hungers and sex grabs, scared to die or even get hurt, encumbered with defects and damages, and essentially inert even when they look like they're moving." They'd called Sam's plane in the middle of my harangue, and I ended up shouting it at him past the gates. "And, listen, Sam, take it easy! Don't get overcommitted! When this Cat thing's over, you're it! You hear? You're it, Sam! Don't get screwed up!"

The next night Sam appeared on television. Sam was good on television, had just the right soft-sell manner. But that night the Cat showed up. It wasn't the first time. He was nearly as hard on us as he was on the Opponent. You could never be sure he entirely understood we were on his side. Sam knew what to do when the Cat turned up: he just got out of the silly bastard's way. Ned and Joe and some of the others weren't always so smart, and usually ended up paying the consequences, suffering the whole course of sleight-of-mind exhibitions with the rest of the hapless populace. This night, the Cat went so far as to leap past Sam and bounce out of every television set in the nation, dragging with him the whole kit and caboodle of commercial TV: spies, cowboys, comics, pitchmen, sob-sisters, cops, preachers, aviators, gumshoes, crooners, talk-ing animals, quarterbacks, and panelists, the whole daffy lot parading through all the bedrooms, living rooms, dens, and bars of the country, shooting it up, wisecracking, blowing whistles, asking irrelevant questions, beating people up. It was pretty unsettling, and a lot of sets got turned off for awhile after that.

At the time, of course, I didn't know about everybody else getting it, too. I thought it was just me he was after. I thought maybe he'd found out about that conversation I'd had with Sam in Albuquerque. I was in a hotel in Zanesville, Ohio. The set in my room was an old one, and I had a hard time focusing Sam in. He kept splitting off diagonally. But I'd finally got it adjusted and had just settled back in an armchair with a cold drink, had my shoes off and was rubbing my toes, when—wham!—there was the Cat leaping out of there, followed by a hockey team from Montreal, a daisy chain of elephants out of a docu-mentary on India, a boxcar of dead American G.I.'s, plus three motorcycle cops, a chorus line, the Olympic swimming team, a mean kid in a toy fire engine, three unwed mothers, and a used-car salesman. A lot more came, but I didn't see them, because a stagecoach and horses rolled right down a mountainside into the room and over me. When I came to, I found myself stripped naked, right down to my fuzzy pot belly and old pale thighs, surrounded by a horde of teeny-boppers from a dance-band show, the audience from a panel game, and the entire membership of the

Mickey Mouse Club, and being poked in the privates by a TV medic. "Hmmm," he was saying solemnly, "looks like we'll have to operate." "Hey! Cut that out!" I hollered. "You're nothing but an *actor!*" And for some goddamn reason they all laughed at that till they cried.

Well, I was sore, and when I heard about the incredible scope of the act, I guessed I wasn't alone. I saw trouble ahead. We got it. The very next day, there was the Cat in the Hat, raining pink ink all over a hostile confrontation of whites and blacks in Jacksonville. Very funny, but it didn't go over in Jacksonville, since it turned out both sides had been spoiling for that fight for a long time. And the Cat's ambivalent blackness, heretofore a political asset, now turned on him: he was suddenly an upstart nigger to whites, a Tom to blacks. Moreover, people like Joe were pretty upset about the pink ink, being sensitive on the Communist issue. On toilet walls across the nation: ONLY A FINK WOULD PISS PINK INK.

Actually, the reaction had begun to set in as early as a week before on some university campuses, though more subtly. Under WE WANT MIGHTY CAT in a Berkeley toilet, somebody had written: TO HELL WITH MIGHTY CAT—ALL I WANT'S A CATAMITE! The *Lampoon* was calling him "The Kook in the Kocked Hat." The Tube Boob Team at Ohio State now hung him in effigy with a sign attached: I CAN BEAT IT ALL BY MYSELF. A Columbia professor delivered a lecture on the Cat, entitled "A New View, or Old Mold?" and a regional meeting of political scientists in Iowa City demanded that the Cat declare himself on the Monroe Doctrine, the United Nations, American military alliances, counterinsurgency, and tariffs. Educators, it turned out, had a lot at stake in the conventional wisdom, had located for themselves a kind of stable verity, if not comfort, in the external desubjectivized physical "reality," and weren't all that excited about romantic journeys into inner realms. They didn't like being ridiculed, either. Neither did the labor leaders, businessmen, minority groups, priests, poets, bureaucrats, warriors, or journalists. And they all got their turn.

What was worse, the Cat could be pretty offensive. Like the time he popped bouncily out of a pregnant womb during an obstetrics lecture at Johns Hopkins, or his feed-

ing of the rats in the city ghettos, or the time he dropped
six planeloads of unsweetened chocolate pies on Disney-
land. Taking a crap onstage in a sandbox while addressing
the Daughters of the American Revolution in Boston didn't
go over very big either. His nakedness was a minor problem
from the outset, of course ("The Nude Dude in the Snood"
was one news headline that never quite made it), but cats
are cats—or so we argued until that Sunday morning in
October when he carried a stiff red peenie through all the
churches in Indianapolis, crying:

> "Look at me!
> Look at me!
> Look at me NOW!
> It is fun to have fun
> But you have to know how!"

I rushed in on Clark. "Stop him before it's too late!" I
cried.

"Too late for what, Mr. Brown?"

I showed him the latest poll. The Cat was down to sixty-
one percent. Which, with no visible opponent, was anything
but overwhelming. "See? You've been wrong, Clark!"

"Wrong? Why, not at all, Mr. Brown." Clark's calm was
spine-shaking. "Oh, by the way, look at this letter we've
just received."

I snatched it up. Oakland postmark. "Hey, man, your
krazy kat turns me on wow like next time try the late late
show send me old lionel barrymoor in a wheelchair I want
to turn him on, man, I mean put me in orbit with carol
lombard and I'll go to bat, man, I really will! *Me-yeah!*"
I threw it down in disgust. "Aw, goddamn it, Clark, that's
just some hippie! He probably won't even bother to vote!"

"So?" The hint of a smile flickered across Clark's pale
face. "Now, don't pout like that, Mr. Brown."

It was hopeless. I stalked out. And the next day, while
Joe was speaking in Washington on the importance of
military preparedness ("Only the strong and the brave are
free!"), the Cat arrived on a tricycle, blowing a rusty
fife, raised the Pentagon off the ground, and spun it like a
top—hilarious to disaffected potheads maybe, but not to the
Joint Chiefs of Staff, all of whom in their cold commitment
ended up in Walter Reed Hospital. Played havoc with all

the Pentagon computers, too, a pretty penny and a lot of history shot to hell.

Well, that did it. Within hours we had received rumors and then anonymous confirmation of an Army-centered take-over plot, and shortly after, we got that other phone call, telling us that the so-called moderate wing of our party —which in reality was just about everybody—was pulling out to support the Opponent.

So the situation that afternoon was this: (1) if the Cat in the Hat threatened to win, and to be sure he still had over fifty percent of the people behind him, the Army would pull their coup the week before elections and install the Opponent as President pro tem, until a new Constitutional Convention could be held; and (2), whether the Opponent won more or less legally or by fiat, we were faced with the prospect of a driveling idiot for President, the virtual political bankruptcy of our party and thus of the American two-party system, and personal lifelong ignominy for each of us.

"A military take-over? Here in the United States?" Sam had asked disbelievingly on answering the earlier call. "Easiest thing in the world," the voice on the other end had replied. Calmly. Coolly. Sam said after, he'd heard the rattle of hospital carts and trays. And true: it no doubt was easy. Who could stop them if they wanted to do it?

> "I can stop them
> With my tricks!
> With my kicks
> And pricks and sticks!"

We stared at the Cat. He sat there in that floppy striped Hat, parody of Uncle Sam's, gloved hands folded over his skinny chest, grinning that silly grin. What about it? Tip the media, expose the generals' plans? Pull a counter-coup? But who'd be with us? That hippie from Oakland maybe. I envied old Riley and Boone their way out.

"Could he do it, Clark?" Sam asked softly.

Clark was staring at us intensely. I'm sure, if it had been pitch dark, we could have seen his glowing eyes. "Why not?" he said. "Dismantling of a few outmoded systems, like the military, the Cabinet, police and espionage organiza—"

"Jesus Christ, Clark!" Joe blurted out angrily. "You're talking about a total violent disruption, man!"

"Of course." That fierce burning gaze. "What did you think this was?"

"But what would we *do* without an army?" Ned asked incredulously.

"Let's try it and find out."

"Now, goddamn it, Clark—!"

"But wait, Clark," Sam interceded, "doesn't a nation in a world like ours *need* a good defense system? I mean, I know what you've been saying about the debasement and insanity of machine-like military and production systems, but how else can we survive as a society?"

"What's more important? Physical survival of an accidental human horde or idea survival? So what if nations more barbarian than ours defeat us militarily? Probably we should just lie down and let them come. Because sooner or later, they'll get it, the exemplary message will sink in—"

"Ohh shiit!" Joe moaned softly.

And then that phone call from the rump group of benedict moderates came, the Cat got booted out, I talked Sam as heir-apparent into absenting himself, and we sat down to some really serious talk. "All right, Sooth, we're listening," Ned said.

A week later, the Cat appeared at a rally outside a small town in Mississippi, along the banks of the Pearl River. We had alerted the personnel of a nearby airbase, the White Citizens Council and the Black Nationalists, the local Minutemen, Klan, Nazis, Black Muslims, and Zionists, the National Guard and the VFW, the different student groups, the local churches, sheriffs, shopkeepers, cops, Mafia interests, farmers, Cubans, Choctaws, country singers, and evangelists, in short, all the Good Folk of the valley. Our precautions were hardly necessary—the same thing would have happened in Walla Walla or Concord by then—but it was only a week before the threatened coup, and since the Cat had a habit of skipping out on scheduled appearances, we were pretty nervous about it. By flattery, cajolery, and just plain hanging on to him, we kept him in sight until we could get him on the scene. Even Clark helped, though I'll never know why exactly.

That they'd kill him, we knew. That they'd do it by

skinning him alive we hadn't foreseen, but those folks along the Pearl are pretty straightforward people. I guess we'd been around him too long and had begun to forget he was a cat. Another thing we hadn't counted on was Sam's showing up. I knew he was upset about the thing, but I thought I'd convinced him to stay away. I have my flaw, I've told you about it, and Sam had his: he believed in reason. He came there to *talk* to those people, for Christ's sake! Oh, poor sweet Sam! "Violence solves nothing!" he cried out, standing in front of the Cat, and somebody shot him in the head. Right between the eyes. Clark talks about reality. Nothing has ever been nor ever will be so real to me as that sick disbelieving expression on Sam's face the instant before the hole opened up. I was backing away, but I came up against a solid wall of people. There was no getting through.

They tied the Cat's feet together and hung him over a peg pounded into the upright beam of a tall cross. He put up no resistance, merely smiled benignly through it all. Oddly, though he was upside down, his Hat did not fall off. For some reason, this enraged the crowd. They all gave a pull on it, including a huge black man, said to be the strongest sonuvabitch this side of the Yazoo. But it wouldn't give. They kicked the Cat in the face, spat on him, punched his belly with pig-stickers, slammed his balls with the blunt end of an ax. But the Hat stayed on. And the Cat just smiled back at them, blinking his long lashes, twiddling his thumbs.

They'd apparently decided on a simple slaying, and a wizened 107-year-old redneck from up in Sunflower County had been handed the knife, but, their blood boiling now, they all went after him with whatever they had at hand, switchblades, hatpins, goads, hatchets, scissors, rusty razor blades. "That is that," the Cat in the Hat was heard to say, and they closed in. There was a mad frenzy of pulling and ripping, cursing and gut-flinging, and they weren't too neat maybe, but it was a thorough job of skinning a cat. Except for the Hat: when they were done, it was still there. And the gloved hands, still folded over a now glistening pink chest. And the placid grin, though now a bit macabre. Ned, Joe, and I, unable to break free, had pulled together. Clark, we noticed, had disappeared.

The crowd stood around now, panting, staring at the dead cat, still dissatisfied somehow. There was a lot of corn liquor getting passed around. Survival, Clark, that's what it's all about, goddamn it, I was saying to myself. Fuck your revelations, I want outa here! About then, somebody thought of matches. As I recall, it was a little kid, about eight years old. They heaped up leaves and old newspapers at the foot of the cross, tossed on the Cat's skin. They were about to light it, when a fat black woman slipped up timidly and dropped her kerchief on the pile. An old sunburned farmer pulled off his straw sun hat, hesitated, then tossed it on. Someone kicked off his boots and pitched them forward. A cop threw his belt on. A man pulled off his shirt. A woman unzipped her dress. A youngster tore off his pants. Before I could grasp what was happening, the whole mob was stark naked. Joe and Ned and I stood out like the strangers we were. Not for long: they jumped us, hogtied us over tree branches, cut our clothes off us, and threw them on the now mountainous pile, put the match to it all.

What followed was a pretty marvelous orgy, spoiled only by the stink of all those burning rags and the pall Sam cast, and I regretted that my situation forced me to play such a passive role in it. While the Cat burned, the throng fucked in a great conglobation of races, sexes, ages, and convictions; it was the Great American Dream in oily actuality, and magically, every time an orifice was newly probed, it uttered the *Me-You!* Cat-Call.

Nor was the Cat in the Hat done with us. His roasted corpse was rescued from the flames, ripped apart, and passed around. I objected, but to no avail, and the burnt flesh was jammed down my throat, ruining forever my taste for charred hamburger. Then . . . VOOM!

Now, I've smoked pot, chewed peyote, and even with an FBI investigative team tripped once on LSD, but the Cat's meat was truly something else. For one thing, like the Cat himself, the vision was all red, white, and blue, shot through with stars, bars, and silver bullets. The whole hoopla of American history stormed through our exploded minds, all the massacres, motherings, couplings, and connivings, all the baseball games, PTA meetings, bloodbaths, old movies, and piracies. We lived through gold-digging, witch-burning, lumberjacking, tax-collecting, and barn-raising. Presidents and prophets fought for rostrums by the dozens. We saw everything, from George Washington reading the graffiti while straining over a constipated shit in Middlebrook, New Jersey, to Teddy Roosevelt whaling his kids, from Johnson and Kennedy shooting it out on a dry dusty street in a deserted cowtown to Ben Franklin getting struck by lightning while jacking off on a rooftop in Paris. It was all there, I can't begin to tell it, all the flag-waving, rip-staving, truck-driving, gun-toting, ram-squaddled, ringtail roaring, ass-licking, bronc-breaking, A-bombing, dragracing Christ-kissing, bootlegging, coffee-drinking, pig-fucking tale of it all. And through it all, I kept catching glimpses of the Cat in the Hat, gunning Japs out of the sky over Hollywood, humping B'rer Rabbit's tar-baby, giving Custer what-for at Little Big Horn, pulling aces out of his sleeves in New Orleans; now he was in a peruke signing the Declaration of Independence with a ballpoint pen, then in a sou'wester going down with the Maine, next leaping with a smirk and a daisy in his teeth out of the President's box onto the stage of Ford's Theater, inventing the cotton gin, stoking Casey Jones' fires, lopping off heads at Barnegat with Captain Kidd, boohooing with Sam Tilden and teeing off with Bing Crosby.

Too much, and the effect finally wasn't so much enter-tainment as mere exhaustion, and I wonder now, sitting here in my Attorney General's office in Washington, if the Cat's whole act wasn't mainly to leave you just sitting quietly, staring blankly out a window, with an empty mind and a body gratefully at rest. Those good Pearl River folks were so tuckered, it was all they could do to smear a little tar on our hind ends, slap on a handful of chicken feathers, and prod us, if not out of the county, at least up the road a little piece.

The Cat in the Hat as candidate was a national calamity; as martyr, he took us to the White House. His death shocked the nation. Sam's should have, but no one paid much attention to it; it was like a normal and almost proper supporting casualty. I wept like a goddamn baby about it. I kept seeing Sam's gentle face with that hole in it. I blamed the Cat. For a couple of weeks, Mississippi was policed by federal troops. The FBI investigated. Our party reconvened solemnly in Philadelphia, where, after stirring tributes to the Cat in the Hat from leaders of every political persuasion, Riley was nominated for President with Boone as his running mate. Our central platform promise was "The New View." The Cat's Hat became a somber symbol, the Cat-Call a moving chant, the Campaign Song a kind of party hymn. Ned penned a new rhyme—he thought of it merely as a last-minute campaign slogan, but it was eventually to enter the American canon, immortalizing that one-time St. Louis shoe salesman . . .

> "Do not fear!
> The Cat is here!
> Where?
> There!
> Near?
> Here!
> There and here!
> Here and there!
> The Cat in the Hat
> Is EVERYWHERE!"

We won in a walk, a cat-walk, as Joe and Ned might have it, backed by the military, labor, Wall Street, the press, the peace movement, Negroes, and the National Society for the Prevention of Cruelty to Animals. President Riley, as his first act of office, declared October 31 as Cat in the Hat Day. What about Sam's day? I asked. He shrugged. The Imperial Grand Wizard of the Ku Klux Klan turned the Cat's Hat over to the National Cat in the Hat Museum and Library in Princeton, New Jersey. Was it the real hat, or just a campaign forgery? Who can tell? Certainly no magic has come of it. Joe, I might mention, is now Undersecretary of State for Latin American Affairs, and Ned is with Bell Telephone.

Ironically, one of my jobs as Attorney General is to keep under constant surveillance my old friend Clark, who is in effect, though he may not be aware of it, under a kind of permanent house arrest; well, that's politics. Legend has it, it's he who has the real Cat's Hat, and that inside it are twenty-six other Cats, ready to be sprung on an unsuspecting world. Oh boy. And where will we go then, Sam, where'll we go?

Bopping

David Henderson

MY MAIN MEN and I bopped
to general agreement
              (like the toast to "the boys upstate"
              before every bottle of Paradise or
              Thunderbird wine)
Down cats
we bopped to give cause to the causes
that died before they got to us.

I remember the arm pumping cap crowned blades
of my boyhood
their elemental gait talking
deep beneath my eyes . . .
              the list at waist and trunk
        whip of an arm
& abrupt then long wing-tipped stride
of days when we had to show ourselves love
in difficult pretensions
        as if speaking words of self-love
      was too remote a performance
    when before the fact
we understood all too well
the action of the thrust.

We maneuvered
to turn that way in dawns or dusk
of the eternal wars
among ourselves our gangs:
              the Crowns   Chaplins   Sportsmen
Boston Baldies   Young Sinners Enchanters   Duschon
    Lords
because talking after all is too little of glamour
to the hungry   the ugly   the mean

we bopped when about to fight
and we bopped when happy
all in our own slight variances
known to the members of the Road
and known to similar bops
of the roaming hordes

From Avenue "D" to Red Hook
through Marcy projects then Crown Heights
Prospect Avenue in the Bronx & also in Brooklyn
The Fifth Avenue Armory on 141st & the Harlem River
Bronx River Housing   forty-three   Fifty-five
99 center   Boston Road
from winters to graduation
from street duels
until
wedlock or the cops
shot us down
bopping
. . .

A Documentary on
Airplane Glue

David Henderson

I HAVE seen the young Negroes & Puerto Ricans
sniffing and nodding in their slums
the young ones
old enough to afford only
the 25-cent Carbona or airplane glue
          the glue so paradoxically manufactured
for the assemblage of model airplanes/

I see the young boys 10   11   13 years
drawing nostrils to bottle lip
and then staring woozily at their tenements
twice & thrice as old as their parents
or gazing at the monotonous pink dormitories
of the Housing Authority
set up so their fathers can remain at their meager jobs
or their mothers on relief/

The pink buildings are tall
the tiny balsa wood planes the glue holds so well
never fly
        try to fly them & they'll break
        leave them lying around & they'll be broken
most of these boys
    have never been on a real plane
               and never will
           (unless they return to Puerto Rico
        flying from poverty to poverty above the clouds/
        . . . & *not* back to Africa)

& for a moment at least   sniffing the glue

can soar one above the pink & gray buildings/

the balsa wood planes are delicate
and crush easily
               Sometimes I wonder how the effects
               of the glue was discovered?

Could it have been an eleven-year-old
bending so close to the tiny construction
piecing & glueing & piecing
gasping with slight exasperation
& then suddenly   wonderfully
                     soaring
        ultimately away/

Politics as Drama as Politics

Conor Cruise O'Brien

A STAGE IS A PLATFORM raised so that the people on it may be seen.

The people on it may be, as they say, "real," doing or suffering something in their own persons; or they may be imitating the doings and sufferings of "real" persons; or—surprisingly often—they may be partly real and partly "imitative," people who are both doing and pretending at the same time.

The most real—in the sense of least feigned—of stage performances is the public execution, where violent death, actually inflicted on the central personage, will deprive him at last of all recourse to mummery. The old word for the gallows was the stage, and "to be staged" once meant to be subjected to public punishment accompanied by public vilification: a vestige of this usage seems to survive in the practice of the New York dramatic critics.

Yet the stage of the gallows has often seen the proof that man, placed on a raised platform before a crowd of his fellows, is apt to turn the real into the theatrical as long as he can, even in the most forbidding of circumstances and sometimes with momentous consequences. The condemned man would play out his part, and the crowd would react as an audience:

> That thence the Royal actor borne
> The tragic scaffold might adorn
> While round the armed bands
> Did clap their bloody hands.

The legitimation of political authority—the coronation of kings—had been a ceremonial performance on a public stage. The Puritan regicides wished to delegitimize monarchy by another ceremonial performance on a public stage, the execution of the king. Yet the king, as Marvell implies,

49

outplayed them by acting his part in the second ceremonial with a demeanor that recalled his part in the first one. Marvell, who was a politician as well as a poet, unerringly though perhaps unconsciously (and of course contrary to his own political intent) brings out the political essentials of this great performance:

> He nothing common did or mean.

That is he succeeded in impressing the audience with the idea that a king was different from common mortals in some essential way:

> Upon that memorable scene

It was intended to be remembered: to become a memory active in a later time, a scene working on imaginations in favor of the Restoration.

> But stooped his Royal head

Though stooped for the moment it remained Royal.

> Down as upon a bed

A man who is going to bed expects to get up; one knows that the Royal Martyr expects a glorious resurrection and the restoration of his line.

The royal actor was thus acting in two senses: he was acting the king, in the theatrical sense, and he was also, and through this piece of theater, engaged in political action. And in fact these two senses of "acting" often combine, have long combined, and do still combine, today. One set of forms and their combination is suggested by the title of my essay: Politics as Drama as Politics. I do not intend to discuss, except marginally, drama as politics—the use of the theater for political purposes such as, in the words of an eighteenth-century writer, "dramatizing the people into loyalty." My subject is not political drama, but the dramatic in actual politics:

Politics:	the decision that the king must be executed.
As Drama:	the ceremony of the king's execution and the way he plays his part.
As Politics:	the political effects of the royal performance on the scaffold.

It will be seen that the politics into which the drama led was not the same as the politics of those who staged the drama; there is a partial reversal, a dialectical process. I think this is inherent in the nature of the dramatic, as distinct from the ceremonial. In pure political ceremonial—a coronation, say, or the installation of a President—the elements of the dramatic and of reversal are almost wholly lacking. But once the political rulers need to move men *against* others, there arises the *agon,* the dramatic, the unpredictable. The anti-monarchical play of 1649 turned, for many, into a pro-monarchical one; the political equivalent of a theatrical director has little or no liberty of choice in his casting and will therefore often face disappointment.

But it is more than a question of involuntary casting: there is a problem of audience, or audiences. The director, in dramatic politics, intends his spectacle for one audience, but it will also reach others, and perhaps with effects the reverse of what he intended. Thus, successive English governments during the eighteenth and nineteenth centuries staged in Ireland a series of State Trials of Irish rebels. From an English point of view, these were solemn public expressions of power under law: of both the strength and the righteousness of English rule in Ireland. When the spectacle was presented to an Irish audience, however, the scenario went wrong: the prisoners, like the Royal Martyr, dominated the scene. The dock became a stage on which the prisoner took the part of the consciousness of an oppressed people. Words spoken from this stage were learned by heart by the young: the volume *Speeches from the Dock* became the best-read book in Ireland; through it, past rebellions became a school for future ones.

Similarly today if a black militant is put on trial for incitement to riot and rebellion, the trial can itself become a school for further riot and rebellion. Indeed, the black militant movement has shown a remarkable grasp of the combined possibilities of dramatic politics and political drama. The pupils at a New York school were able to stage an act of dramatized defiance through the use of appropriate dramatic performances. LeRoi Jones's militant charades are in part provocations to the established order, attempts to force it into acts of legal coercion, which themselves will be turned through the workings of dramatic politics into far more telling incitement than the original dramatic fiction. The funeral of Martin Luther King, with blacks in the roles of silent accusers, whites in the roles of penitents, was natural dramatic politics and at the same time prologue to the deliberately staged political drama of the Poor People's March, in which the accusers sought to exact a tangible penance through a symbolic action.

The natural political drama of trials and executions, assassinations and funerals normally reaches two audiences, who respond to it not only in opposite ways, but with different degrees of intensity. The audience which is on the side of the court or in tacit sympathy with the assassin has a response of satiety: "Justice has been satisfied" is a phrase which suggests that the matter is closed.[1] But the audience which is on the side of the prisoner experiences unappeased anger, a dynamic emotion. Because of the unevenness of the reaction, this kind of political drama has always a subversive thrust, or list, quite contrary to the intentions of those who originally provide for its staging. It is not surprising, therefore, that modern administrations, competently advised about the manipulation of public opinion, tend to be cautious about recourse to such methods.

This does not mean, however, that members of governments, and other public men working within the limits of the established political system, do not dramatize their politics. If certain forms of dramatic politics have a revolutionary tendency, other forms, like a sort of real-life soap opera, are calculated to have a sedative effect. These forms are of their nature rather diffuse and tend to elude our intellectual grasp. There are difficulties of vocabulary: the language in which we discuss politics is full of dramatic terminology; words like "scene," "stage," and "role" recur frequently. These of course are also part of our general

---

[1] Similarly, most whites probably wanted to see Dr. King's funeral as a close: the eminence of the white leaders attending, and the fervor of their panegyrics, had cleansed the white community of such guilt as it felt. The speeches and editorials after his death served essentially the same function as the legal proceedings before his death would have done had he been executed instead of assassinated. The function is that of a dramatic ritual seeking to make vengeance illegitimate.

vocabulary, and one might easily dismiss them as dead metaphors. Yet, in a political context they show a curious tendency to come back to life. Thus, in one recent issue of *The New York Times,* on the editorial page, I found the word "role" used politically, and sustaining itself in a kind of life, if not in perfect health, in three different places. One editorial suggested that "Senator McCarthy may have found the means of dramatizing his underdog role." One has a role but may find the means of "dramatizing" it; the metaphor is buried deep but will not rest. Another editorial, dealing with the election of a new Secretary-General to the Organization of American States, described how this good man bravely lived down what the writer called "the handicap" of being "tagged—unfairly—as the United States candidate" and how despite this handicap he was nonetheless elected as a result of "the quiet pressure-free diplomacy of Ambassador Sol. M. Linowitz." This little gem of pastoral closed with the reflection that "the United States played throughout the role of 'partner of the enterprise rather than boss of the enterprise.'" It seems that one can have one role and play another, like the squire joining in charades in the servants' hall. Finally, on the same page Mr. C. L. Sulzberger quoted Dean Acheson's well-known observation that Britain had lost an empire but not yet found a role. His imagination stimulated by the Achesonian metaphor, Mr. Sulzberger went on to say that "by the time successive British governments had resolved to join, de Gaulle was running the road show and determined that Britain should be limited to a noise offstage."

How FAR IS this sort of language merely a literary usage, and how far does it reflect an apprehension of something inherently dramatic in the proceedings discussed?

We can, I believe, construct a span of references of this kind, ranging from the purely literary or subjective—where the dramatic metaphor is simply a way of describing behavior not dramatically intended—out to the absolutely literal, where dramatic terminology is simply descriptive.

Thus, one might have said of the time the credibility of "The Great Society" was crumbling: "President Johnson has been playing Oedipus—an Oedipus who doesn't seem quite able to make out what the oracle has been saying."

This would have been a literary form of political criticism without any literal element, since obviously the President did not intend to be seen in this way.

One can also have a literary, and even a far-fetched, use of dramatic reference in relation to effects which are, at least in part, intended. Thus at the time of the settlement of New York's garbagemen's strike *The New York Times* published, under the heading "Political Drama," a letter from a correspondent in Flushing who discerned an *agon:* "the intense manifestation of qualities resembling the heroic ideal and that of the golden mean in the two leading protagonists, the mayor and the governor." This seems a little fevered, yet it does describe effects which seem to have been intended: the mayor and the governor did appear to some of their followers to embody some such qualities.

We are further from the literary use of words and nearer to the literal when we say: "President Johnson, in trying to justify the Vietnam war, played the role of President Lincoln." For there is no doubt that President Johnson did deliberately seek to persuade people to see him as the latter-day Lincoln, "sad but steady," "brooding" over a war, and even over "dissent, riot, and rebellion." Mr. Johnson also took occasion to remind the audience, at his performance at the Lincoln Memorial, that Lincoln saw 600,000 Americans die; this would have left the new Lincoln a considerable margin for further feats of stoic perseverance. This particular use of dramatic politics for legitimation by historic analogy is extremely important, and I shall return to it. It should be noted, however, that in this case the performance was a flop and that the jeers which greeted the Johnsonian Lincoln gave this particular show a short run.

At a further distance in the span from the literary toward the literal, we are told by the most intellectual and introspective of the candidates for the Presidency that he is in the habit of viewing himself and his political rivals in terms of the development of a drama: "Act I people" and "Act II people." Here is dramatic metaphor, but it is no longer simply part of the spectator's description—it is part of a protagonist's way of envisaging his performance and presumably affects his action. It was Senator McCarthy who did most to close the run of Johnson's appearances in the role of Lincoln.

The final example, in our span of references, is one in which the language of the theater can be applied literally, without any admixture of metaphor at all, to a political performance. This is the example: "The Governor of California is a movie actor who uses his professional skills to play on television the part of governor of California."

II

ON THE DOMESTIC STAGE, there are obvious and definite limitations to the operation of dramatic politics. Histrionic skill will not alone persuade workers to accept lower wages or farmers to accept lower prices.[1] People know about wages and prices and where the shoe pinches. Domestically, the processes of electoral democracy have considerable rational significance. But the foreign policy options of the most powerful of democratic states are in a different sphere. To the extent that they are rational, these options are not easily affected by democracy; and to the extent that they are affected by democracy they are not often rational. The electorate knows little about the world outside the United States and has been conditioned to imagine this world in Manichaean terms, which are of course inherently dramatic. They run something like this: foreigners are not all bad; some of them are enrolled in something called the "free world," where they are quite happy, and love America, from which they receive aid. Their freedom, which they prize above all things, is, however, menaced by communism; not only are communist armies massed on their borders, but native communists, or communists disguised as natives, are undermining them from within. The nations of the free world, much as they hate communism, suffer from a mysterious incapacity to protect themselves, even against their own communists. America therefore must protect them, both for their own sakes and because any country ruled by communists automatically threatens the American people. It will be necessary, therefore, from time to time to occupy free-world countries in order to save them. Since the com-

[1] Farmers can, however, use histrionic methods to try to secure higher prices. Thus television commentators recently described farmers who killed and buried hogs as "dramatizing low hog prices."

munists are determined, ruthless, and wily, and since the American government, for security reasons, must keep to itself its knowledge of their plans and activities, it is necessary for the American public to let the American government decide what it may be necessary to do in and to any given country of the free world at any given moment. Whatever it decides to do will automatically be in the ultimate interests of the free world and will deserve the support of all patriotic Americans and of all other good men.

I don't think this account seriously distorts the network of prevailing American assumptions about international affairs—a network that results from fifty years of anticommunist indoctrination through the press and other media and from the ideas propagated by four successive Presidents about the containment of communism.

These assumptions are not only prevalent, but deeply rooted; in many circles the mere fact of questioning these assumptions suggests either bad faith or extreme naïveté on the part of the questioner. This is the case among the unsophisticated, the majority of the electorate. But not only among them. It is a mistake to suppose that members of an elite are not themselves affected by the values and concepts which they commend to the public. People tend to grow into the parts which are assigned to them. "Man in business," as was noted in the year of the execution of King Charles, "is but a theatrical person and in a manner but personates himself." Professor John Kenneth Galbraith, in his amusing and frightening fable about Washington, *The Triumph*, describes the prevalence in official circles of a theory of what he calls "multiple interconnected blind spots": a theory through whose application all criticisms of official anticommunist policy automatically discredit themselves and are eliminated from the system. The theory is explained by a member of the State Department who has doubts about the official line: " 'Miro is believed by Washington to have a blind spot where communism is concerned. So when I argue that Miro is okay, it means that I have a blind spot where Miro is concerned. O'Donnell argues that I am right. It follows that he has a blind spot where I am concerned. Besides he is a Catholic, and Catholics are now thought to have a special blind spot where communism is concerned—that includes the Pope. The boys at the White House are sympathetic. That is because they have a general blind spot resulting from inexperience. In other words, all who disagree with the official line are disqualified by blind spots. They are a great handicap.' "

The anticommunist assumptions therefore can hardly be modified; rather they modify reality as it is apprehended. The official mind breaks down the flow of information out of its initial complexity into a series of tentative anticommunist scenarios, which are required to make information relevant and assimilable. On the basis of this mode of cognition, decisions are taken, and once that has been done, new, simplified scenarios are developed for the benefit of the public. The simplified scenarios resemble the original tentative ones and, like them, fit into a system of assumptions common to the official mind and to the wider public. But the simplified scenarios are governed not only by the original tentative ones but also by the decisions taken, which determine the story line to which the dialogue and staging must conform. Thus, whatever the intrinsic nature of the Tonkin Gulf incident, the nature of its presentation to the public depended not on an intrinsic element but on an extrinsic one: the decision to begin bombing North Vietnam, and to use the Tonkin Gulf incident for the legitimation of the decision and for the establishment of a consensus in its favor. This required the solemn and dramatic proclamation, at the highest level, of a deliberate and unprovoked attack by the communists on the American vessels. On the other hand, a decision to do nothing about the matter would have required a somewhat different scenario, as was the case with the presentation of the intrinsically graver *Pueblo* incident, about which it was not expedient to excite the public mind excessively.

THE UNITED NATIONS has often been the theater for the symbolic presentation and legitimation of dramatized versions of international episodes and decisions. Indeed, it was the consideration of the actual, as distinct from the apparent, significance of United Nations debates and decisions that brought home to me the large element of the theatrical in the conduct of the more visible aspects of foreign relations and suggested the exploration of the general theme of this essay.[1] The United States is, of course, not alone either in dramatizing its international decisions or in making use of the United Nations for this purpose. As the richest and most powerful nation, however, the United States has resources of staging not available to others, and a larger share in the use of the United Nations theater; also its practices are of the most immediate concern to us here.

The presence of United Nations headquarters here in New York and the televising of most of its proceedings—and especially of all important statements by U.S. spokesmen—have made possible a continuous holy dramatization of United States foreign policy. U.S. spokesmen in the United Nations—Warren Austin, Henry Cabot Lodge, Adlai Stevenson, Arthur Goldberg—have had to be actors and preachers, or actors playing preachers, at least as much as diplomats. Their parts have been extremely demanding, because the rules and conventions of the theater are liable to change with the demands of the story line for each successive episode. Thus, when the United States decides on an armed intervention, this will be presented as a United Nations action if circumstances permit (Korea); if circumstances do not permit, if United Nations blessing is not available, the United States, if it deems it expedient to do so, will intervene anyway (Vietnam, Santo Domingo) and will justify such unilateral action, as Ambassador Goldberg did, by regretting the "present weakness" of the United Nations which would, if it were stronger, carry on the war itself. On the other hand, where the United States decides *not* to intervene, as in the time of the Soviet crushing of the Hungarian uprising in 1956, it claims that its hands are tied by its obligations under the United Nations Charter and by the Soviet veto. It is not surprising that American public opinion has become confused and, in some cases, resentful, about the nature and purpose of the world organization which is sometimes relevant and sometimes irrelevant, sometimes furiously active, sometimes sunk in lethargy, and sometimes mysteriously holding back the United States from some virtuous course of action. It is often said that

[1] For a fuller discussion see the present author's *The United Nations: Sacred Drama* (Simon & Schuster, 1968).

the United States public has become disillusioned about the United Nations, but this is far from the case. The truth is that this public is suffering from a surfeit of successive and conflicting illusions about the world organization, so that the public now becomes nervous, irritated, and tired when the subject is again brought to its attention. The way in which the United States has used the United Nations has caused a slow attrition in that organization's reputation, but has on the whole been remarkably successful in directing away from the United States government any popular dissatisfaction with the conduct of international affairs. It must be added that it has also, on occasion, helped to save the peace. The uses and abuses of the United Nations theater are a complex subject which I can only touch on here.

The dramatic element in politics is in itself both neutral and ambiguous. It can be used for revolutionary or counter-revolutionary purposes, for war or for peace; those who use it cannot, up to now, precisely calculate its effect. It is a basic element, and it shows no signs of beginning to disappear: modern communications extend its range and speed up its operation without, however, changing its nature.

In *The Armies of the Night,* Norman Mailer has discerned and brilliantly described some of the workings of dramatic politics. But I think he exaggerates the novelty of such proceedings when he says that in the March on the Pentagon, the New Left and the hippies were coming upon the opening intimations of a new style of revolution—revolution by theater and without a script. In fact it was not entirely without a script—as Mr. Mailer's own account shows—and past history, including the history of the French Revolution, is rich in revolution by theater, partly scripted but diverging from its script. Dramatic politics is an ancient phenomenon taking new forms in modern conditions. Thus television and radio have the effect of making dramatic politics more continuous and versatile. This does not, however, make them proportionately more effective; repetition tends to dull responses, which have in any case already been overstimulated by people trying to sell deodorants.

THE MALAISE of the American people is great and growing; or rather the malaise of the American peoples is great and growing, since the malaise of the white people and that of the black people are not identical. The questions which arise or half arise out of this dual malaise are answered in terms of dramatic politics, and this is what makes our theme an important one. There is no need to exaggerate its importance: the sources of the malaise are historical, social, economic; the politics, and the drama of the politics, are secondary phenomena. Yet the fact that they are secondary does not make them inactive, or wholly predetermined by blind forces, or without influence on the choices of the society, or altogether beyond the reach of effective criticism. No criticism is likely to eliminate dramatic politics itself, or even a certain permanent element of illusion in such politics; but criticism can deter and help to drive from the stage the grosser forms of deception, which incapacitate their victims and can carry a society to self-destruction.

As an example, let us touch once more on that notable creation, the Johnsonian Lincoln. In its crude, shambling, impudent way, that was a cunning piece of political theater, a clever pseudo-answer to the dual malaise. For three things were generally known about Lincoln: he *fought a war*, he *saved the country*, and he *freed the blacks*. So to those who were worried about the country and those who were worried about the blacks, the new Lincoln had the answer: help him to win the war, and all would be well. Insofar as this performance was found convincing, or even plausible, it would have worked toward lengthening the war and impressing the toll of unnecessary deaths. Conversely, the fact that it was hooted offstage brought on negotiations. The questions of how good a performance is, and how it is criticized, are therefore not a light matter, although the element of the ridiculous often inherent in the spectacle itself might suggest that it is. Through such performances as this, government tends to develop into what Ruskin called "a certain polluted theatrocracy." Criticism can help to reduce the pollution levels.

Now there are those who think that neither the polluted theatrocracy nor any possible criticism of it really matters very much. Those in power, it is claimed, will always manipulate public opinion, and public opinion cannot significantly affect their options. This school of thought is certainly more realistic than that which believes American foreign policy to be under effective democratic control, subject to considered adjustments by exercise of the popular will every four years. Yet the school which thinks of itself as realistic has its own kind of romanticism, an unacknowledged cult of the stern inflexibility of vast, impersonal forces. Public opinion is indeed largely amenable to manipulation, but it can also be in some degree recalcitrant; not all the effects of the manipulators always come off; if they did, Castro would no longer be in power in Cuba. And the fact that public opinion must have *some* effect on policy options is demonstrated by the very fact of the trouble which those in power take in order to manipulate public opinion. Nor is such manipulation a simple, monolithic, or unilateral thing. There are competing forms of drama, as well as competing forms of criticism. The drama of the status quo fears the drama of black power. And even among those at the center of power in American society, there are conflicting tendencies, manifested in conflicting attempts at manipulation of public opinion. And the very existence of potential alternatives in the manipulation of public opinion can influence foreign policy and even determine the most momentous choices. Mr. Roger Hilsman in *To Move A Nation* has described how President Kennedy was led to allow Mr. McNamara his head in beginning to involve American forces in fighting the Vietnam war. President Kennedy, according to Mr. Hilsman, would have liked to hold back Mr. McNamara but feared to do so, because if he had, the Joint Chiefs would have made trouble for him in Congress. Behind this capacity to make trouble, lay of course the Manichaean world-view of the American electorate and the vulnerability of the Democrats to the charge of absent-mindedness—"losing Vietnam" as they had "lost China." So McNamara had his way, and the descent down the slippery slope began.

What this suggests is that the struggle for public opinion is more important, more complex, and less predictable in its outcome than some of the "realists" are prepared to allow. Has the intellectual community, so conscious of its alienation, adequately grasped its opportunities and responsibilities in this domain? The very subject of the question raises further questions; it would be easy to say of the intellectual community that when it is intellectual it is not a community and when it is a community it is not intellectual. Let us be less ambitious, then, and ask—as it is appropriate we should in this context—whether the world of the universities in its widest sense—students, graduates, faculty, and people sufficiently interested to read essays like this—might not produce out of itself a more conscious and concerted effort to educate the public opinion of this country out of the present dangerous crassness of its assumptions about the world?

The university world, as a whole, will not of course make any concerted effort in this or any other matter; nor is it desirable that it should. But already within the university world there has formed a sizable body of opinion, mainly of young people, which rejects the mythology of political Manichaeanism and consequently rejects America's world counterrevolutionary role, of which the war in Vietnam is the present, scandalous symbol. These people, in the protest and resistance movements, have provided their own form of dramatic politics—some of it very effective natural drama, like that acted out before the Pentagon last October. Among the protesters and resisters have also been a few highly effective older critics of the mythology, notably Professor Noam Chomsky. The movement of minds among the young has had its effects; among intellectuals, the "liberal-but-anticommunist" position no longer has its old appeal: the best of its former tenants have abandoned it, and some of those who still cling to it confess to feeling a little seedy.

MOVEMENTS OF OPINION among intellectuals have in the past—in France and Russia for example—rippled out rather slowly among the population at large; I think they are so rippling out here and now. But this not enough. We need to use such skills and knowledge as we have in order to reach and educate a much wider public. We have ourselves made use of dramatic politics, but like our opponents, we have not always used it wisely. Burning has always had a dramatic impact, but one should be careful about what one burns. Burning a draft card carries a clear, specific message —rejection of an unjust war—but burning an American flag works on the public mind simply as propaganda in favor of President Johnson. And of course the political dramatists on the other side do what they can, within the mass media, to select from the drama of protest those scenes which best suit their purposes.

The drama in any case is interpreted according to prevailing assumptions and takes effect within them, modifying them only slightly. It is at the level of assumptions, through criticism and analysis, that the main work has to be done. Much of this work will have to be done by teachers, inside and outside the classroom. For years, under the guise of patriotism and the designation of history, American youth has been indoctrinated in conservative chauvinism, the ideological preparation for counterrevolutionary action and the seed-bed of the present disasters. There are probably now quite a large number of teachers who are sufficiently conscious, sufficiently determined, and sufficiently aware of their own numbers and strength to refuse to allow themselves to be used for such indoctrination and to try to give their pupils, to the best of their own knowledge and belief, a relatively undistorted picture of the world today and of America's position in it. If this can be done—and of course efforts will be made to counter it—the political audience, which in any case will increasingly be an educated one, will come to show radically different responses, and the character of the political drama will change accordingly.

I do not wish to imply, like the more simpleminded of the eighteenth-century enlighteners, that education automatically makes men better. You do not educate man away from his interests and appetites. But it can, I think, be shown that the interests of most Americans, and even the interests of the white middle-class generally, do not in fact require a counterrevolutionary strategy in the world, and do require an equivalent effort for the improvement of domestic conditions. If that can be shown, and if it is shown, then education can work for peace and progress. But it will have to be the educators themselves, and not the government, that do the showing. The government is itself to a great extent the prisoner of its own political drama, more than half believing it itself, and frightened by it; frightened also of the people whom in the past it has helped to frighten, and frightened of others who might frighten the people afresh. This self-sustaining politics of fantasy and fright has acquired a momentum of its own, carrying it away from its original base in interest and toward collective disaster at home and abroad.

It is not necessary to accept this process as inevitable, still less to welcome it—as some on the extreme Left are doing, and as members of the German extreme Left welcomed the rise of Hitler as the dark harbinger of brighter days to come, only attainable by a passage through fascism and world war. Those brighter post-Hitler days, in which we now live, are hardly so bright as to encourage us to cooperate in venturing on a further, similar passage through certain dark toward possible light. It seems worthwhile, rather, to try to break the cycle; and for those of us who are in one way or another concerned with communication, it seems most promising to break it across its lines of communication, to criticize the established form of dramatic politics out of credibility into absurdity, and to offer other forms of drama in its place.

In Robert Frost's *A Masque of Reason*, God says to Job:

> Society can never think things out:
> It has to see them acted out by actors.
> Devoted actors at a sacrifice—
> The ablest actors I can lay my hands on.

The present leading actors are hardly the ablest God could lay his hands on, but the element of sacrifice is undoubtedly present. Those who are being sacrificed in what is now being acted out, have been assigned to the crowd scenes: they are the young men of this country and the population of Vietnam. Those young men who refuse to play the parts assigned to them in this scenario but instead prefer to give the drama a new turn of their own, the young men who won't take their cue from the draft board and who prefer the role of prisoner to that of soldier in an unjust war—these are indeed the ablest actors. *Devoted actors at a sacrifice* in the drama which this society, not having thought out, has now to act out.

Bayonet Training with Loudspeaker, Fort Leonard Wood, Mo.

Charles David Wright

WHAT IS THE SPIRIT OF THE BAYONET?
We knew he knew. No sergeant is that dumb.
Just yesterday we told him fifty times
as by the number in meatlocker cold
we lunged in lines and disemboweled the air.
My gloves stolen, I couldn't feel the stock,
much less the spirit of the bayonet.

WHAT IS THE SPIRIT OF THE BAYONET?
We knew he knew. Could he perhaps forget
what was entrenched in bunkers of his mind?
Next to me Klein, whose father was a moyel,
couldn't control his bladder or his blade
and dropped out of the drill with chafing legs.
Piss on the spirit of the bayonet.

WHAT IS THE SPIRIT OF THE BAYONET?
We had to answer and he had to know.
Over the mike he led our litany,
constraining us to yell to save our lives.
So, having upheld painfully the same
position in this pointed dialogue,
numb to the wrist, I made my bloodless thrust
and shouted with my company, "TO KILL!"

The Drive Home

Russell Banks

"I thought how just, americans
still love morally with many preliminary questions."
—*Ed Dorn* ("Hawthorne, End of March, 1962")

. . . So FAR AS I can see now, there are but two directions available to me, just two, and no more: In and Out.
All others, which many people will claim are different, new
directions, simply are not. They must be either In or Out.
If she thinks to ask me:

Up or Down?
North or South?
East or West?
North by Northwest or South by Southeast?
That or This?
From or To?

I will have to answer, No. For these, as well as any
others already mentioned inadvertently in passing, all these
sets of directions are best understood as In or Out. Whether
in or out of context.

I simply can't see it as being any other way. Not even
circular (an absurd notion, relevant perhaps to the experiences of plants and some lower animals, but thankfully
no longer regarded by *any*one in *any* field as even remotely
relevant to human experience—which disregard, admittedly,
imposes a bit of a come-down on us human animals, regardless of the pride we take in the efficiency with which truth
is being served).

No. Not even circular.

I don't want to digress, but it's strange, how every time,
when I seem to begin, I have the distinct impression that I
am absolutely alone, as if standing in the middle of an
enormous room, whose walls are too far away for me to see
in this gloomy light; and then in a very short time I dis-

cover that what all along I thought I was presenting to myself alone, was actually being uttered to someone else. And then I realize that either I am not alone, or else I am what is usually called "mad." Viz., I speak: therefore I'm heard. Yet *that* makes absolutely no sense whatsoever, even to me, and surely not to anyone who happens to be listening out for something worth listening to.

But to return. In and/or Out. The move In and/or the move Out.

The first is nearly completed now; the second will begin soon. An arrival, as such, should not be looked for, any more than a point of departure should. They have been ignored here, as everywhere . . .

This is so damned *difficult!* It's not even circular. I sometimes try to console my self and family by saying that if we weren't alive, we wouldn't even be interested in life. Some consolation.

(Surely, the dreams that afflict other people's lives are not so fucking ultimate! What I wouldn't give for a little symbolism now and then. Or myth, even.)

(All my dreams, and therefore, all my acts as well, seem to end parenthetically, even when busted apart by the alarm clock. The alarm clock! Now *there's* a symbol for you!)

. . . A WILLING GIRL spreads like a coffee-colored flower with a still-darker center, and I grow heavy with infamy by midafternoon.

Driving home in sleet to wife and tiny daughter. Windshield wipers shuffling the scene before me with each swipe of the blade.

Boston.

The industrial suburbs.

The residential suburbs.

Moving out from the tight black center, like a pale insect —sated, bloated, staggering heavily away. . . .

Driving. Bent over my work intently, one hand on the inside of either thigh, thumbs working the brown flesh, working it up, palms and fingers pressing thighs down; brown, round ass down flat against the mattress; holding her down; down; down. . . .

Outside, icy rain noisily slops into the streets, falls across these high narrow brick buildings, sloshes along gutters, choking the sewers.

I tell her none of this, I tell her nothing, except what she expects and desires to hear from me, here, doing this infamous thing to her. Later, I tell her what I was thinking at the time—because she asks. (You want to know what I was thinking while I was fucking her? All right, if that somehow gratifies you, I'll tell you. I wonder what you'll make of it.) This:

I was worrying about how I could not forget where I was and what I was doing. No, really. Who can forget where they are and what they are doing, when they are fucking in these cities, these cold, blackened crematoriums, where all the people crowd up against the fences, pushing and shoving weakly for a chance to stare out at the ones who years ago, when there must have been more room for fewer people, got away. They smile back from outside, looking somehow quaint, the men reading their newspapers, the women dressed in white, starched aprons, beating tan batter in wooden bowls. Even . . . no, *especially*, my wife and daughter, seen from here, seem no longer to have anything to do with me. I recognize them as distant dead relatives seen in a daguerreotype. My daughter chirps like a bird in a warm kitchen. My wife prepares an evening meal, smiling as she works. They have no names.

I am all name, and as a result am heavy with infamy . . .

You crazy, she says, thinking something else (but not the *fact* of thinking something else).

I'm not insane. No sir. Nor am I ashamed. I'm guilty, that's what. Shame can be but for a single act; guilt is for all existence. The price and the consequence.

There ain't no way around it, I tell her. One simply must go for the center, the dark hole that opens for him, and with hands, feet, and mouth wide open and reaching, to touch everything—wet ceilings, flaking walls, scaly floors cold against bare feet; and lifting suddenly, he will come to life, like a huge motor starting up. The past turns into a picture-magazine that he flipped through once while waiting for someone to come into the room and call his name (The Doctor will see you now, Mr. Bass.) and tell him what he's dying of. Of being a father. A husband. A Caucasian.

A Ph.D. A twenty-seven-year-old American male. A high-school teacher of American history. Of being the owner of a 1959 Chevrolet Impala sedan. Of being a registered Democrat in the town of Wakefield, Massachusetts. Of being the husband of a nineteen-year-old blonde from Hartford, Connecticut. Of being the only child of parents dying silently, slowly, in Crawford, New Hampshire. Of being the friend of a friend, with no friends of his own. Of being an insomniac who dreams. Of being an adulterer. A wife-beater. A cheater at cards. A tall man. A heavy man. Of being a quiet man. A formal man. A cold man. A stingy man. Of being a ridiculous man . . . a woefully ridiculous man full of pity for himself. *These* kinds of things, presumably, one needs to hear from others. It is for these, we are told, that one needs to hear from others. This is why they must keep on talking to us. For we are taught to believe, by each other, that we cannot exist without first coming to know, and constantly coming to know again, these kinds of things about ourselves. And then, as a consequence, we die—as if to prove the truth of what we've been told. . . .

The truth is subtler stuff, though. And less easily complied with. For the truth is that I cannot need to know these kinds of things, if I also need to exist. They are important to me only if I'm in a hurry to die. They are the things for which I can feel only passing pride or redeemable shame.

No. Guilt is the meaningful consequence, the one meaningful consequence . . . and therefore, the one desirable consequence.

Give it to me, baby! she cries to the ceiling.

Take it! I reply. Take it, take it!

Give it to me, baby! Don't hurt me!

Take it, take it, take it!

Give it to me! Oh Jesus, Jesus!

Take it . . . take it . . . take it . . . !

And then I come, deep inside her, all at once and from every direction, like a full jug, shattering. . . .

She pounds me on the head with her fists, beats at my ears and eyes, cheeks, nose, and lips, moaning. . . .

While dressing, I peer through the soot-covered window and watch the people down below on the street. Cringing

in gray light beneath the cold rain. Hiding under newspapers, hats, umbrellas. Scurrying along sidewalks in dark,
heavy clothing.

You good, baby. You make it. Honey, you really make it.
More of the same, I tell her. That's all it is.

. . . AND I HAVE dreams of being caught, as by a photo-
graph, in certain postures and with facial expressions representing me at the precise instant of the climax of some
athletic event. (Here I am exhibiting my now-famous,
high-Yankee bellyroll, as I go up and over the high-jump
bar. As if I am actually floating in the air! Notice, in the
background, the curious mixture of disappointment, cha-
grin, and sheer disbelief beginning to spread across the
Russian's face. . . .)

Yet I also have dreams of suddenly spinning on my
heels and raising a high-powered rifle to my shoulder,
aiming coolly down the barrel at a creature moving rapidly
along the rocky bank of a mountain stream, and—when I
have let the tip of the barrel cruelly hover above the
creature's head for barely a second—dropping it to the
head, squeezing the trigger. As if one move necessitated the
other! (Here the dream ends, for it is not of my killing
the creature but of my firing the gun. . . . Then it repeats.)

These two types of dreams in recent years have literally
plagued my sleep and have now become as images for me.
Images *to* me, actually. And *for* my "identity." Insofar as
my identity can be said to concern me.

This is because I am a thief and a murderer. (Aside:
Like all thieves and murderers, he is many other things as
well, but it is only as a thief and a murderer that he con-
cerns himself with his self. For while we are asleep here,
we are awake elsewhere, and thus every man is at least two
men.)

Images, however, have no psychological or psycho/
sociological significance for me. None whatsoever. I feel
able to affirm this, to employ it as a basic premise in any
examination of my self, because I have no doubt but that I
am located at the very center of the universe and am,
thereby, its prime mover. My attitude toward the universe

and its center and the necessary relation between the two (i.e., one of them being necessarily the mover of the other, and thus the "prime" mover) may well be little more than an unconscious response to the all-pervasive notion of a heliocentric solar system; but even if this *is* so, I cannot help it, nor can I ever know it for sure, and so I do not intend to try (helping or knowing).

Therefore, when I am asked, Why, Fletcher, do you steal? I am able to answer freely, Because I am a thief. And to, Why do you murder? I reply: Because I am a murderer.

The nub of me, then, must be metaphysical.

And the nature of my enterprise—to uncover the nub—casts me in the role of metaphysician. Given my premises, I am perhaps the diagnostician of my own soul, but only if the diagnosis gives up evidence that a prognosis will be required. Otherwise, my enterprise will have been purely analytical, which, while not a totally fruitless activity, still doesn't give me quite the ethical dignity of the other.

The most recent—and in many ways the most clear-cut—evidence that I am a thief and a murderer turned up this very morning, shortly before dawn. This must be regarded as incontrovertible proof. Then I will move on confidently to a much more tangled matter, i.e., the question of meaning. That is, the "So what?" end of the question.

But to cite the evidence:

This morning, before it had begun fading into light, I stole a small glass of Irish whiskey from a bottle that had been left out on a liquor cabinet the night before, and I killed a little girl, who was about ten years old, I would guess, and who had gotten up before anyone else in the house. Passing the door to the living room while on her merry way to the bathroom, she discovered me there and demanded to know what I was doing, drinking her Daddy's whiskey. I hit her on the head with a poker and left the house by the cellar door, the same way I had entered the house hours before. As always, I was confused but not, as in the past, mortified. (Mortification is essentially the result of having been surprised. Once such things no longer were capable of surprising me, they were unable to mortify me. This, in spite of my continuing to become horribly confused.)

Well and good, but "So what?" one might say.

Indeed. So this:

So now I endure dreams of standing before a liquor cabinet in an unfamiliar, shadow-banked living room, a half-filled glass of excellent Irish whiskey in my hand. Old Bushmill's.

A little girl, probably about ten years old and dressed only in her flannel nightgown, pads barefoot down the hall, passes the living room, and accidentally, casually, peers into the gloom of the room and sees me.

What are you doing, drinking my Daddy's whiskey? His very favorite, too! she adds, amazingly unruffled for a child her age.

I put the glass down, grab a poker from beside the fireplace, and before the tyke has had a chance to realize what I am up to, I have killed her, felled her with a single blow, have wiped all fingerprints from all touched objects and am disappearing silently down the cellar steps, like a genie returning to his lamp. . . .

Images, then, multiply uncontrollably, and with incredible speed. And so must the things they represent. Or I would have been wakened and punished long ago.

. . . It's not unusual for me to while away an evening at home by sitting in my green chair listening to Verdi. *Falstaff*, his swan-song, is my favorite. Thus it is even less unusual if I happen to be tapping my foot to *Falstaff* (Act II).

The Boston Globe, refolded along original creases, lying beside the chair like a good dog, headlines pressed to the floor. The apartment silent, except for the music. The roars of Falstaff's courting, emitted from a machine squatting across the room from me, seeming to emphasize the silence of the other five rooms in the flat. Maroon, cracked-leather slippers on feet. Necktie loosened. Cardigan unbuttoned. Eyeglasses on the table next to the chair, thumb and forefinger of right hand rubbing dents on either side of bridge of nose. Gray odor of boiled cabbage still hanging in the air, sneaking up nostrils, spreading corrosively through convoluted passageways up behind eyes and forehead. . . .

None of this is unusual for me.

None of it.

None of it. . . .

(Aside: Our hero need not despair of continuing this dreary normalcy, however. He is a cocksman now. And in a second or two, he will rise from his green, thick-limbed chair's hug, will turn up the volume of his portable record player, and will tramp authoritatively down the dim hall to the bathroom at the end. For he is a cocksman now, and a cocksman, as Archilochos says, must keep his prick clean and dainty.)

Mistress Quickly's voice in the background, Falstaff's barreling from the huge wicker hamper next to the wall, Mr. Ford's raging on either side of Mistress Quickly's . . . I flop my prick over the cold, white edge of the sink, watch it shrink back and feel my balls (still inside my pants) drawing up from the shock of the cold. Rather small for a cocksman's.

Not so much small, actually, as temperamental: enormous, scarlet, quivering, when enticed; tiny, brown, and flaccid, when challenged or ignored. And having rid myself of wife and child, I am prepared to have it enticed. I slosh it around in warm water for a few moments, dry it carefully with a face towel and place it back into my pants, dropping it and feeling its nice weight down there in the warmth and darkness of my crotch.

Checking (coat and muffler on): record-player off, no gas jets left on in the kitchen, all but the hall light turned off, wallet in pocket, money in wallet, cigarettes, matches, comb in shirt pocket. He closes the door, steps into the gloom of the stairwell landing, turns back to the door and locks it. Drops the keys back into his coat pocket. Sniffs: the cooking smells of five kitchens—two on the first floor, two on the second, and one on his, the third—sweep through his head like a swarm of houseflies. Descending two flights of stairs to the street will be unpleasant for him. . . .

Checking again: gloves in coat pocket, one in each, keys in right pocket, car key on key ring.

Then I remember: Oh, the *car!* She took the car with her!

You take the car and I'll have you arrested for stealing it! I had screeched into her face. I mean it! We're not just a-playing around now, lady! No sir! You take that car and I'll have a warrant for your arrest sworn out in five minutes!

You've been watching too much television, she muttered,

going back to the task of buttoning Laura's coat. Laura sat on the chair, unable to move in her clothes and looking, inside coat, leggings, hat, scarf, mittens and fur-lined boots, like an overheated teddy bear being pushed, prodded, and pulled about by an angry teen-ager.

That's no teen-ager; that's my wife.

What're you going to do, Dagmar? I calmly asked, leaning back against the kitchen sink, folding my arms complacently across my chest. Run home to Mama and Papa, taking *them* your child, like a teen-ager again? Is that what you want? Is that what I'm keeping you from? Huh? C'mon, let's hear it! I'm keeping you from being a teen-ager! That's *really* it, isn't it! I smiled—as if I had just explained some self-evident truth to my students. American History 101-A. The "bright" students. Hah! I'll show 'em who's bright. Compared to them, to her, I'm a goddam Christmas tree.

You know, I observed, lighting a cigarette and blowing jets of blue smoke out my nostrils, you know, Dagmar, you really aren't too different from all the little teen-age tarts I see sitting out there in front of me every day. Cud-chewing, empty-headed, purple-sweatered cunts. That's *all* they are, you know. The correspondences are self-evident, m'dear.

She stood up, slowly, stiffly. Laura, at last, was capable of facing the elements. Will you *please* shut up? she said to me, lifting the child off the chair and placing her onto the floor in a standing position. Then she went to the coat closet, took her long, gray tweed coat from a wire hanger and climbed into it.

And the same goes for Laura too! I yelled to her, with Laura, having heard her name mentioned, struggling vainly to turn around and face her accuser. I mean, the same as goes for the car! You take this child out of here and I'll swear out a warrant for your arrest on kidnapping charges! Then I'll get a divorce on grounds of desertion, which'll give *me* custody of the child!

You can't win, I smiled, as she returned to the kitchen.

Fletcher, she said in a low voice, Fletch, please. You've got to stop this now . . . please. You've taken just about everything I have . . . *including* my love for you. Please know that. Please know that I don't love you anymore. I don't even care what comes out of your mouth anymore. So please know what is happening now . . . to you . . .

to me, and for God's sake, know what is happening to
Laura! The marriage is over, Fletcher . . . You've killed it.
Please recognize the fact of its *death!* Don't you know that
we can't fight anymore? Fighting with each other is something people can do only when there's still some kind of
life left in their marriage . . . and ours is dead. It doesn't
even matter who killed it. . . .

You're perfectly right, I told her. Which is why I'm so
concerned about Laura and the car. When there's nothing
else, one turns to protecting his property, and as for Laura,
my concern is simply that you don't take her out in the
streets at this late hour with no definite place to go. Your
parents live several hundred miles from here, as you know,
and you have no money to get there by public transporta-
tion. Your friends . . . well, if you have any friends who
will put you up, *I* don't know them.

She sighed. She was very tired by then. Fletcher, give
me the key to the car. I have a credit card for gas and I'll
only use it to buy enough gas to get to Hartford . . .

See! You *are* running home to Mama and Papa!

Just until I can figure out what to do after that. Now
give me the key. Please.

Sorry, Dagmar. I refuse to aid you in this . . . this
escapade, in any way whatsoever. Nor will I force you to
stay, of course. As far as I am concerned, you are an adult.
Regardless of your desires to be treated like a teen-ager.

Fletcher . . . please.

Laura began to cry. I looked at her.

I think that you have gone insane, Fletcher, she announced quietly. I don't know what else to think . . .
because if you haven't gone insane, then everything else has
been insane all along . . . right from the beginning. Never
mind about the car key. I think I have my own in the glove
compartment. (The first time I knew *that.*) Then she
picked Laura up in her arms and walked out of the
kitchen, down the hall, and out the door. I listened to her
clump, clump, clump, down the stairs, her heavy steps
growing fainter and fainter as she descended, until finally
I couldn't hear them anymore.

It was so quick . . . and so easy.

I walked out onto the landing. Heard the building door
hissing as it closed on the street, and a few seconds later,

the easily recognizable, clear, sweet rumble of the Corvette coming to life where I had parked it out in front of the building this afternoon. The blood rushed into my head and then as quickly drained, and I felt suddenly chilled standing out there on the landing.

(Aside: He locks the door slowly behind him, walks down the hall to the coat closet, sheds his coat and goes into the living room. Loosening his tie and unbuttoning his cardigan, kicking off loafers and sliding his feet into old slippers, he sets Verdi's *Falstaff* on the record player, flicks the machine on and drops his body into his green armchair. This is the way he usually spends his evenings. Toward the end of the second act, he falls asleep. Sitting up. In the chair. Thumb and forefinger of his right hand pressing. Into either side of the bridge. Of his nose.)

. . . THERE IS an order to all this. There is a continuum. Though they are not the same here, no more than anywhere else. But nevertheless, there is no beginning, nor is there an ending: I can't say otherwise, for I can express things no more honestly than I can experience them. If I go backwards, or cross over, it is only toward what I mean. And while there may well be uncovered a progression here, there is no progress as such. . . .

The young lady next to me on the bus keeps smiling primly straight ahead, across her bony knees and out the huge, wall-like windshield, to the road that seems to be laying itself down before us, a black ribbon between mounds and fields of snow on either side. The girl's light blue ski sweater is covered with fine, white angel-hair, making her look hazy from neck to waist. Her face is a young Christian's: confident, complaisant, and pitying, all at once, and consequently, she looks at me with gratitude and pity when she can no longer stare straight ahead and be polite about it.

Bored, I give up trying to impress her stolid taste with intellectual filigree and go back to looking out the window on my other side.

Across the aisle from the girl sits a big, blond, crew-cut boy of twenty or so, no larger than I am but in much better shape, and he knows her needs instinctively, whereas I would have difficulty even learning them by rote. His is the suggestion that we sing. We—the skiers and I. His, too, the guitar. And the songs.

Which they all sing with gusto. Two or three songs that they must have learned from Pete Seeger records owned by their roommates at college. I nod my head in time to the music, smiling gently—to show her the range of my tolerance, I suppose.

Then the blond guy across the aisle from her, seeing that not quite all of the skiers on the bus appreciate his enthusiasm for music (since it *is* still rather early in the day), suggests loudly that whoever wants to have a "sing-along" (his expression) should join him and his trusty guitar at the rear of the bus, where there happen to be many vacant seats. He stands up in the middle of the aisle, guitar in hand, and coaxes the Christian lady to follow him to the rear of the bus, where, we all know, it will be darker, more intimate, and further from the father-figure in the military uniform, the fat man driving the bus implacably northward, than where we are now seated—in the front row, with only the driver and the exit steps between us and the great wall of glass.

Hey, c'mon, whyn't we all go sing in the back! C'mon, everybody, there's loads of room back there and we won't have to bug the driver that way! C'mon! Everybody who wants to sing move to de back ob de bus! (Suburban white wit, I smile tolerantly to my Christian lady, who missed it and thus cannot comprehend my response, its dignity.) C'mon, he says to my lady. Say, what's your name, anyhow? Mine's Buzz, he says proudly.

Mine's Fletcher, I murmur into her tiny ear. Fletcher Bass.

Mine's Cynthia, she tells Buzz. Cynthia, she repeats to me compassionately, lifting her hard, broad, and nearly shapeless wool-skirted ass from the seat, stepping clumsily to the aisle, as Buzz, grinning heartily at the other grinning passengers (who are actually relieved to see him and his guitar moving away from them), strolls toward the empty seats at the back.

I follow them, one or two of the others ahead of me—between me and Cynthia—and one or two more sliding along behind. We all sit around Buzz, presumably because he has the guitar and it was his idea in the first place to come here and sing. Cynthia is next to him, leaning toward him carefully, almost touching his beefy, sweatered shoulder with her hamburger-bun breasts. Several young American skiers, all of them looking like overfed Swedes, place themselves on the wide end-seat on either side of Cynthia and Buzz. I am draped over the back of the next to the last seat, staring Buzz right in his blue eye and talking quietly all the while to Cynthia: about order, the continuum, and the differences between the two, about beginnings and endings, their absence in our experience, about progression and the lack of progress. All my obsessions. But Cynthia keeps her baby-blue eyes fixed on Buzz's thick fingers as they do a stumbling imitation of Carlos Montoya's fingers.

Hey, swell! Here's a great one to start with! Buzz shouts, beginning immediately to bang on the strings, crump, crump, crump. Yeah! Everybody knows this one! He commences the singing, with everyone (except me) joining by the second word: We-shall-o-ver-cu-um! We-shall-o-ver-cu-um! We-shall-o-ver-cum-sum-m-m-m-day!

And so on. I don't bother to keep time with head-noddings now. At the right moment, I reach across the space between Buzz and the back of my seat and grab his bass-string just as he brings his hand down to crump all six strings evenly, and I yank the string straight out, so that his hand, rippling across the upper five, bangs into the sixth and bounces back up, killing the song, naturally, and probably hurting his hand, too. He stops, and everyone else piles up on top of whomever he has been secretly following. Except Cynthia, who seems to have been following a chorus of singers not on this bus, who simply goes on singing, alone, sweetly and slightly off-key: We-shall-o-ver-cum-sum-day-ay-ay-ay . . . ! Deep-in-my-heart-I-know-that-we-shall-o-ver-cum-m-m-sum-m-m (moving straight through to the finish now, all alone, smiling, mouth wide open) day-y-y-y-y-y!

What did you do *that* for? Buzz barks at me.

Let th' broad sing, ya creep! Whaddaya, Melchior or somethin, ya gotta drown the broad out? (Aside: *This* is what our hero came to see—not the "Christian Lady," not the happy songsters one and all, but the confused anger of the blond young man with the guitar. For he, the one called Buzz, he is the only one in the group not counting F.B., whose mere thoughts can drown out the very voices of the others, whose pride is greater than all their vanities and whose guilt is greater than all their trivial shames. *He* is the one to be encountered, for he is the only one capable of, and thus driven to, the feat of swallowing up the others, F.B. included.)

Lissen, mister, Buzz snarls, I don't know what kinda game you're playing, but I'm not innarested. Now, whyn't you just go on back down to the front of the bus and stop bothering people? he suggests, nipping angrily at the words with his even, perfectly white teeth.

I look to Cynthia, as if for understanding and pity. Securing assurances of same, I turn back to Buzz, who has much more understanding than Cynthia will ever have, but naturally, and as a direct result, no pity whatsoever. Look, I say, if this is some kinda closed group I'm breaking into, I mean, if this is some kinda *clique* or something and strangers belong elsewhere whenever you people get together to sing together, I'd be the last one to want to bust in and ruin the sanctity of the thing. (Aside: Outflanked him, though he probably saw it coming. Not the language, though. He never could've anticipated F.B.'s freedom from language, which is what allows *him* to employ *it*, rather than vice versa, even though Buzz probably possesses that very same freedom himself. Simply hasn't realized it yet, that's all.)

Just don't keep the rest of us from enjoying *our*selves, okay? We won't ask you to do anything you don't want to do, so long as you do the same for us. Okay? And right now, we want to sing. So if you can't join us and if you want to keep on interrupting like you just did, we'll have to insist that you leave us. Okay?

Not okay.

What???

I said, *not* okay.

Wal . . . well, then, you'll just have to take off, pal. Just move on outa here. That's all. G'wan, beat it!

C'mon, forget it, Buzz. He's just looking for trouble. Let's ignore him, huh?

Buzz glares the suggestion down, sends it flying back to

its owner's original anonymity and silence with a wave of his thick hand. What are you after, mister? he asks, and I know it's all over for him now: he's too close to genuine curiosity and too far from direct challenge, and the only way he can ever get back will be if I decide to allow him back. Which, of course, I simply cannot do. Not now. No, he'll have to get back on his own now.

What am I after, Buzz? I'm glad you asked that question. Because *this* is what I'm after: I want you to take your guitar and march yourself right down to the front of the bus and request the driver to stop and let you off right now, or as soon as it's possible for him to do so safely. I smile benignly at him.

What??? You . . . you're out of your head! This is crazy! He looks to the others for confirmation, but they are looking to him for confirmation. Even Cynthia—whose pity has finally turned its light onto its real object, herself.

Do you think you can accomplish that, Buzz? I ask nicely.

Look, you're nuts! You don't know me, so I don't know what you're talking about!

I know you now, fella. Don't I? So let's hop to it. We're almost to Concord, the driver'll have to make a stop there, and you can catch a bus back to Boston in a few hours with no trouble at all. You'll even have time to take in a bit of the city. It's small, but it is the state capital, you know. So pack up your guitar, Buzz, and get moving. Right now, fella! I add sharply.

Lissen, mister, *you're* the one who's going to get moving! he shouts, and he grabs my arm with one hand, his other hand moving quickly to assist his violence and, consequently, letting go of the guitar's neck—a lost, hopeless, desperate move. For I simply grab the guitar by its neck where he had been clutching it, yank it down onto the floor next to my seat and stamp my foot through it, ruining the instrument with one blow. Buzz lets go of my arm, horrified, and falling back into his seat, he turns into a miserable, utterly miserable, young man staring down at his smashed guitar.

This is where you get off, I inform him, as we glide down Concord's main street.

This bus finally hisses to a stop before a small brick building which serves as a railroad station—taxi stand—bus depot. Buzz stands up weakly and moves slowly past me. You bastard, he says quietly. If I ever see you . . . if I ever catch you where I can deal with you . . . someplace like a dark alleyway . . . I'll beat the living shit out of you!

Buzz! Cynthia exclaims, shocked. You mustn't be vengeful. Try to *forgive* him, Buzz. *Pity* him. He's a man we must all feel *sorry* for, not *hate,* she says. Please, Buzz. Stay. Don't get off the bus.

If I stay here, I'll kill the bastard!

Buzz! Cynthia cries, pitying him for his wrath.

You'd better get a move on, Buzz, I remind him.

I just hope you're happy, mister. . . . Cause if you set out to make me sick, don't worry, you did! And *that's* why I'm getting off this bus . . . because you make me sick! I'd stay if you'd leave . . . but you're not enough of a human being to do anything like that! No!

Don't beg me, Buzz. It's unbecoming. And it won't do you a bit of good. Not now.

You shit! he says, moving down the aisle for the door, grabbing his satchel from the luggage rack above his original seat at the front of the bus and his loden coat from the seat itself, then stalking glumly down the steps and out the door.

The remaining five or six at the back of the bus, including Cynthia, file past me in abject silence and return to their original seats, all of them, as they sit down, glancing out their windows at Buzz. Then, not understanding their embarrassment, their own senses of loss and secret joy, very quickly turning away.

A few miles down the road, with the bus passing through a small country village called Boscawen, New Hampshire, I walk forward and ask the driver to let me off as soon as he can safely do so. He is able to stop the bus after a few seconds in front of a barn-red general store. I pull my coat off the rack above Cynthia's head, drape it over my shoulders like a cape, and say good-bye to Cynthia. Take good care of yourself, baby, I sagely advise. And don't worry about ol' Buzz or me. You'll be wasting your time, cause we're both fine. Just do what comes natural, baby. Worry about Cynthia.

You gettin off or not, buddy? the driver inquires.

Off, I say, and so I do.

Nobody looks out his window at me as the bus wheezes from the gravel parking lot to the road, heads north to the mountains.

Surrounded by head-high snow banks, I began to hitch-hike back to Concord. The third car to pass me heading south, an old Ford station wagon driven by a tall middle-aged woman in an army surplus field jacket, stopped.

. . . HOME: Crawford, New Hampshire. Where one's parents reside.

There is snow on the ground, on the trees. Recently fallen, with no chance to melt from crotches and forks among the branches of the trees.

The house: squat, fat in the middle, and tapered at both ends where rooms, porches and garages have been tacked on over the years—haphazardly added and never quite able to merge with the main design of the house, even after decades. The house, its barn, the entire country-side—languishing warmly in late morning beneath the chill blanket of snow. . . .

The dirt road, cleared by scraping off most of its snow cover, looking stark and brown, like dog shit, against the scrupulously white snow. Winds cross and finally flee the shadowed valley, dashing quickly along the road and dis-appearing in the north with the road, behind tall, slope-shouldered pine trees.

There are gray hills in the north beyond the pines. And huddling like sleeping bears beyond the hills, there are the White Mountains. The Presidential Range. There are lakes and rivers and streams; the tracks of glaciers everywhere. And the buildings seem almost as old as the land forms.

Among these buildings: the house. It sets back from the road about seventy-five feet. In the front yard, between the house and the road, loom two enormous elm trees. Crossing the yard, cutting between the two elms, a blue 1949 Ford panel truck, the chains on its rear wheels grab-bing at the dead grass and frozen turf beneath the snow, yanking the truck backwards to the front door of the house, where it stops. Two men dressed in plaid wool mackinaws and caps jump out of the truck, disappear into the house, and soon return with armloads of articles from inside the house. Back, and forth, disappearing together into the house, then reappearing with their arms full, or at either end of some huge piece of furniture or trunk, then disappearing into the truck and coming out again empty-handed. Back and forth. Back and forth. Their faces cannot be seen from where I am (wherever *that* is); only their broad backs.

On the south side of the house there is a porch that runs the depth of the structure. A man is sitting on the porch. He rocks a rocking chair and peers off the porch to the ground below, seeming to let his attention casually gather in the subtle details of the snow-covered meadow before him. He is a heavy man, though not fat, and rather tall. He appears to be in his late twenties.

The two workmen busily carry furniture from the insides of the house to the insides of the truck. End tables, lamps, cartons ostensibly filled with kitchen implements, beds, mattresses, curtains, rugs, chairs, a sewing machine. The truck long ago should have been filled to overflowing, but still the men come and go with their arms full of large, unwieldy objects, disappearing each time into the back of the small panel truck like a long line of circus clowns disappearing into a tiny, scarlet automobile parked in the middle of the center ring.

Finally, the two burly men come out of the truck for the last time, and instead of returning to the house for more, they step aside and face the open door, their backs against the truck's open door, standing at attention, like footmen for Cinderella. The man on the porch continues to rock and look at the ground dropping away and spreading out like water before him.

An old woman suddenly appears from inside the house. She is tall and slender, with white hair tied up beneath a black pillbox hat, and she is carrying a small, dark green steel box and several large brown mailing envelopes. She walks purposefully out the door, leaving it open behind her, and steps gracefully into the rear of the truck. The footmen quickly close the truck door as soon as she is inside. Then they walk around and get into the front seat of the truck, start the motor, and drive quickly across the yard, driving in their original set of tire tracks in the snow between the two elms, turning right when they reach the road (turning toward the south) and disappearing.

The man on the porch continues as before. The front door of the house is still open. This house is my parents' house. I am the man on the porch (Aside: Look at his *face*, for God's sake, not to mention his posture!). I do not recognize the two men who have been removing all that the house contained. The woman, clearly, is my mother. Although I did not get a good look at her face. They ignored me on the porch, all three of them. They behaved as if I weren't even there. I leap from my rocking chair and rush into the cold, stripped house, to see if maybe my father has been left hanging around somewhere. To see if *anything* has been left me. Anything at all!

Nostalgia of the Infinite

Robert Watson

FLAGS FLY from a white tower's top in a green sky.
The dark couple at its base do not embrace
Look up or down. This is the nostalgia
Of the infinite,
Of the infinite set on the retina,
On the base of the brain when the rain wipes clean
The brain pan and the wind bangs the pan on its nail.

Holcomb, Kansas

William Stafford

The city man got dust on his shoes and carried
a box of dirt back to his apartment.
He joined the killers in jail and saw things
their way. He visited the scene of the crime
and backed people against the wall with his typewriter
and watched them squirm. He saw how it was.
And they—they saw how it was: he was
a young man who had wandered onto the farm
and begun to badger the homefolk.
So they told him stories for weeks while he
fermented the facts in his little notebook.

Now the wide country has gone sober again.
The river talks all through the night, proving
its gravel. The valley climbs back into its hammock
below the mountains and becomes again only what
it is: night lights on farms make little blue domes
above them, bright pools for the stars; again
people can visit each other, talk easily,
deal with real killers only when they come.

The Night Is Dark and I Am
Far from Home

Eric Bentley

THE WORD "ALIENATION" has been used in a variety of ways. What I have in mind is the feeling that many Americans have of not belonging to the American Way of Life. They write the American Way of Life with initial capitals or within quotes, that is to say, they dissociate themselves from it even as they mention it. It has *alienated* them, made them *enemy aliens*. All their actions are *Un-american Activities* and have to be looked into by Committees and punished by literal or figurative jail sentences, deportation, exile, death. They are the disaffiliated, the disenfranchised. They are public enemies, foreigners, refugees, displaced persons, outlaws . . .

The opposite of being alien is being native, indigenous, fulfilled, in harmony with one's surroundings, at home. The environment makes one welcome, and one gratefully repays it with respect, praise, loyalty. Such is patriotism in a healthy situation. It is not an opinion, it is a formed attitude to a fact, the fact of belonging.

If the opposite of being alien is to belong, belonging may be either active or passive. The passive belonger acquiesces in, approves, applauds what the active belonger does. The active belonger plants the flag on the conquered territory; the passive belonger salutes it—and him. In modern times, the lower middle class as a whole has delighted in the passive role. And modern society has therefore aimed at giving the working class a lower middle-class mentality.

Active belonging means belonging to what nowadays is called the power élite, the Establishment. Such belonging doesn't necessarily *look* active. It is the privilege of the rich to be passive personally while operating actively through their wealth. Because *it* dominates, *they* can exercise domination without lifting a finger. Yet listless aristocrats are no longer the persons the society most respects. Our society prefers people who not only do dominate but look and sound as if they do, like Hitler: a doubly active form of belonging. It is in this perspective that we should see the modern preference for the social climber over the born gentleman. The latter is still something, but the climber is more. "From the log cabin to the White House." From the Austrian village to mastery of the world. That is the great modern image, the archetype of archetypes.

What is really shocking about Norman Podhoretz's book *Making It* is that the author, if we take him seriously, believes this archetype to be irresistible and is telling us that those who might claim to find it resistible are hypocrites. In the light of this "insight," the alienated are only those who failed to "make it," and all their plaints are cries of sour grapes.

There is another aspect to the Podhoretz case: the Jewish aspect. Until Podhoretz, young Jews had the option of either trying to "make it" or of renting a cold-water flat and belonging to the intelligentsia. Podhoretz claims to be making the revelation that the stairs of the cold-water flat lead ultimately to Westchester. And so the Jewish intelligentsia is the WASP Establishment's loyal opposition. Not even opposition. The Jewish Mafia can be Dean Rusk's bodyguard. Chosen some time ago by Jehovah, the Chosen Race has now "made it" in Washington. The model from now on won't be Maimonides or Spinoza, Heine, Marx, or Freud; it will be Arthur Goldberg or Abe Fortas.

What is the essential strategy of *Making It*? On the face of things, it is to force an admission from the reader—"vous! hypocrite lecteur, mon semblable, mon frère"—that he himself is no better and either enjoys making it or envies those who do. The name for the philosophy behind this is cynicism. Cynicism, however, is always either ironical or uncertain of itself, and Norman Podhoretz either meant just the opposite of what he pretended to mean or he is *not sure* whether he meant what he pretended to mean. Now, if he is not sure, his uncertainty could contain the mute appeal: "*show* me I don't really mean it"; as when a man says: "I'm in despair. Isn't this weak of me?" in the hope of making someone retort: "Oh no, you're not, you're very brave."

I tend to think that Norman Podhoretz is trying to convince us he has overcome alienation. On the face of it, the evidence is overwhelming. He gets phone calls from the White House. But alienation and integration are not synonyms for failure and success, nor yet for opposition and conformity. The words represent *a state of being*, which the outer circumstances may conceal. Sometimes one wonders if our present society is one which even the people it rewards most extravagantly can be at home with. James V. Forrestal committed suicide at precisely the time when the scope of the present military-industrial complex defined itself. He was the first Secretary of Defense that the U.S. had. His death, as well as his life, opened a new era . . . There is also a sense in which Miss Dorothy Day is at home in this world while Lyndon Johnson is a frantically maladjusted intruder. But these are paradoxes which, when unravelled, only confuse one's original understanding of what the words mean. It is by a profound alienation from society as it is—its conditions and its ideology—that a saintly person can sometimes find a real home in holiness. In such instances—Buddha and St. Francis are examples— the rejection of society is quite overt. The fine clothes are stripped off, and the saint moves from the city, which society made, to the fields, which society didn't make. The comrades sought after by such figures—Jesus is another example—are specifically society's rejects. The New Testament is very clear about this. "Give all you have to the poor and follow me," says Jesus to the rich young ruler. This is not the establishment of a new society. This is the rejection of all society. Those whom society has *not* rejected must themselves do the rejecting, says Jesus. To those who reject the kingdom of this world, he offers his kingdom, which is not of this world. To those who leave home he offers a home from home.

WHAT JESUS OFFERED the poor in spirit has an analogue in what, at a much later date, the Romantic poets offered the impoverished imagination. William Wordsworth is a St. Francis of poetry, finding in a oneness with the countryside and country folk the communion which society proper denied him. And so the Lake District, in those days before autos and planes, could also be a home from home.

It was the habit of radicals a generation ago to scoff at these religious and poetical conquests of alienation. A wiser radicalism will not feel any need to do so; it will, in fact, need *not* to scoff, for saints and poets were not running away from the home which all modern radicalism chiefly has in view but (a) were finding it where it could be found and (b) were at the same time defining it for any who might later find it elsewhere. Hence they are not to be seen as enemies of the future. That they befriended a certain aspect of the past—peasant culture or whatever—does not make them enemies of the future: it only makes them enemies, like ourselves, of the present.

Karl Marx said that religion was the opium of the people; and it was. But this religion had little in common with that of a St. Francis. Literature and the other arts also function mainly as drugs, but that is because most art is bad art, as most religion is bad religion. And even good art and good religion can be badly used.

Alienation is overcome by a St. Francis or a Wordsworth, yet the limitation of this conquest is obvious: it is only a personal one, a solution for *them* and perhaps a small circle of intimates. The new home provided by religion or poetry is a home from home. The original non-home—the City, the Civilization, the communal entity, polis, nation or what not—is unaffected. Today we are not content to think that a saint or a poet can construct a little home from home for himself. We presume to envision that our civilization itself can become a home, not just for an Establishment but for a people, and not just for one people but for all.

Since nothing like this has ever been achieved in all history, it is a vision of remarkable audacity. We need look no further afield than the streets of the city where these words were written—New York—for the evidence that civilization is still the direct opposite of a home for men. The other evening, seeing a film on TV, my son heard one of the characters say people could learn to live by giving instead of grabbing. His comment was that this must be an old film, since today people wouldn't have that much faith in goodness. My son is eight years old. Yet his environment—protected, comfortable, middle-class—has already demonstrated to his satisfaction that the United States is not a home for man. If and when I let him see the daily exploits of American military power on the seven-o'clock news, he will find out just how right he was. We cry peace when there is no peace. We cry brotherhood and drop atomic bombs. Is it, then, a giant error, an absurdity, that in a time of unprecedented violence we envision an unprecedented fraternity?

If violence has the last word, it *will* have been an error and an absurdity; though there may be no one left to see the joke. However, those of us who make the affirmation are not at all disposed to minimize the threat to it. That the possibilities have been polarized seems to us in the nature of the case. This may be hard for the imagination to grasp; but that's the imagination's problem. As in the garden of Eden—after the fall—possibilities for good are also, and equally, possibilities for evil. If the goodness we envision is colossal, so the disaster, if it comes, will be colossal.

YES, TO THINK of this subject is to think of both Eden and Armageddon, Creation and Doomsday. And of course the two sets of forces—those of birth and those of death—are not separate. There is a specific relationship between them, the relationship between violence and transformation. What *is* this relationship? From the Marxist tradition we have received such images as: violence the midwife of social change. Which is not misleading. Conventional liberals are shocked by it, particularly if anyone proceeds to act on it. Yet American history affords examples: its Revolution and its Civil War. Let me cite a much smaller piece of evidence. I recently paid a call on a local Congressman. He seemed to be against the war in Vietnam, and I wanted to know if he would do something about it in Congress. Instead he lectured me on the restraints placed upon action by the two-party system. Very little could ever be done, he stressed: one must simply learn not to expect much. Then he added: except in a time of social chaos. Then he added: and of course we may be headed for just such a time.

I was tempted to say at once: *"Well, I can only hope so,"* since it was the one chance he offered me. Revolt. Black Power. Rioting. If we could prove to him that things had gone so far, he would go down to Washington and say: "In *these* circumstances, yes, I can ask for speedy withdrawal from Vietnam." And in this manner the program of Rap Brown and Stokely Carmichael is conjured up and, in a sense, even justified by the hedging, "square," white middle class . . .

Violence is the midwife of social change. Not the *only* midwife of social change; but the choice lies first and foremost with those who resist change. The Bastille fell in 1789 largely without violence. That was because there were no guns to defend it. The French monarchy did *not* fall without violence. That is because it was defended with guns.

The wars that stand between us and the realization of the goal—making a home for man—are not, then, to be seen as roadblocks only: rather, they are the road itself—to the goal. The logic of Ché Guevara and Régis Debray is not far-fetched. It boils down to the most straightforward proposition conceivable: since battle is the road to the goal, make sure you win. Dean Rusk and Lyndon Johnson should have no quarrel with this logic since they propose to do likewise —fighting, of course, on the other side. Yet the fact that their people killed Ché, and that his people didn't kill *them*, forces us to reconsider the matter. Guns do not win all struggles; and this is lucky for radicals, since, in many struggles, their enemies have all the guns.

Certain it is that the struggles—both those with guns and the others—will decide whether the goal which modern humanity has set itself will ever be reached. These struggles will decide if our alienation will be overcome, if the planet can be a home for man and not just for the imagination of individual saints and poets. War will have to be abolished. The nation state will have to be abolished. Capitalism will have to be abolished. The road is long in struggle and suffering. It may not be long in years. Many now living might live to see the day if they live out their three score years and ten. One question is whether they *will* live that long.

We can expect to live out all the days that remain to us in alienation. That is why we are justified in looking the phenomenon in the face. We can hardly glory in it. But we can come to terms with it. What are its dangers and possibilities?

The dangers stem from misjudged self-congratulation,

from forgetting that alienation is a misfortune. To make a parade of being alienated is like making a parade of a wooden leg. It also confuses alienation with mere opposition and presupposes that all members of the Establishment are not alienated, whereas in fact the Establishment draws constantly on alienated intellectuals of a certain type and plays their alienation for all it is worth. (Many alienated intellectuals went to John F. Kennedy's Inaugural . . .)

THE THOUGHT of self-congratulation among the alienated brings to mind the Hippies. I wouldn't want to join in any of the current jeering against Hippies. They are a more admirable group of Americans than will be found in the country clubs or in the Conventions of the Republican and Democratic Parties. The trouble is that they are *children* of the country club and of the Republican and Democratic Parties. My complaint against them is, in a sense, that they are not alienated enough. It is when rebellion is incomplete that it runs to external display. A real rebel, like A. J. Muste or Dave Dellinger, is willing to wear the uniform of the bourgeoisie, like any labor leader.

One should not limit this kind of criticism to Hippies. The wish to look like a rebel is commoner than the wish to be one. This supposedly individualistic country has always, as Stendhal and Tocqueville noted long ago, lived under the tyranny of public opinion. As much as Germans, Americans like, above all else, to run with the pack. So, if they leave the Established pack, they run with the Alienated pack. Their uniform clothes—in either case—mean too much to them, like their uniform hairstyles, modes of speech, and so on. One danger of alienation, then, is that it brings the dangers of non-alienation with it, or, more precisely, that people don't tackle the problem of alienation at all but think merely in terms of staying in or dropping out. At a recent peace meeting which I attended in Town Hall, one speaker got a round of applause immediately after he said he was a college drop-out—before he explained why he dropped out or what he *did* with his freedom from education. That applause indicates a prejudice in favor of something entirely negative and without content.

To the Hippies, as I've implied, it is not easy to be fair. Lecture audiences, I find, begin to titter as soon as Hippies are mentioned. Also, they are not a compact group. The views of the various persons called Hippies are neither identical nor unchanging. Sometimes there are changes toward an attitude I can recognize as more satisfactory—in which case Hippie-ism may have been a necessary stage along life's way. But among many who have been called Hippies there is a dangerous degree of passivity. This shows itself in their profession of the religious virtue of humility, as well as in their code of Live and Let Live. These high principles can be the mask of mere non-interventionism and indifference.

In relation to war, for example, it always has to be asked how many of those who are against it today will drop their opposition when the heat is on, that is, when American casualties are really heavy and when the government announces that it has to have national unity, high morale, belief in God, etc. Some Hippies like to say there would be no wars if everyone was a Hippie, a remark which shows too easy a disregard for human intelligence. And indeed another common fault of Hippies is that they are anti-intellectual, or even unintelligent, *on principle*. There would be no wars if everyone was a Quaker; or even if everyone was a sheep or a stone. So what? Everyone isn't; and war is. And war has so strong a personality—has so much, as we say, "going for it"—that it will drag us all along in its iron chariot unless our opposition is *much tougher than this*. "Religion is the opium of the people," said the young Karl Marx. Today this is not always so. Religiously inspired individuals stand at the head of the peace movement. But religion can too easily be the opium of the Hippies; just as opium—or other drugs—can be their religion.

This last comment is not an idle quip. The drug-addicted sub-culture makes up one large constituency of the Alienated. Without pursuing the experiments oneself, one can grant what is claimed for drugs by the experimenters—that they do something which, by metaphor at least, can be called expansion of consciousness. This fact has suggestive value. It suggests what pleasures may be awaiting us on the other side of alienation. But drug experience is not the only experience that does this. Bernard Shaw wrote of plain, undrugged sexual intercourse: "I liked sexual intercourse because of its amazing power of producing a celestial flood of emotion and exaltation of existence which, however momentary, gave me a sample of what one day may be the normal state of being for mankind in intellectual ecstasy."

One day. When this earth is a home for man. Meanwhile it is the fate of such experiences to be occasional, momentary, unpredicted, casual, or accidental. I would not be taken as expressing merely Puritanical disapproval of drug culture or the sexual explorations of today—though Puritanism has its point—but rather, while admitting that such pleasures might one day proceed naturally from the life of the community, I regard their function now as escapist.

Art was defined in the nineteenth century as "the quickest way out of Manchester," and drugs in the twentieth are the quickest way out of Manhattan. To wish to get out of Manhattan is natural enough, but if we are addressing ourselves to the question of a home for man, our task is to re-make the places where men are, not to get out of them.

"To get out of Manhattan." Gauguin's Tahiti no longer beckons, and the Virgin Islands are full of the Manhattan rich. There is no escape except into fantasy. That is the solid material base of drug subculture, and that is also what is wrong with it.

The wrongness is evident in more ways than one. What starts out as the exploration of an alienated avant-garde can easily end up identical with the masturbation fantasies of the business executive and his staff. Andy Warhol's movies are an instance. The avant-garde here makes itself the source of supply for stag movies in Scarsdale and Greenwich, and so what was a flight *from* the Establishment becomes a headlong rush back *into* the Establishment—and provides a flight—or should I say a trip?—*for* the Establishment. Andy Warhol told the press in 1967 that New York City under Lindsay was perfect. Which is to say that he denied the very existence of alienation: New York was already a home for man. Such is the decadence of one section of our intelligensia. I offer it as a sample of the refuse that any revolution would have to sweep away.

JUST AS THE *im*perfections of New York City have to be seen with a cold, clear eye, so alienation—if it is to have possibilities—must be seen as the unhappy state that it is.

And even when possibilities open up, we need to be constantly aware of the hazards. The Alienated have their hysterias. Their detachment lends itself all too easily to every sort of irresponsibility, and to sudden changes of direction—especially capitulations and betrayals. Cut loose from their moorings, the Alienated have the freedom—excessive, dangerous, and pointless—of a boat adrift; which, of course, is no freedom at all, since such a vessel's course is determined by the winds and waves. It is very important that Alienated man not mistake himself for Liberated man. (Classical instance: Ibsen's Gregers Werle.)

On the other hand, if alienated man does not see himself as moving *toward* liberation, his alienation has dangers but no positive possibilities. Are there such possibilities and, if so, what are they?

We should undoubtedly not be discussing alienation in New York, in 1968, had it not been discussed by the young Karl Marx in his *Economic-Philosophic Manuscripts,* written in 1844, published in 1932. And it was Marx and Engels who claimed to see in the negative phenomenon of alienation certain positive possibilities. Indeed, in their exposition, it is from the very negativity that the possibilities arise. I quote from Engels' *Housing Question:*

> In order to create the modern revolutionary class of the proletariat it was absolutely necessary to cut the umbilical cord which still bound the worker of the past to the land. The handweaver who had his little house, garden, and field, along with his loom, was a quiet, contented man "in godliness and respectability" despite all misery and despite all political pressure. He doffed his cap to the rich, to the priests, and to the officials of the state; and inwardly was altogether a slave. It is precisely modern large-scale industry which has turned the worker, formerly chained to the land, into a completely propertyless proletarian, liberated from all traditional fetters and free as a bird. It is precisely this economic revolution which has created the sole conditions under which the exploitation of the working class in its final form, the capitalist modes of production, can be overthrown.

I am reading from the translation published in Moscow, and it contains an error which shows that even the Moscow translator was confused by Engels' dialectic. The worker is *not* free as a bird, *at home* with nature. He is free, at best, as a Robin Hood *exiled* in nature. And this is what Engels said. The mistranslated word is *vogelfrei*, which looks as if it means "free as a bird," but actually means proscribed, banned, banished, outlawed. Such a passage provides the basic reason why Marxism placed its hope of revolution in the proletariat. The reason was not a liberal and sentimental admiration of the moral character of workers, though Engels at times, like subsequent Marxists, does show such admiration. The reason lay not in the workers' characters but in their historical situation. Being stripped bare by the bourgeoisie, they did not even wear the spiritual clothing of that class and its civilization. They were without prejudice, and so could see the world as it was. They were without property, and so had no inducement to be defensive. Passivity offered only continued and increasing oppression. "You have nothing to lose but your chains and a world to win." The Communist Manifesto states the objective side definitively. There is a subjective side. Whether or not the world was won, revolt gave a positive meaning to existences become wholly negative, made men out of things, offered a foretaste of community and home to the dispossessed, homeless slum-dweller.

Now Mr. George Meany's well-heeled following does not resemble the forlorn proletariat classically described in Engels' *Condition of the Working Class in 1844* and the first volume of Marx's *Capital*. Instead, it supports colonialism and war.[1] From being the great hope for revolution through its character as a disaffiliated group, the working class in America has effected a merger with the lower middle class and become a principal source of cohesion for the established social system. This, more than any other single factor, is what has enabled the ruling group in the United States to follow its interests as it sees them with a minimum of interference. It did not need to suppress the traditional freedom of dissent, because there was no dissent of the kind that counted, and it's always nice to have around the kind of dissenting chatter that makes no difference.

[1] By about 56% to 44%, however, not 600 to 1, as Mr. Meany would have us believe. *The New York Times*, February 18, 1968.

IN THE LIGHT of these facts it is interesting to look back on the history of American radicalism in our time. In the thirties, there was much militancy—it was the era of the Depression and the New Deal—but World War II brought national unity, which meant that the Left was lost, like a drop in a bucket. An attempt was made to revive it in 1947–48. But there were at least two strongly countervailing factors: 1. the compromising of the Socialist movement all over the world by Joseph Stalin, which could no longer be passed over as it had been in the thirties; 2. the launching of a counteroffensive in the United States by the House Un-American Activities Committee and a little later by the other Joseph, Joseph McCarthy. When the Left was not disenchanted and discouraged by one Joseph, it was intimidated and discouraged by the other. Even in the sixties, one often stumbled on further evidence of the vast power of both Josephs, in large and small things. I know, for example, an actress who will not join in any of the current anti-war activity even though she agrees with it. She told me that she had been so hurt by McCarthyism she could never again "do anything of that kind." So, you see, McCarthyism works; and if you are twenty years old now, you should ask yourself whether you will be able to withstand all future attempts to cripple the radical in you.

Had the trend of the late forties and early fifties continued, by 1960 the American people would have been handed over, bound hand and foot, to what is variously called the military-industrial complex, the power élite, the Establishment. Such a Grand Design was in the cards, and certain very influential people worked hard to achieve it. Hard and subtly, for it could all have been done without recourse to the very un-American style of Adolf Hitler. There would have been no little black moustaches. No straight-arm salutes. No swastikas. Possibly no anti-Semitism. It could probably all have been done within the proprieties. Without an extension of censorship. With the press free in the sense in which it is free now. And all around, the *dolce vita* of the affluent society: on the money you make off wars in the Pacific you can take your cruises in the Mediterranean. Such is the American dream, new style. And the dream is, furthermore, to impose it on everyone else under the name *Pax Americana*.

Between United States power and the realization of this dream abroad stands the military might of her official enemies among the Great Powers and the determination of the guerrillas and NLFs. But what stands between United States power and the realization of that dream here in the United States? Neither of the political parties. No leaders of organized labor. The possibilities narrow themselves down to two groups: Negroes and a section of the largely white professional classes—and of course, these are the people who come closest to Marx and Engels' description of the alienated, even though they aren't all proletarian or even poor.

It is possible that United States power will be contained by China and the Soviet Union, especially if other countries follow the lead of France in withholding support. It is possible that the United States will be defeated by the guerrillas in Vietnam and in all countries its Army intrudes upon. But another possibility is that the United States will win. For, if there is still a group of "Great Powers," America is really the single Super-power, and, if the others cannot unite, they may simply be unable to hold America off.

If this should be the case, then the hope of the world rests with the dissidents in America itself, and only Americans will be able to save the world from America. Now, if this *may* be so, it becomes their job to provide for the possibility that it *is* so. From which much follows. Leaving America would not seem a good idea until it becomes clear that the dissidents here are totally blocked. Which is not so now. Even United States power has not abrogated laws of human dialectics; so things still work both way. That freedom of speech which may be conceded by the ruling group as a-luxury-they-can-afford can also be exploited by a non-ruling group to the point where it becomes something different. It is up to the dissidents to *make use* of such freedoms against the powers that concede them.

How was it that the Grand Design of the McCarthy era went wrong? Why wasn't, finally, every section of the nation "included in"? Here Negroes are a topic to themselves. I will only remark in passing that the Grand Design would have encompassed Negroes too, had *all* Negro leaders praised Freedom House and LBJ, and had *all* the rank and file shown nothing but an interest in joining the white middle class. It is in this perspective that Black Power shows a plus, not a minus, sign.

BUT BECAUSE I am a white writer, artist, scholar, teacher, student, writing chiefly for other white writers, artists, scholars, teachers, students, it behooves me to speak more especially of *our* part in things. This would be a point, too, at which to speak of the Hippies in a more friendly fashion. Insofar as they are well-heeled boys and girls who, at some cost to themselves, and with real difficulty, reject the Westchester way of life, the Greenwich (Conn.) way of life, all honor to them. What they are doing at least proves that the Great American Way doesn't work. The affluent society would like to declare social conflict abolished. Success and money provide gracious living in the suburbs and exurbs, there's your brave new world, and what else is the aim of it all? What other happiness has life to offer? What else is being defended against greedy yellow Communists? This is the thesis anyway; the antithesis has been told to get lost.

Only, true to the logic of human nature and human history, it refuses. The sons and daughters of suburban high living rebel. Quit. Drop out. They *feel* alien; and they move to alien ground. This moving does no good. But without it —without what is implied in it—nothing could be done.

Something happened around 1960 for which the world may someday be grateful. It was a reversal of a main trend. I have represented it as happening according to dialectical law: trends develop their own contradictions, and friends give birth, as it were, to their enemies. Whether it's really as inevitable as that I don't know. We may just have been lucky. And credit should perhaps be given to human will as well as to historical forces. Whatever the explanation, a revolt happened. And this revolt differed from other revolts—including the Negro revolt—which are revolts against acknowledged failures, because it was a revolt not only against failure *but also against what America considered its notable successes*. It was a revolt precisely against the American Way of Life. The parents had said: "We have labored three generations to give you this, darling." And the younger generation replied: "You know where you can stick it."

For the alienated middle class, this revolt comes before

any concern with civil rights, poverty, or war. But, of course, the concern is *connected* with the revolt, and what the connection is might be expressed this way: "After feeling the worthlessness of your affluent culture to the marrow of our bones, we are compelled to look into it all a little further, to ask how it happened. Well then: we ask *at whose expense* and we discover the poor. We look at the poor and we see they are not the same *color* as we are. Looking at all those who are not the same color as we are, our eyes make the journey from Mississippi to Vietnam. And there finally we have it: the primal shame and the ultimate one. The bombs that kill the Vietnamese today were manufactured yesterday and sold to the government for money. On that money our parents live in nice places. The garden party at Greenwich is as elegant as anyone could wish. Truman Capote is there with Princess Lee Radziwill. The fine flower of our society. The peak of Western Civilization. But look at these people closely: they are dripping with blood." However high the wages, however gracious the living, this is a civilization that lives by oppression at home and aggression abroad. It is when young people first see this nightmare—a nightmare they do not invent but discover—that they become deeply alienated.

The most optimistic conclusion that could be drawn from the facts as I have presented them would be that what Marx hoped from the proletariat could be delivered by an alliance between the Negroes and the white professional classes; and this is a dream we do see gleaming in the eyes of some radicals these days. Since protest is having no effect, the argument runs, let us follow the lead of Ché Guevara, Régis Debray, and Stokely Carmichael, and become guerrillas. I note, though, that what is used in defense of this position is, above all, *contempt for peaceful methods*. A remark made at the recent Havana Congress is worth citing. "When they hear the word revolver," said one militant about the less militant, "they reach for their culture." A very rough joke. Rough because it is drawn from Nazi sources, and what the Nazis meant by it is not reversed by the new formulation. That is one point. There is a more important one. In the United States, the most guns—and the biggest and best ones—belong to the cops, the National Guard, and the Army.

As far as Black Power goes, I have already suggested what must be conceded in its favor. On its limitations I am in agreement, not with its outright enemies, but with its radical critics such as Christopher Lasch. In assigning the blame for errors and excesses, I would definitely place it not on those who have been provoked, but on those who did the provoking. Not the least horrible aspect of a horrible general situation is that United States power drives so many into acts and attitudes of futile desperation. I attended a gathering lately when a speaker got a quick round of applause by stating that if we couldn't change America at least we could destroy it. One appreciates the excruciating sense of impotence out of which such a declaration comes. It remains simple-minded and infantile, because the point is never reached at which the alienated can conclude that America cannot be changed. *I* may fail to change it but *you* younger people may yet succeed—provided that *I* don't destroy it. And, even if it could be proved that America is unchangeable, what would be the interest in the building of funeral pyres? If America is unchangeable, it will destroy itself without assistance from the likes of us.

Another small incident. I met a girl who very much agreed with the proposition: "if you can't change it destroy it." Finding her so much more radical than myself, I whipped out of my pocket a couple of documents for her to sign. One would have committed her to tax-refusal; the other to aiding and abetting draft-resisters. Before deciding that America should be totally destroyed, would she change America this little bit? To my dismay she declined. It was the universal bonfire that appealed to her, not positive change. I conclude that we have a lunatic fringe on the left and that it fully matches the one on the right in lunacy.

Was this girl excessively alienated? I don't think so. Consider. Our Establishment believes above all in violence, while infuriating us with hypocritical speeches *against* violence. We say to Ho Chi Minh: "Stop your violence and come reason with us." Then we add: "And if you don't we'll smash your face in." In this situation it is inevitable that some of our radicals should wish to match the Establishment's violence with their own. *In doing so, though, they want "in."* They want to be invited to the Garden Party, and are promising that their hands, too, will drip blood.

WHAT THEY SHOULD address themselves to instead is the fact which prompts all the futile gestures: it is that America is *not* on the verge of that total overturn which we would like to see, which we feel to be necessary. Therefore it is futile to say: a few more fires this summer, a few more guns, and a revolution will occur and our alienation will be overcome. As far as politics are concerned, the alienated must concentrate on immediate goals, above all on the stopping of the war. As far as the longer term is concerned, what is needed is the *preparation of the radicals themselves* for the future they should like to create. They have by all means to endure alienation. But it need not be a passive endurance. They can fight alienation if they have a vision of a promised land, an eventual home. In this suffering and in this fight, they will need what some people call an ideology, some a religion, and others yet again a cultural program. The aggressions of the United States in this time would be wrong in any case but they are doubly wrong because the culture which the United States has to offer the other nations is a bad one, made up of bad religion, bad philosophy, and bad art. America is smashing up old cultures, and preventing new ones from being born: both at the same time. And is replacing what it destroys with the corrupt rhetoric of its public relations and the cultural junk of its mass media. What Newark and Detroit are today, cities conquered by the United States—if they remain standing—can hope to become tomorrow. (Mary McCarthy has observed such a development in Saigon.)

Let them assimilate, in our own population, those who are assimilable, but let those who are too alienated for that have the courage of their alienation and accept the responsibilities. This means holding on to good ideology, good religion, good poetry—holding on, in short, to the *imagination* in its purity, its nakedness—and not only holding on but making new ideology, new religion, new poetry.

I was saying earlier that the artist, like the saint, could only achieve in personal fantasy what we hoped would eventually be achieved in social actuality. This statement needs now to be modified and enlarged. Precisely what begins as personal fantasy may become social reality. It is then that the artist is, in Shelley's phrase, an unacknowledged legislator. The word "prophet," in this connection, is misleading: it only suggests that the artist, like Nostradamus or readers of tea leaves, has his own strange ways of guessing what others will do. What I am asserting is that he contributes, and can contribute at a very early stage. This is the stage not of a guessing game, nor of systematic planning, but of the formation of images. In saying this I am thinking not only of Shelley but of Blake.

The alienation of the middle class will not be overcome by individual action alone, but certain individual actions prepare us for the change. Any such change *has* to be prepared by being imagined in the heads of individuals. It has been said that in science nothing can be invented until it has been imagined. Is not the same true of history? Of both its disasters and its achievements? Auschwitz existed in the fantasy of anti-Semites long before it was actuality. The fantasy of American planes and ships running wild in the skies and seas of the whole world was to be found in "Superman" and other comic strips before America's U2 was brought down over Russia and her spy-ship was seized off Korea. Shall we assign the fantasy of man a lesser role in his positive achievements?

The Communist parties a generation ago were preaching something called Socialist Realism. It was corrupted by Stalinism and deservedly came in for much ridicule. Nonetheless, the original rationale had been right. The premise was that literature had bogged down in mere description of conditions, and that something more positive was needed. Now if you look at, say, fiction in America today it is still in that Naturalistic tradition. What floats the fictional successes of the Grove Press is still what floated fictional successes half a century ago: *shocking frankness*—that is, mentioning a little more than was mentioned the last time of what goes on in bedrooms in the dirtier parts of town. This literature has had great value; but it is now used up. I see *A Day in the Death of Joe Egg*, and I say: not *another* play telling us that everyday life is trivial, empty, sordid, and contemptible? Even our negative literature will have to be different—like *Catch 22* and *Candy*, perhaps, grotesque, fantastic, far out. An alienated class, if it is not to drown in its Alienation, needs a literature that does not merely reflect Alienation.

It needs literature and art that begin to prefigure the

integration in which Alienation will be ended and tran-
scended. In this, literature and art join with religion, not
the decadent kind that is the opium of the people, but
active and fresh religion as it has been seen in our time in
Pope John XXIII, in Martin Buber, and in A. J. Muste. For
if I am speaking, now, of faith, hope, and love (and I am),
I am speaking of them as facts of life, big with earthly possibilities.

In Noah's Wake

Allan Block

The giraffes already had sea legs.
Busy smelling out the corners, the moles
Were steady travelers. Placid too
Were hibernating adders. It was the people,
Eternally on edge, who unbalanced the ark.
Uncles, country cousins, distant kin,
All handpicked, good churchgoers, they
Had been shepherded aboard ship
By a craven old man, and for what?
The rain came down, there was nothing to do
But continue in public the mutiny
Each had always conducted privately.
And, as it happened, they never struck
The right climate for regeneration.
Down in the hold, the beasts did better,
Egged on by what they thought was home,
Nothing clogging their pleasure, least of all
What others rankled most over:
Stale fodder, cramped quarters, sour weather.

White and Fast Water

Alan Distler

Tʜɪs," said my father, looking out from between the strands of my mother's hair, "is a mad house."

"Edward," said my mother, unhooking his belt and unbuttoning his pants with the thin hand that was crushed between them, "will you ever stop talking?"

"If I did not talk," my father said, "I would not be. I talk therefore I exist. Or, better: I talk therefore."

I was eleven and in the flower garden where my father addressed the roses as "Thorny Bitches."

"By the time you grow," he said to them, "I won't even care. You'll bloom in a void. I'll teach you denial."

He hoed their roots and watered their stems and cried for them to come out now that the need was the strongest. The drops of water hung to the thorns.

"Father," I said, "how did we come here?"

"Your Grandfather," he said, and crushed hard clots of earth in his fists until the dirt rained down through his fingers onto the garden. "Your Grandfather was going someplace and stopped here on the way. That's how we came here."

"You mean he just stopped and stayed?"

"He stopped for a drink, I suppose. That's all. And he forgot."

"Was he an explorer or a covered wagon man?"

"He was a tailor," my father said. "And he wore heavy glasses."

"Did I ever know him?"

"No. Not you. He died before your brother Aaron came. He remembered one morning where he was going and he put down the coat he was sewing, threaded the needle on the machine, got up, walked out, and fell dead on the pavement. He was always a silent man."

But not him. The tailor's son. My father was a hod carrier of words and he stumbled through life letting them tumble about him until there were piles of them, walls of them, empty rooms of them, kitchen middens of them, where trapped and intrigued he wandered and dallied and the years flowed outside his window like traffic bound out from the fair that had just closed.

"Father," I said, when I had become nineteen and was in love with a breastless girl who liked to wash my hair, "are you always going to stay here, just because Grandfather stopped for a drink?"

"No," he said, "someday we'll go; if we are lucky."

And the girl was fiendish about removing the blackheads from my face while my hands searched her blouse trying to find out if there was a chance that breasts might ever bloom.

"Edward," said my mother. She had begun to sweat. "If you would stop thinking you would have an erection."

"If I stopped thinking," said my father, "I would starve."

My mother wept. Weeping was her country. She would have been anything else than herself, my mother. She was a giant of a woman who tried all her life not to walk heavily on her heels and to believe herself shorter than she was. She had breasts and they warmed her. But out of him she had to cajole, bargain, force three children and a glance. She pushed him to look at his food, comb his hair and get up in the morning. She whipped her children with a cloth belt that she kept twenty years and piled dishes from one side of the kitchen to the other, slammed oven doors, shined floors and thumped about the house trying to have her sanity as a sanctuary.

And the children grew up so that they too could look away from her, even over her. Toward the wall, the other side of the room, the water stain on the ceiling that came from the bathroom above.

"This," said my father, as if it were a rite, when he awoke each morning, "is an asylum."

My sister Lillian, beaten for spitting at her teacher when she was seven, nailed her teddy bear to the wall. My father sat by it all night reading Santayana and ruminating. Looking at it, pointing to it with the stem of the pipe that his teeth had broken through. "After puberty," he said, "you'll forsake wisdom." And my sister lay in the bed sobbing. She was naked and would not put on her pajamas.

He composed jingles. They were his furies. You could hear them coming from the house, the windows, and the cars that came down the street in the evening. When it grew dark and the lights went on and the sound of the tires grew louder; and the air, colder, should have been still, they flew about. The night was a fever of soda pop and cigarette celebrations that had blown from my father's pen. And he would not allow a radio in his house. The Green Hornet was a secret activity that we listened to, like the underground awaiting instructions, in the darkened garage on the horsehair seats of his Dodge.

When we smelt the deep damp odor of tobacco we fell to the floor and waited desperately for him to come in, putter with his tools and drag out a sack of rose food so that we could return to strange countries.

Oh, we grew. The weeds of his garden and the plants of my mother's calculations.

"Mother," my sister Lillian asked her, "will father be a famous writer someday?"

"Let us be thankful," she answered, "for the bounty that is here."

"Anything you want," he said to me, when I was older, "you can have if first you learn not to desire it too much."

"How is that? It's an absurdity."

"The madmen have planned it all out. It's that way."

There was my brother Aaron. He caught a brown-eyed girl with a simple face for seven years. Held her like a timid hopeful bird by salting her sweet tail with his eyes. She was a girl like any other, with two tits and a cunt where one ought to be and she spoke softly and followed him about and ran her hand through his hair and said things to him like: "Why don't you try" and "I believe you can" and "You're such a wonderful person." A girl like any other, with great want in her eyes and a hand to rest on his cheek and a rump to lie against. She had a father who never said the right thing to her and a mother who was prettier. And she told Aaron that his eyes were deep and his lips soft and there was a spot on his neck that was delicious to kiss. And Aaron tossed himself about and asked

what love was and if this was right and how much should
one know before one said that one knew. He was like a
stick in the water, tumbling here and beaching there and off
again. Up the narrows and down the straits. Idylling
and into the fast water. And the green swirled all about
him. Oh, he was a great one for thinking too.

"You are a lunatic," my father told him, "I confirm it."

Oh, he was. He thrashed about, looked into walls, read
self-help books, talked of moving, changing careers, took
his own temperature, bought an old sports car, disappeared
on trips to Boston, Albany, New York, Springfield until he
was exhausted. Then he died into love and he told her he
loved her. He loved her! To make her his wife. His one.
His own. Their life together forever and a dream. He was
the stick turned to bird. He reached delight. He went to
ecstasy.

And he proposed and proposed and proposed until the
pavements of the town were red with the blood of his knees.

And she, the brown-eyed one, took her hands out of his
hair and looked at him. There was a little flesh folded over
his belt now. A crease in his brow. Had she seen that before? His rump was bigger than she had intended. Or had
she? And the plans and the promises of seven years before.
In the heat they had all melted. What were they? Were
they?

She was a girl like any other and she knew a lunatic
when she saw one. That was someone who saw a whore and
the madonna in her face. Oh, she knew that for sure. She
was a thinker that one! So she took Aaron's hands off her
breasts. Once it had been delight, his and hers, now it
seemed to hurt. When did he start pinching? When did that
begin? She put them back into his pockets and she, herself, closed his pants for him. She was gentle and kind to
the end. And she looked at him in terms of houses, and cars,
and movies on Friday nights, and the baby-sitter who
would have to stay overtime once in a while and all the
things his own father's jingles called out to her and told
him what a great person he was and a fine human being
and she loved him very much. But he wasn't marriage
material.

A soft fall evening, on a bench in the park where the
moon made shadows of the tears on his face and she tried

to explain how much harder for her than for him it really was.

So Aaron went back to the water and on a cold night scattered his clothes among the garbage receptacles and walked out. Further and further he went until there was more water than there was Aaron and the sound of his thinking was gone and he swayed gently up and back, beaching here and floating out there, forever and ever. Amen.

She married a red-haired Pontiac salesman, with hair on the back of his hands, who sometimes fell asleep half-way in her at night, forgetting just what it was he had started and sinking into his own breath while she squirmed out from under him. He had two cars and a passion to sit or lie on top of everyone he knew. He had a twelve-year-old voice that had forgotten to change when the rest of him grew and he never used it. He grunted to seduce her, he grunted in his sleep and when he woke in the morning. If he did speak she would listen. But he did know kindness and anger, like passion, always came to him too late to use. An afterthought. And she loved something about him that she spent the rest of her life trying to determine. He was a great sports fan. He knew all the batting statistics. And he combed his hair each morning.

He was marriage material.

They had three reticent children who went through life with a shock of red hair and one thumb in their mouth and the other in their ass. They were all professional men, always had new sports cars, and traded streams of mistresses with each other.

"Aaron," said my father, "outraged himself."

"He was very foolish," my mother said.

"And he never listened," my father mused.

But I did and he showed me that the trick was to be neither creator nor critic. I spent long years at school studying art and art history, and meaning and non-meaning. I became an appraiser. A value maker. I knew a Savoldo from a Correggio by the stroke and told age by a thread from the back of the canvas.

The first girl I talked into bed, when I came to the city, told me what I was. I talked to her from eight in the evening to six in the morning on the street, in bars, restaurants, coffee houses and finally in my apartment, where clothes and books lay scattered about the floor and the garbage truck keened and shuffled below.

In the early chill I lay nude and exhausted on the bed and she sat, her slip around her waist, her breasts falling over it; carefully, tenderly inspecting, handling my genitals like three new born kittens.

"You," she said, running a cold hand over my stomach so I quivered, "are the one who tells the fake fake from the true fake!"

She cupped me, kissed me, knew me. Oh she knew me! I tell the fake fake from the true fake. But later on when I was on top of her, my hands clutching her wrists and pulling out her arms, my mouth rummaging through the corner of her neck, she said that I was "emotionally stunted."

And Lillian, my sister, quit her job one day as a welfare worker and went to Europe for the summer and stayed ten years; wandering from one Bohemian camp to another until she came back and met me in New York.

"I always coveted you," she said to me at dinner.

"How do you mean?"

"I don't really know you. Do you know me?"

"I think so."

"Pass the salt," she said.

We drove home on the thruway in an old Ford that I kept together with wire hangers and thought myself clever for it. She didn't say a word or move until New Haven.

"You've been away a long time," I said.

She looked at me. Her black eyes and large nose glinting in the reflections of the on-coming headlights. Then she leaned down into my lap.

"I want to know you," she said. I did not stop her. The cold was on my belly and the warmth of her mouth, there, until Hartford where I went off the road. I meant to say: "Lilloe, what are you doing?" But I never did.

She was a strong one and holy. And when she was home my father gave up looking at walls and looked at her. She had small black eyes and moved into the corners of any room she was in. She waited out life like a nervous traveler at a strange station furiously reading the local paper, where she could not identify a thing, waiting for the train that would take her on. It never came. She chased up the track for years after anything that looked like it. Sometimes it was only a lost black dog, sometimes a cow or a large unidentifiable bird.

There was a sober jew from Buffalo, desperately in love with her and she would never let him talk, which was a great difficulty for him. He was a student of philosophy and Kierkegaard and Heidegger and Hegel wanted to spill from him with the same necessity of his urine. But she made love to him on streets, in piles of leaves, on the beaches and in dark busses until he could not distinguish between her madness and his so he went home to his family and wrote her that he would have to admit that intermarriages did not work.

Lillian did not even read the letter. By that time she was in love with a Swedish engineer who called up his wife first and told her to get out of the house when he brought Lillian home. He would tie her to the bed with his neck ties and take her that way and wait and take her again. He made her leave early in the morning when it was still dark and the moonlight smelled of the sea and he would go out to the garage and bring his wife in. She had been sleeping in the car. And Lillian would walk home alone. Her skin damp with sweat and stung with bites. Her mind filled with the warmth of beer that was always on his breath. And she thought how nice it would be if he would have her tied to the tree in the garden or throw her out one morning still tied, still wanting, onto the lawn where the town would find her squirming toward the sun. She was enslaved to him until the night he did not find his wife in the car, but found his friend the Public Relations man in her, instead. Then he left home and Lillian spent six months getting him out of her apartment. He cried a great deal and disgusted her. By that time she was in love with an actor that she did not even like.

She was a very talented girl. A great painter. Her abstracts were brown smears and dark circles and red sticks that filled whole walls. She loved orange and terra cotta. She painted furiously. She hated museums as houses of the dead. She called up millionaires, taking their names out of the phone book, and told them they must support her; and some of them did. She slept with none of them; but she was religious about going to their cocktail parties and they loved her for that.

She believed that while she was in the midst of painting she mustn't have an orgasm. She "must preserve the primitive energy and let it come out upon the canvas." So she would strip and kneel in front of her men and her ass blossomed out and broke like a soft seed pod in fall and her breasts explored their legs and she drank them and then, without rising, said in the small voice of a little girl of seven: "It's me. Me. Do you know me? Oh love me always."

Oh I knew what she looked like. I knew her. I have not forgotten the voice. It is no confession. If she were here now I would hear it again. She made a rite out of ancient torment. She said that the only things really to know were dark things, ancient ones, that fell like old runes in the mind when you touched them and she said that she was to serve me who was lonely and afraid. She knew what it was, she said, if I did not and if she was to be humbled before some unknown flow, then knowing me was what saved her.

I was the only one who returned home over the years. For both of us. My mother shrank into silence, holding her hands to her breasts and talked to herself constantly of disappointment. My father befriended his plants and questioned them. He knew that they had been there before him.

"He worries about you," my mother said.

"What is to become of you?" he asked me. The white hair fell over his face and the soil of the garden hung to his knuckles. "Where are you going?" He did not smoke any longer but the smell of old tobacco hung to his lips.

"I'm working," I said. "And I have a girl. I'm not unhappy."

"You're lying," he said. "Talking out riddles."

"How is that?"

The wrinkles of his eyes fell down onto his cheeks.

"When anyone talks of happiness they are lying."

"What should I talk of?"

He waited.

"I've stopped for a while," I said. "Later I will go on."

"I'll meet you there," he said, satisfied, and went back to his garden.

They are all dead now. Lillian in the ground of Texas where her car fell into the Rio Grande, never stopping as it went off the road, but in one endless leap it broke the heart of the river.

She was on her way to Mexico to reclaim her "primitive energy" with a writer ten years younger than she. Oh, she is the milk of the cactus now and the white of the fast water.

My mother and father waited long enough and then they went.

And I. I waited too. And am here. And have come to nothing. And do not talk of happiness. And tell the lonely girl who I will not have only because if I would, she would not have me, that love is to be made in silence and living in waiting; and that nothing is to be believed. We are all inmates.

"Hosanna!" my father cried. And he was dying.

"Edward," said my mother. "When will you ever stop exaggerating?"

And she washed the soil of the flower bed from his feet.

A Sense of the Ridiculous:
Paris; 1951 and After

Mordecai Richler

For MASON HOFFENBERG
and JOE DUGHI

LAST SUMMER, our very golden Expo summer, I was drinking with an old and cherished friend at Montreal airport, waiting for my flight to London, when all at once he said, "You know, I'm going to be forty soon."

At the time, I was still a smug thirty-six.

"Hell," he added, whacking his glass against the table, outraged, "it's utterly ridiculous. Me, forty? My father's forty!"

Though we were both Montrealers, we had first met in Paris in 1951, and we warmed over those days now, *our* movable feast, until my flight was called.

A few days later, back in London, where I have been rooted for more than ten years, I sat sipping coffee on the King's Road, Chelsea, brooding about Paris and watching the girls pass in their minis and high suede boots. Suddenly, hatefully, it struck me that there is a generation younger than mine. Another bunch. And so we are no longer licensed to idle at cafés, to be merely promising as we were in Paris, but are regularly expected to deliver the goods, books and movies to be judged by others. At my age, appointments must be kept, I thought, searching for a taxi. Time counts.

As it happened, my appointment was with a Star at the Dorchester. The Star, internationally known, obscenely overpaid, was attended in his suite by a bitch-mother private secretary, a soothing queer architect to keep everybody's glasses filled with chilled Chevalier Montrachet, and, kneeling by the hassock on which his big bare feet rested, a chiropodist. The chiropodist, black leather toolbox open before him, scissors-filled drawers protruding, black bowler lying alongside on the rug, was kneading the Star's feet, pausing to snip a nail reverently or caress a big toe, lingering whenever he provoked an involuntary little yelp of pleasure.

"I am ever so worried," the chiropodist said, "about your returning to Hollywood, sir."

"Mmmnnn." This delivered with eyes squeezed ecstatically shut.

"Who will look after your feet there?"

The Star had summoned me because he wanted to do a picture about the assassination of Leon Trotsky. Trotsky, my hero. "The way I see it," he said, "Trotsky was one of the last really, really great men. Like Louis B. Mayer."

I didn't take on the screenplay. Instead, on bloody-minded impulse, I bought air tickets and announced to my wife, "We're flying to Paris tomorrow."

Back to Paris to be cleansed.

As my original Left Bank days had been decidedly impecunious, this was something like an act of vengeance. We stayed on the Right Bank, eating breakfast in bed at the Georges V, dropping in to the Dior boutique, doing the galleries, stopping for a *fin de maison* here and a Perrier there, window-shopping on the rue de Rivoli, dining at Laperouse, Tour d'Argent, and La Méditeranée.

Fifteen years had not only made for changes in me.

The seedy Café Royal, on Boulevard Saint-Germain, the terrace once spilling over with rambunctious friends until two in the morning, when the action drifted on to the Mabillion and from there to the notorious Pergola, had been displaced by the sickeningly mod, affluent Le Drugstore. In Montparnasse, the Dôme was out of favor again, everybody now gathering at the barnlike La Coupole. Strolling past the Café le Tournot, I saw no sign of the abundantly confident *Paris Review* bunch (the loping Plimpton in his snap-brim fedora, Eugene Walter, Peter Mathiessen) either conferring on the pavement or sprawled on the terrace, dunking croissants into the morning café au lait, always and enviably surrounded by the most appetizing college girls in town. Neither was the affable Richard Wright to be seen working the pinball machine any more.

Others, alas, were still drifting from café to café, cruelly winded now, grubbiness no longer redeemed by youth, bald, twitchy, defensive, and embittered. To a man, they had all the faults of genius. They were alienated, of course, as well as being bad credit risks, rent-skippers, prodigious drinkers or junkies, and reprobates, and yet—and yet—they had been left behind, unlucky or not sufficiently talented. They made me exceedingly nervous, for now they appeared embarrassing, like fat bachelors of fifty tooling about in fire-engine red MG's.

The shrill, hysterical editor of one of the little magazines of the fifties caught up with me. "I want you to know," he said, "that I rejected all that crap Terry Southern is publishing in America now."

Gently, I let on that Terry and I were old friends.

"Jimmy Baldwin," he said, "has copied all my gestures. If you see him on TV, it's me," he shrieked. "It's me."

On balance, our weekend in Paris was more unsettling than satisfying. Seated at the Dôme, well-dressed, consuming double scotches rather than nursing a solitary beer on the lookout for somebody who had just cashed his GI check on the black market, I realized I appeared just the sort of tourist who would have aroused the unfeeling scorn of the boy I had been in 1951. A scruffy boy with easy bigoted attitudes, encouraging a beard, addicted to T-shirts, the obligatory blue jeans, and, naturally, sandals. Absorbed by the Tarot and trying to write in the manner of Céline. Given to wild pronouncements about Coca-Cola culture and late nights listening to Sidney Bechet at the Vieux Columbier. We had not yet been labeled beats, certainly not hippies. Rather, we were taken for existentialists, by *Life* if not by Jean-Paul Sartre, who had a sign posted in a jazz cellar warning he had nothing whatsoever to do with these children and that they hardly represented his ideas.

I FREQUENTLY FEEL I've lost something somewhere. Spontaneity, maybe, or honest appetite. In Paris all I ever craved for was to be accepted as a serious novelist one day, seemingly an impossible dream. Now I'm harnessed to this ritual of being a writer, shaking out the morning mail for check-size envelopes—scanning the newspapers—breakfast—then upstairs to work. To try to work.

If I get stuck, if it turns out an especially sour, unyielding morning, I will return in my mind's eye to Paris.

Paris, the dividing line. Before Paris, experience could be savored for its own immediate satisfactions. It was total. Afterward, I became cunning, a writer, somebody with a use for everything, even intimacies.

I was only a callow kid of nineteen when I arrived in Paris in 1951, and so it was, in the truest sense, my university. Saint-Germain des Près was my campus, Montparnasse my frat house, and my two years there is a sweetness I retain, as others do wistful memories of Harvard or Columbia. Even now, I tend to measure my present conduct against the rules I made for myself in Paris.

The first declaration to make about Paris is that we young Americans, and this Canadian, didn't go there so much to discover Europe as to find and reassure each other, who were separated by such vast distances at home. Among the as yet unknown young writers in Paris at the time, either friends or those with whom I had a nodding café acquaintance, there were Terry Southern, Alan Temko, Alfred Chester, Herbert Gold, David Burnett, Mavis Gallant, Alexander Trocchi, Christopher Logue, Mason Hoffenberg, James Baldwin, and the late David Stacton.

About reputations. A few years ago, after I had spoken at one of those vast synagogue-cum-community plants that have supplanted the poky little *shuls* of my Montreal boyhood, all-pervasive deodorant displacing the smell of pickled herring, a lady shot indignantly out of her seat to say, "I'm sure you don't remember me, but we were at school together. Even then you had filthy opinions, but who took you seriously? Nobody. *Can you please tell me,*" she demanded, "*why on earth anybody takes you seriously now?*"

Why, indeed? If only she knew how profoundly I agreed with her. For I, too, am totally unable to make that imaginative leap that would enable me to accept that anybody I grew up with—or, in this case, cracked peanuts with at the Mabillion—or puffed pot with at the Old Navy—could now be mistaken for a writer. A reputation.

Two years ago, when Alexander Trocchi enjoyed a season in England as a sort of Dr. Spock of pot, pontificating about how good it was for you on one in-depth TV discussion after another, I was hard put to suppress an incredulous giggle each time his intelligent, craggy face filled the screen. I am equally unconvinced, stunned even, when I see Terry Southern's or Herb Gold's picture in *Time*.

I also find it disheartening that, in the end, writers are no less status-conscious than the middle-class they—we, I should say—excoriate with such appetite. As my high school friends, the old Sunday morning, scrub team, have been split by economics, this taxi driver's boy now a fat suburban cat, that tailor's son still ducking bailiffs in a one-man basement factory, so we, who pretended to transcend such matters, have, over the demanding years, been divided by reputations. Our yardstick may be more exacting, but it still measures without mercy, coarsening the happy time we once shared.

Paris.

It would be nice, it would be tidy, to say with hindsight that we were a group, knit by political anger or a literary policy or even an aesthetic revulsion for all things American, but the truth was we recognized each other by no more than a shared sense of the ridiculous. And so we passed many a languorous, pot-filled afternoon on the terrace of the Dôme or the Select, improvising, not unlike jazz groups, on the hot news from America, where Truman was yielding to Eisenhower. We bounced an inanity to and fro, until, magnified through bizarre extension, we had disposed of it as an absurdity. We invented obscene quiz shows for television and ad-libbed sexual outrages that could be interpolated into a John Marquand novel, a Norman Rockwell *Post* cover, or a June Allyson movie. The most original innovator and wit amongst us was easily the deceptively gentle Mason Hoffenberg, and one way or another we all remain indebted to him.

Oddly, I cannot recall that we ever discussed "our stuff" with each other. In fact, a stranger going by our cultivated indifference, the cool café posture, could never have guessed that when we weren't shuffling from café to café, in search of girls—a party—any diversion—we were actually laboring hard and long at typewriters in cramped, squalid hotel rooms, sending off stories to America, stories that rebounded with a sickening whack. The indifference to success was feigned, our café cool was false, for the truth is we were real Americans, hungering for recognition and its rewards, terrified of failure.

The rules of behavior, unwritten, were, nevertheless, rigid. It was not considered corrupt to take a thousand dollars from Girodias to write a pornographic novel under a pseudonym for the tourist trade, but anybody who went home to commit a thesis was automatically out. We weighed one another not by our backgrounds or prospects, but by taste, the books we kept by our bedsides. Above all, we cherished the unrehearsed response, the zany personality, and so we prized many a bohemian dolt or exhibitionist, the girl who dyed her hair orange or kept a monkey for a pet, the most defiant queen, or the sub-Kerouac who wouldn't read anything because it might influence his style. Looked at another way, you were sure to know somebody who would happily bring on an abortion with a hat pin or turn you on heroin or peddle your passport, but nobody at all whom you could count on to behave decently if you were stuck with your Uncle Irv and Aunt Sophie who were "doing Europe" this summer.

Each group had its own conventions, which is to say we were not so much nonconformists as subject to our own peculiar conformities or, if you like, antibourgeois inversions. And so, if you were going to read a fat Irwin Shaw, a lousy best-seller, you were safest concealing it under a Marquis de Sade jacket. What I personally found most trying was the necessity to choke enthusiasm, never to reveal elation, when the truth was that I was out of my mind with joy to be living in Paris, actually living in Paris, France.

My room at the Grand Hotel Excelsior, off the Boul' Mich, was filled with rats—rats and a gratifyingly depraved past, for the hotel had once functioned as a brothel for the Wehrmacht. Before entering my room, I hollered and whacked on the door, hoping to scatter the repulsive little beasts. Before putting on my sweater, I shook it out for rat droppings. But lying on my lumpy bed, ghetto-liberated, a real expatriate, I could read the forbidden, outspoken Henry Miller, skipping the windy cosmic passages, warming to the hot stuff. Paris in the fabled twenties, when luscious, slavering American schoolteachers came over to seek out artists like me, begging for it. Waylaying randy old Henry in public toilets, seizing him by the member. Scratching on his hotel room door, entering to devour him. *Wherever I travel I'm too late. The orgy has moved elsewhere.*

Moving among us, there was the slippery, eccentric Mr. Soon. He was, he said, the first Citizen of the World. He had anticipated Garry Davis, who was much in the news then. Mussolini had deported Mr. Soon from Italy, even as he had one of our underground heroes, the necromancer Alistair Crowley, The Great Beast 666, but the Swiss had promptly shipped Mr. Soon back again. He had no papers. He had a filthy, knotted beard, a body seemingly fabricated of meccano parts, the old clothes and cigarettes we gave him, and a passion for *baklava*. The police were always nabbing him for questioning. They wanted to know about drug addiction and foreigners who had been in Paris for more than three months without a *carte d'identité*. Mr. Soon became an informer.

"And what," he'd ask, "do you think of the poetry of Mao Tse-tung?"

"Zingy."

"And how," he'd ask, "does one spell your name?"

MY AMERICAN FRIENDS were more agitated than I, a nondraftable Canadian, about the Korean War. We sat on the terrace of the Mabillion, drunkenly accumulating beer coasters, on the day General Ridgway drove into Paris, replacing Eisenhower at SHAPE. Only a thin, bored crowd of the curious turned out to look over the general from Korea, but the gendarmes were everywhere, and the boulevard was black with Gardes Mobiles, their fierce polished helmets catching the sun. All at once, the Place d'l'Odéon was clotted with Communist demonstrators—men, women, and boys—squirting into the Place out of the back streets, whipping out broomsticks from inside their shapeless jackets and mounting anti-American posters on top.

"*RIDGWAY*," the men hollered.

"*À la porte*," the women responded in a piercing squeal.

Instantly the gendarmes penetrated the demonstration, fanning out, swinging the capes that were weighed down with lead, cracking heads and smashing noses. The once disciplined cry of "Ridgway, à la porte!" faltered, then broke. Demonstrators retreated, scattered, clutching their bleeding faces.

A German general, summoned by NATO, came to Paris, and French Jews and Socialists paraded in somber silence down the Champs Élysées, wearing striped pajamas, their former concentration camp uniforms. A Parisian Jewish couple I had befriended informed me at dinner that their newborn boy would not be circumcised, "Just in case." The Algerian troubles had begun. There was a war on in what we then still called Indo-China. The gendarmes began to raid Left Bank hotels one by one, looking for Arabs without papers. Six o'clock in the morning they would pound on your door, open it, and demand to see your passport. "I am a ci-ci-citizen of the world," said Greenblatt, then something called a nonfigurative poet, now with Desilu Productions.

One night the virulently anti-Communist group, *Paix et Liberté,* pasted up posters everywhere that showed a flag, the Hammer and Sickle, flying from the top of the Eiffel Tower. HOW WOULD YOU LIKE TO SEE THIS? the caption read. Early the next morning the Communists went from poster to poster and stuck up the Stars and Stripes over the Russian flag.

With Joe Dughi, a survivor of Normandy and the Battle of the Bulge, who was taking the course on French civilization at the Sorbonne, I made the long trip to a flaking working-class suburb to see the Russian propaganda feature film, *Meeting on the Elbe.* In the inspiring opening sequence, the Russian army is seen approaching the Elbe, orderly joyous soldiers mounted on gleaming tanks, each tank carrying a laurel wreath and a portrait of Stalin. Suddenly, we hear the corrupt, jerky strains of "Yankee Doodle Dandy," and the camera swoops down on the opposite bank, where the unshaven behemoths who make up the American army are revealed staggering toward the river, soldiers stumbling drunkenly into the water. On the symbolically lowered bridge, the white-uniformed Russian colonel, upright as Gary Cooper, says, "It's good to see the American army— even if it's on the last day of the war." Then he passes his binoculars to his American counterpart, a tubby, pig-eyed Lou Costello figure. The American colonel scowls, displeased to see his men fraternizing with the Russians. Suddenly, he grins slyly. "You must admit," he says, lowering the binoculars, "that the Germans made excellent optical equipment." The Russian colonel replies: "These binoculars were made in Moscow, Comrade."

In the Russian zone, always seen by day, the Gary Cooper colonel has set up his headquarters in a modest farmhouse. Outside, his adorable orderly, a Ukrainian Andy Devine, cavorts with sandy-haired German kids, reciting Heine to them. But in the American zone, seen only by night, the obese, cigar-chomping American colonel has appropriated a castle. Drunken enlisted men parade enormous oil paintings before him, and the colonel chalks a big X on those he wants shipped home. All the while, I should add, he is on the long-distance line to Wall Street, asking for quotations on Bavarian forests.

RECENTLY I HAVE been reading John Clellon Holmes' *Nothing More to Declare*, a memoir which makes it plain that the ideas and idiom, even some of the people, prevalent in the Village during the fifties were interchangeable with those in Paris. The truculent Legman, once a *Neurotica* editor, of whom he writes so generously, inevitably turned up in Saint-Germain des Près to produce his definitive edition of filthy limericks on rag paper and, incidentally, to assure us gruffly that the novel was dead, absolutely dead.

Even as in the Village, we were obsessed by the shared trivia and pop of our boyhood, seldom arguing about ideas, which would have made us feel self-conscious, stuffy, but instead going on and on about Fibber McGee's closet, Mandrake's enemies, Warner Brothers character actors like Elisha Cook, Jr., the Andrew Sisters, and the Katzenjammer Kids. To read about such sessions now in other people's novels or essays doesn't make for recognition so much as resentment at having one's past broadcast, played back as it were, a ready-to-wear past, which in retrospect was not peculiar to Paris but a fifties commonplace.

At times it seems to me that what my generation of novelists does best, celebrating itself, is also discrediting. Too often, I think, it is we who are the fumbling, misfit, but *unmistakably lovable* heroes of our very own fictions, triumphant in our vengeful imaginations as we never were in actuality. Only a few contemporaries, say Brian Moore, live up to what I once took to be the novelist's primary moral responsibility, which is to be the loser's advocate. To tell us what it's like to be Judith Hearne. Or a pinched Irish schoolteacher. The majority tend to compose paeans of disguised praise of people very much like ourselves. Taken to an extreme, the fictional guise is dropped and we are revealed cheering ourselves. And so George Plimpton is the pitcher and hero of *Out Of My League* by George Plimpton. Norman Podhoretz, in *Making It,* is the protagonist of his own novel. And most recently, in *The Armies of the Night,* Norman Mailer writes about himself in the third person.

This is not to plead for a retreat to social realism or novels of protest, but simply to say that, as novelists, many of us are perhaps too easily bored, too self-regarding, and not sufficiently curious about mean lives, bland people. The unglamorous.

ALL AT ONCE, it was spring. One day shopkeepers were wretched, waiters were surly, concierges mean about taking messages; and the next, the glass windows encasing café terraces came down everywhere, and Parisians were transmogrified: shopkeepers, waiters, concierges actually spoke in dulcet tones.

Afternoons we took to the Jardin du Luxembourg, lying on the grass and speculating about Duke Snider's arm, the essays in *The God That Failed,* Jersey Joe Walcott's age, whether Salinger's *The Catcher in the Rye* could be good *and* a Book-of-the-Month, how far Senator McCarthy might go, was Calder Willingham overrated, how much it might set us back to motorcycle to Seville, was Alger Hiss lying, why wasn't Nathanael West more widely read, could Don Newcombe win thirty games, and was it disreputable of Max Brod to withhold Kafka's "Letter To My Father."

Piaf was big with us, as was Jacques Prevert's *Paroles,* the song *Les Feuilles Mortes,* Trenet, and the films of Simone Signoret. Anything by Genet or Samuel Beckett was passed from hand to hand. I tried to read *La Nausée* in French, but stumbled and gave it up.

Early one Sunday morning in May, laying in a kit bag filled with wine, pâté, hard-boiled eggs, quiches and salamis and cold veal from the charcuterie, cheeses, a bottle of armagnac, and baguettes, five of us squeezed into a battered Renault *quatre-chevaux* and set off for Chartres and the beaches of Normandy. Nineteen fifty-two it was, but we soon discovered that the rocky beaches were still littered with the debris of war. Approaching the coast, we bumped drunkenly past shelled-out, crumbling buildings, *VERBO-TEN* printed on one wall and *ACHTUNG!* on another. This moved us to incredulous laughter, evoking old Warner Brothers films and dimly recalled hit parade tunes. But, once on the beaches, we were sobered and silent. Incredibly thick pillboxes, split and shattered, had yet to be cleared away. Others, barely damaged, clearly showed scorch marks. Staring into the dark pillboxes, through gun slits that were still intact, was chilling, even though gulls now squawked reassuringly overhead. Barefoot, our trousers rolled to the knees, we roamed the beaches, finding deep pits and empty shell cases here and there. As the tide receded, concrete teeth were revealed still aimed at the incoming tanks and landing craft. I stooped to retrieve a soldier's boot from a garland of seaweed. Slimy, soggy, already sea-green, I could still make out a bullet hole in the toe.

Ikons.

We were not, it's worth noting, true adventurers, but followers of a romantic convention. "History has not quite repeated itself," Brian Moore wrote in a review of *Exile's Return* for the *Spectator*. "When one reads of the passionate, naïve manifestos in Malcolm Cowley's 'literary odyssey of the 1920s,' the high ambitions and the search for artistic values which sent the 'lost generation' to Paris, one cannot help feeling a touch of envy. It would seem that the difference between the American artists' pilgrimage to Europe in the twenties and in the sixties is the difference between first love and the obligatory initial visit to a brothel."

Our group, in the fifties, came sandwiched between, largely unmoneyed, except for those on the GI Bill, and certainly curious about French writing, especially Sartre, Camus, and, above all, Céline. We were also self-consciously aware of the twenties.

We knew the table at the Dôme that had been Hemingway's and made a point of eating at the restaurant on rue Monsieur le Prince where Joyce was reputed to have taken his dinner. Not me, but others regularly sipped tea with Alice Toklas. Raymond Duncan, swirling past in his toga, was a common, if absurd, sight. *Transition* still appeared fitfully.

Other connections with the twenties were through the second generation. David Burnett, one of the editors of *New-Story*, was the son of Whit Burnett and Martha Foley, who had brought out the original *Story*. My own first publication was in *Points*, a little magazine that was edited by Sinbad Vail, the son of Lawrence Vail and Peggy Guggenheim. It wasn't much of a magazine, and though Vail printed four thousand copies of the first issue, he was only able to peddle four hundred. In the same issue as my initial mawkish short story, there was a better one by Brendan Behan, who was described as "27, Irish . . . Has been arrested several times for activities in the Irish Republican Army, which he joined in 1937, and in all has been sentenced to 17 years in gaol, has in fact served about 7 years in Borstal and Parkhurst Prison. Disapproves of English prison system. At present working as a house-painter on the State Railways."

Among other little magazines coming out at the same time there was *Id* and *Janus* ("An aristocrat by his individualism, a revolutionary against all societies," wrote Daniel Mauroc, "the homosexual is both the Jew and the Negro, the precurse and the unassimilable, the terrorist and the *raffiné* . . .") and *Merlin*, edited by Trocchi, Richard Seaver, Logue, and John Coleman, who is now *The New Statesman*'s film critic. *Merlin*'s address, incidentally, was the English Bookshop, 42 rue de Seine, which had once belonged to Sylvia Beach.

In retrospect, I cannot recall that anybody, except Alan Temko perhaps, was as yet writing fantasy or satire. Mostly, the stories we published were realistic and about home, be it Texas, Harlem, Brooklyn, or Denver. Possibly, just possibly, everything can be stripped down to a prosaic explanation. The cult of hashish, for instance, had a simple economic basis. It was easy to come by and cheap, far cheaper than scotch. Similarly, if a decade after our sojourn in Paris a number of us began to write what has since come to be branded black humor, it may well be that we were not so much inspired as driven to it by mechanics. After all, the writer who opts out of the mainstream of American experience, self-indulgently luxuriating in bohemia, in the pleasure of like-minded souls, is also cutting himself off from his natural material, sacrificing his sense of social continuity; and so when we swung round to writing about contemporary America, we could only attack obliquely, shrewdly settling on a style that did not betray knowledge gaps of day-to-day experience.

For the most part, I moved with the *New-Story* bunch, David Burnett, Terry Southern, Mason Hoffenberg, Alan Temko, and others. One afternoon, Burnett told me, a new arrival from the States walked into the office and said, "For ten thousand dollars, I will step in front of a car on the Place Vendôme and say I did it because *New-Story* rejected one of my stories. Naturally, I'm willing to guarantee coverage in all the American newspapers."

"But what if you're hurt?" he was asked.

"Don't worry about me, I'm a paraphrase artist."

"A what?"

"I can take any story in *Collier's*, rewrite it, and sell it to the *Post*."

New-Story, beset by financial difficulties from the very first issue, seldom able to fork out the promised two bucks a page to contributors or to meet printer's bills, was eventually displaced by the more affluent *Paris Review*. But during its short and turbulent life, *New-Story* was, I believe, the first magazine to publish Jean Genet in English. Once, browsing at George Whitman's hole-in-the-wall bookshop near Notre Dame, where Bernard Frechtman's translation of *Our Lady of the Flowers* was prominently displayed, I overheard an exasperated Whitman explain to a camera-laden American matron, "No, no, it's not the same Genêt as writes for *The New Yorker*."

Possibly, the most memorable of all the little magazines was the French publication, *Ur, Cahiers Pour Un Dictat Culturel*. *Ur* was edited by Jean-Isador Isou, embattled author of *A Reply To Karl Marx*, a slender riposte hawked by gorgeous girls in blue jeans to tourists at Right Bank cafés—tourists under the tantalizing illusion that they were buying the hot stuff.

Ur was a platform for the Letterists, who believed that all the arts were dead and could only be resurrected by a synthesis of their collective absurdities. This, like anything else that was seemingly new or outrageous, appealed to us. And so Friday nights, our pockets stuffed with oranges and apples, pitching cores into the Seine, scuffling, singing "*Adon Olam*," we passed under the shadows of Notre Dame and made our way to a café on the Île St. Louis to listen to Isador Isou and others read poems composed of grunts and cries, incoherent arrangements of letters, set to an antimusical background of vacuum cleaners, drills, car horns, and train whistles. We listened, rubbing our jaws, nodding, looking pensive.

—*Ça, alors.*

—*Je m'en fou.*

—*Azoi, Ginsberg. Azoi.*

Ginsberg was the first to go home. I asked him to see my father and tell him how hard up I was.

"Sometimes," Ginsberg told him, "your son sits up all night in his cold room, writing."

"And what does he do all day?"

Crack peanuts on the terrace of the Café Royal. Ruminate over the baseball scores in the *Herald Tribune*.

WE WERE ALL, as Hemingway once said, at the right age. Everybody was talented. Special. Nobody had money. (Except, of course, Art Buchwald, the most openly envied ex-GI in Paris. Buchwald, who had not yet emerged as a humorist, had cunningly solved two problems at once, food and money, inaugurating a restaurant column in the *Herald Tribune*.) We were all trying to write or paint, and so there was always the hope, it's true, of a publisher's advance or a contract with a gallery. There was also the national lottery. There was, too, the glorious dream that today you would run into that fabled lady Senator from the United States who was reputed to come over every summer and, as she put it, invest in the artistic future of five or six promising, creative youngsters. She would give you a thousand dollars, more sometimes, no strings attached. But I never met her.

Immediately before Christmas, however, one of my uncles sent me money. I had written to him, quoting Auden, Kierkegaard, *The Book of Changes*, Maimonides, and Dylan Thomas, explaining we must love one another or die. "I can hear that sort of crap," he wrote back, "any Sunday morning on the Manischewitz Hour," but a check for a hundred dollars was enclosed, and I instantly decided to go to Cambridge for the holidays.

Stringent rationing—goose eggs, a toenail-size chunk of meat a week—was still the depressing rule in England, and, as I had old friends in Cambridge, I arrived laden with foodstuffs, my raincoat sagging with contraband steaks and packages of butter. A friend of a friend took me along to sip sherry with E. M. Forster at his rooms in King's College.

Forster immediately unnerved me by asking what I thought of F. Scott Fitzgerald's work.

Feebly, I replied that I thought very highly of it indeed.

Forster then remarked that he generally asked visiting young Americans what they felt about Fitzgerald, whose high reputation baffled him. Forster said that though Fitzgerald unfailingly chose the most lyrical titles for his novels, the works themselves seemed to him to be without especial merit.

Unaccustomed to sherry, intimidated by Forster, who in fact couldn't have been more kind or gentle, I stupidly knocked back my sherry in one gulp while the others sipped theirs decorously. Forster waved for my glass to be refilled and then inquired without the least condescension about the progress of my own work. Embarrassed, I hastily changed the subject.

"And what," he asked, "do you make of Angus's first novel?"

Angus being Angus Wilson and the novel, *Hemlock And After.*

"I haven't read it yet," I lied, terrified lest I make a fool of myself.

I left Forster a copy of Nelson Algren's *The Man With The Golden Arm,* which I had just read and admired enormously. A few days later the novel was returned to me with a note. He had only read as far as page 120 in Algren's novel, Forster wrote, which had less vomit than the last American novel he had read, but . . .

At the time, I was told that the American novelist Forster found most interesting was Willard Motley for *Knock On Any Door.*

CAMBRIDGE, E. M. FORSTER, was a mistake; it made me despair for me and my friends and our shared literary pretensions. In the rooms I visited at King's, St. Mary's, and Pembroke, gowned young men were wading through the entire *Faerie Queene*, they had absorbed Beowulf, Chaucer, and were clearly heirs to the tradition. All at once, it seemed outlandish, a grandiose *chutzpah*, that we, street-corner bohemians, kibitzers, still swapping horror stories about our abominable Yiddish mamas, should even presume to write. Confirmation, if it were needed, was provided by John Lehmann, who returned my first attempt at a sub-Céline novel with a printed rejection slip.

"Hi, Keed," my brother wrote. "How are things in Gay Paree?" And there followed a list of the latest YMHA basketball scores.

Things in Gay Paree were uncommonly lousy. I had contracted scurvy, of all things, from not eating sufficient fruit or vegetables. The money began to run out. Come midnight, come thirst, I used to search for my affluent friend Armstrong, who was then putting me up in his apartment in the Étoile. I would seek out Armstrong in the homosexual pits of Saint-Germain and Montparnasse. The Montana, the Fiacre, L'Abbaye, the Reine Blanche. If Armstrong was sweetening up a butch, I would slip in and out again discreetly, but if Armstrong was alone, alone and sodden, he would comfort me with cognacs and ham rolls and take me home in a taxi.

Enormous, rosy-cheeked, raisin-eyed Armstrong was addicted to acquired Yiddishisms. He'd say, "*Oi*, bless my little. I don't know why I go there, Mottel."

"Uh-huh."

"Did you catch the old queen at the bar?"

"I'm still hungry. What about you?"

"*Zut!*"

"You know I've never eaten at Les Halles. All this time in Paris . . ."

"I don't care a tit if you *ever* eat at Les Halles. We're going home, you scheming *yenta*."

When we were both students at Sir George Williams College, Armstrong had taken out the most desirable girls, but two years ago he had tossed up everything to come to Paris and study acting. Now he no longer put up with girls and had become an unstoppable young executive in a major advertising company. "I would only have made a mediocre actor," he was fond of saying to me as I sat amid my rejection slips from the *New Yorker* and *Partisan Review*.

Once more I was able to wrangle money from home, three hundred dollars, and this time I ventured south for the summer, to Haut-de-Cagnes. Here I first encountered American and British expatriates of the twenties, shadowy remittance men, coupon-clippers, who painted a bit, sculpted some, and wrote from time to time. An instructive but shattering look, I feared, at my future prospects. Above all, the expatriates drank prodigiously. Twenties flotsam, whose languid, self-indulgent, bickering, party-crammed life in the Alpes-Maritimes had been disrupted only by World War II.

Bit players of a bygone age, they persisted in continuing as if it were still burgeoning, supplying the *Nice-Matin*, for instance, with guest lists of their lawn parties; and carrying on as if Cyril Connolly's first novel, *The Rockpool,* were a present scandal. "He was only here for three weeks altogether, don't you know," a colonel told me.

"I'm only *very* thinly disguised in it," a lady said haughtily.

Extremely early one morning I rolled out of bed in response to a knock on the door. It was Mr. Soon.

"I have just seen the sun coming up over the Mediterranean," he said.

In spite of the heat, Mr. Soon wore a crushed greasy raincoat. Terry Southern, if I remember correctly, had given it to him. He had also thoughtfully provided him with my address. "Won't you come in?" I asked.

"Not yet. I am going to walk on the Promenade des Anglais."

"You might as well leave your coat here, then."

"But it would be inelegant to walk on the Promenade in Nice without a coat, don't you think?"

Mr. Soon returned late in the afternoon and I took him to Jimmy's Bar, on the brim of the steep gray hill of Haut-de-Cagnes.

"It reminds me most of California here," Mr. Soon said.

"But I had no idea you had ever been to California."

"No. Never. Have you?"

I watched—indeed, soon everyone on the terrace turned to stare—as Mr. Soon, his beard a filthy tangle, reached absently into his pocket for a magnifying glass, held it to the sun, and lit a Gauloise. Mr. Soon, who spoke several languages, including Chinese, imperfectly, was evasive whenever we asked him where he had been born in this, his twenty-third reincarnation. We put him down for Russian, but when I brought him along to Marushka's she insisted that he spoke the language ineptly.

Marushka, now in her sixties, had lived in Cagnes for years. Modigliani had written a sonnet to her, and she could recall the night Isadora had danced in the square. Marushka was not impressed by Mr. Soon. "He's a German," she said, as if it was quite the nastiest thing she could think of.

I took Mr. Soon home with me and made up a bed for him on the floor, only to be wakened at two A.M. because all the lights had been turned on. Mr. Soon sat at my table, writing, with one of my books, *The Guide For the Perplexed*, by his side. "I am copying out the table of contents," he said.

"But what on earth for?"

"It is a very interesting table of contents, don't you think?"

A week later Mr. Soon was still with me. One afternoon he caught me hunting mosquitoes with a rolled newspaper and subjected me to a long, melancholy lecture on the holy nature of all living things. Infuriated, I said, "Maybe *I* was a mosquito in a previous incarnation, eh?"

"No. You were a Persian prince."

"What makes you say that?" I asked, immensely pleased.

"Let us go to Jimmy's. It is so interesting to sit there and contemplate, isn't it?"

I was driven to writing myself a letter and opening it while Mr. Soon and I sat at the breakfast table. "Some friends of mine are coming down from Paris the day after tomorrow. I'd quite forgotten I had invited them to stay with me."

"Very interesting. How long will they be staying?"

"There's no saying."

"I can stay at the Tarzan Camping and return when they are gone."

WE BEGAN TO sell things. Typewriters, books, wrist-watches. When we all seemed to have reached bottom, when our credit was no longer good anywhere, something turned up. An ex-GI, Seymour, who ran a tourist office in Nice called SEE-MOR TOURS, became a casting director for extra parts in films, and we all got jobs for ten dollars a day.

Once more, Armstrong tolerated me in his Paris flat. One night, in the Montana, Armstrong introduced me to an elegant group of people at his table, including the Countess Louise. The next morning he informed me, "Louise thinks you're cute, boychick. She's just dumped Jacques and she's looking for another banana."

Armstrong went on to explain that if I were satisfactory I would have a studio in Louise's flat and an allowance of one hundred thousand francs monthly.

"And what do I have to do to earn all that?"

"*Oi vey.* There's nothing like a Jewish childhood. Don't be so provincial."

Louise was a thin, wizened lady in her forties. Glittering earrings dripped from her ears and icy rings swelled on the fingers of either hand. "It would only be once a week," Armstrong said. "She'd take you to first nights at the opera and all the best restaurants. Wouldn't you like that?"

"Go to hell."

"You're invited to her place for drinks on Thursday. I'd better buy you some clothes first."

On Thursday I sat in the sun at the Mabillion, consuming beer after beer before I risked the trip to the Countess's flat. I hadn't felt as jumpy or been so thoroughly bright and scrubbed from the skin out since my bar mitzvah. A butler took my coat. The hall walls were painted scarlet and embedded with precious stones. I was led into the drawing room, where a nude study of a younger Louise, who at one time was a patroness of the Surrealists, hung in a lighted alcove. Spiders and bugs fed on the Countess's ash-gray bosom. I heard laughter and voices from another room. Finally, a light-footed American in a black antelope jacket drifted into the drawing room. "Louise is receiving in the bedroom," he said.

Possibly, I thought, I'm one of many candidates. I stalked anxiously around an aviary of stuffed tropical fowl. Leaning against the mantelpiece, I knocked over an antique gun.

"Oh, dear." The young American retrieved it gently. "This," he said, "is the gun Verlaine used in his duel with Rimbaud."

At last Louise was washed into the room on a froth of beautiful boys and girls. She took my hand and pressed it. "Well, hullo," I said.

We sped off in two black Jaguars to a private party for Cocteau. All the bright young people, except me, had some accomplishment behind them. They chatted breezily about their publishers and producers and agents. Eventually one of them turned to me, offering a smile. "You're Louise's little Canadian, aren't you?"

"That's the ticket."

Louise asked me about Montreal.

"After Paris," I said, swaying drunkenly, "it's the world's largest French-speaking city."

The American in the black antelope jacket joined me at the bar, clapping me on the shoulder. "Louise will be very good to you," he said.

Azoi.

"We all adore her."

Suddenly Louise was with us. "But you must meet Cocteau," she said.

I was directed to a queue awaiting presentation. Cocteau wore a suede windbreaker. The three young men ahead of me, one of them a sailor, kissed him on both cheeks as they were introduced. Feeling foolish, I offered him my hand and then returned to the bar and had another whiskey, and yet another, before I noticed that all my group, including my Countess, had gone, leaving me behind.

Armstrong was not pleased with me, but then he was a troubled man. His secretary, a randy little bit from Guildford, an ex-India army man's daughter, was eager for him, and Armstrong, intimidated, had gone so far as to fondle her at the office. "If I don't screw the bitch," he said to me, "she'll say I'm queer. *Oi*, my poor *tuchus*."

Armstrong's day-to-day existence was fraught with horrors. Obese, he remained a compulsive eater. Terrified of blackmailers and police *provocateurs*, he was still driven to cruising Piccadilly and Leicester Square on trips to London. Every day he met with accountants and salesmen, men in shiny office suits who delighted in vicious jokes about queers, and Armstrong felt compelled to prove himself the most ferocious queer-baiter of them all.

"Maybe I should marry Betty. She wants to. Well, boy-chick?"

In the bathroom, I looked up to see black net bikini underwear dripping from a line over the tub. Armstrong pounded on the door. "We could have kids," he said.

The medicine cabinet was laden with deodorants and sweetening sprays and rolls of absorbent cotton and vaseline jars.

"I'm capable, you know."

A few nights later, Armstrong brought a British boy home. A painter, a Taschist. "*Oi*, Mottel," he said, easing me out of the flat. "*Gevalt*, old chep."

THE NEXT MORNING I stumbled into the bathroom, coming sharply awake when I saw a red rose floating in the toilet bowl.

After Armstrong had left for work, the painter, a tall fastidious boy with flaxen hair, joined me at the breakfast table. He misunderstood my frostiness. "I wouldn't be staying here," he assured me, "but Richard said your relationship is platonic."

I looked up indignantly from my newspaper, briefly startled, then smiled and said, "Well, you see I could never take him home and introduce him to my family. He's not Jewish."

Two weeks later my father sent me enough money for a ticket home and, regretfully, I went to the steamship office at l'Opéra. An advertisement in the window read:

liked Lisbon, loved Tahiti. But when it comes to
getting the feel of the sea . . .
give me the crashing waves and rugged rocks
give me the gulls and nets and men and boats
give me the harbors and homes and spires and quays
GIVE ME NEW BRUNSWICK
              CANADA

I had been away two years.

John Ruskin:

A Message to Denmark Hill

Richard Howard

MY DEAREST father, it is the year's First Day,
    Yet so like the Last, in Venice, no one
        Could tell this birth from the lees.
           I know it is some while
Since you received a word of mine: there has been
    The shabbiest sort of interruption
        To our exchanges (to mine,
           At least) in the shape
Of a fever—nights of those imaginings,
    Strange but shameful too, of the Infinite
        By way of bedcovers and
           Boa constrictors,
With cold wedges of ice, as I thought, laid down
    At the corners of the bed, making me
        Slip to its coiling center
           Where I could not breathe.
You knew from my last, I think, I had again
    Gone to the Zoological Gardens
        And seen the great boa take
           Rabbits, which gave me
An idea or two, and a headache. Then
    I had too much wine that same night, & dreamed
        Of a walk with Nurse, to whom
           I showed a lovely
Snake I promised her was an innocent one:
    It had a slender neck with a green ring
        Round it, and I made her feel
           The scales. When she bade
Me feel them too, it turned to a fat thing, like
    A leech, and adhered to my hand, so that
        I could scarcely pull it off—

And I awakened
(So much, father, for my serpentine fancies)
    To a vermilion dawn, fever fallen,
        And the sea horizon dark,
        Sharp & blue, and far
Beyond it, faint with trebled distance, came on
    The red vertical cliffs in a tremor
        Of light I could not see without
        Recalling Turner
Who had taught me so to see it, yet the whole
    Subdued to one soft gray. And that morning
        I had your letter, father,
        Telling of the death
Of my earthly master. How much more I feel
    This now (perhaps it is worth noting here
        The appearance of my first
        Gray hair, this morning)
—More than I thought I should: everything
    In the sun, in the sky so speaks of him,
        So mourns their Great Witness lost.
        Today the weather
Is wretched, cold and rainy, dark like England
    At this season. I do begin to lose
        All faith in these provinces.
        Even the people
Look to me ugly, except the boys from eight
    To fourteen, who here as in Italy
        Anywhere are glorious:
        So playful and bright
In expression, so beautiful in feature,
    So dark in eye and soft in hair—creatures
        Quite unrivaled. At fifteen
        They degenerate
Into malignant vagabonds, or sensual
    Lumps of lounging fat. And this latter-day
        Venice, father! where by night
        The black gondolas
Are just traceable beside one, as if Cadmus
    Had sown the wrong teeth and grown dragons, not
        Men. The Grand Canal, this month,
        Is all hung, from end
To end, with carpets and tapestries like a street

Of old-clothes warehouses. And now there is
 Even talk of taking down,
  Soon, Tintoretto's
Paradise to "restore" it. Father, without
 The Turner Gallery, I do believe
  I should go today and live
   In a cave on some
Cliffside—among crows. O what fools they are, this
 Restoring pack, yet smoothing all manner
  Of rottenness up with words.
   My Turner would not
Phrase like these, and only once in all the years
 I knew him said, "Thank you, Mr. Ruskin."
  My own power, if it be that,
   Would be lost by mere
Fine Writing. You know I promised no Romance—
 I promised them Stones. Not even bread.
  Father, I do not feel any
   Romance in Venice!
Here is no "abiding city," here is but
 A heap of ruins trodden underfoot
  By such men as Ezekiel
   Angrily describes,
Here are lonely and stagnant canals, bordered
 For the most part by blank walls of gardens
  (Now waste ground) or by patches
   Of mud, with decayed
Black gondolas lying keel-upmost, sinking
 Gradually into the putrid soil.
  To give Turner's joy of this
   Place would not take ten
Days of study, father, or of residence:
 It is more than joy that must be the great
  Fact I would teach. I am not sure,
   Even, that joy is
A fact. I am certain only of the strong
 Instinct in me (I cannot reason this)
  To draw, delimit the things
   I love—oh not for
Reputation or the good of others or
 My own advantage, but a sort of need,
  Like that for water and food.

I should like to draw
All Saint Mark's, stone by stone, and all this city,
Oppressive and choked with slime as it is
(Effie of course declares, each
Day, that we must leave:
A woman cannot help having no heart, but
That is hardly a reason she should have
No manners), yes, to eat it
All into my mind—
Touch by touch. I have been reading *Paradise*
Regained lately, father. It seems to me
A parallel to Turner's
Last pictures—the mind
Failing altogether, yet with intervals
And such returns of power! "Thereupon
Satan, bowing low his gray
Dissimulation,
Disappeared." Now he is gone, *my* dark angel,
And I never had such a conception
Of the way I must mourn—not
What I lose, now, but
What I *have* lost, until now. Yet there is more
Pain knowing that I must forget it all,
That in a year I shall have
No more *awareness*
Of his loss than of that fair landscape I saw,
Waking, the morning your letter arrived,
No more left about me than
A fading pigment.
All the present glory, like the present pain,
Is no use to me; it hurts me rather
From my fear of leaving it,
Of losing it, yet
I know that were I to stay here, it would soon
Cease being glory to me—that it *has*
Ceased, already, to produce
The impression and
The delight. I can bear only the first days
At a place, when all the dread of losing
Is lost in the delirium
Of its possession.
I daresay love is very well when it does not

Mean *leaving behind,* as it does always
   With me, somehow. I have not
     The heart for more now,
Father, though I thank you and mother for all
   The comfort of your words. They bring me,
     With *his* loss, to what I said
     Once, the lines on this
Place you will know: "The shore lies naked under
   The night, pathless, comfortless and infirm
     In dark languor, still except
     Where salt runlets plash
Into tideless pools, or seabirds flit from their
   Margins with a questioning cry." The light
     Is gone from the waters with
     My fallen angel,
Gone now as all must go. Your loving son, John.

The Disciple of Bacon

Leslie Epstein

HOCHBRUCKER CLIMBED the dark stairwell as if it were a mountain, plucking at handholds on the wrinkled walls, gasping for breath amid the fumes of cantaloupes and pears, pushing through the cumuli of California dates which roiled about the second landing and broke upon his sharkskin vest. He paused only once, in the middle of the flight, when an unfamiliar odor scudded past his nose. "Radishes," he thought, "bringers of luck," and resumed his climb, pleased, relentless, so intensely propelled that when a produce truck backed against its loading ramp below and the full stairway arched in response, he did not falter but pressed his awkward volumes, leather bound, between elbow and hip and careened upward off the crackling banister. At the top of the stairs he reached on tiptoe for the light cord, grazed and caught it in his out-stretched fingers, and only then remained for an instant motionless and illuminated—the white cap of the mountain straddled with mists, Fuji with figs—before sinking to his heels and entering his room.

The perfect square of Hochbrucker's room was empha-sized by the way everything in it kept to the corners. A sofa, upper left, rested diagonally across from an old, up-right record player; along the other axis, a deep, enameled sink sat catercorner from a wooden chest of drawers. Each fixture was joined to the others by a row of books which, emerging from under the sofa, marched in an unbroken line along the base of the four walls, under the sink and airshaft window, right past the door, around corners with the chest (its bottom drawer thus blockaded) and phono-graph player, and then disappeared under the sofa again to meet head with tail, A to Z, Adlgasser's great work on counterpoint and organic rhythm clandestinely pressed to Zuchovsky's green-backed *Pieśni Ukochych*, "A Lover's Songs."

Caught in the open, in the center of the room, a pedestaled table strained upward to reach a suspended electric fan, the two of them forming the spindle of the room, from whose eternally frustrated embrace sofa and sink, phonograph, chest, and books turned chastely, centrifugally away. There was no other furniture, no paintings on the whitewashed walls, no rug on the unstained floor, "no nonsense anywhere," thought Hochbrucker, tripping over the hopelessly tattered copy of Niccolò Jommelli's *Armida Abbandonata* (the first, or 1769, edition of the score) as he crossed the threshold, "a perfect scholar's room."

Recovering balance, Hochbrucker closed the door and bent to restore the file of books he had overturned. Then he crossed to the bare, pedagogically correct window, opened it, and—his heart pounding more from apprehension than from his recent climb—craned eastward out of the frame. Across the airshaft, behind the smoking, helmeted pipes, a round red sun hung on a quivering pane of glass. "No, no—how could it be?" moaned Hochbrucker, fighting the sudden pain at his bladder; yet even as he watched, the sun began to bulge over its frame and onto the sheet of glass beneath it. He was noted for his mathematics. The sun was now on the sixth panel from the bottom and total darkness. In twenty-five minutes it will have slipped entirely onto the fifth. At thirty minutes for each remaining pane, that meant less than—and here his fingers drummed on the sill—three hours' working time. Could it be done? Was so little light worth so much effort? Half in and half out the window, the corners of the leather volumes biting into his groin, he wavered, dizzily watching the New York afternoon spill away. Only a chance gust of uncrated dill struck him like smelling salts and brought him from his trance. "All the parsleys are propitious," he thought and resolutely banged the window to.

There was no time to dawdle now. Hochbrucker quickly set the two large books in the center of the table, between a glass of water, a glass of pencils, a loose-leaf notebook, and an ashtray. Then, standing on the sturdily boxed set of Adalbert Gyrowetz's *Hármonia i Seksualnosè*, he pulled down the front of his pants and shot a thin white stream of urine over the lip of the sink and ran some water from the iron tap over his hands. He crossed the room and pulled from the top drawer of the bureau a brown waxed-paper bag, then jogged back across the floor and shook the bag vigorously at arm's length over the sink, following which he extracted a loaf of rye bread and carelessly flipped it into the damp basin. Out of the top of the sack Hochbrucker fashioned a crude funnel and, turning the bag upside down and tapping gently on its bottom, he managed to coax a steady fall of caraway seeds into the waiting glass ashtray. He then folded the depleted sack and replaced it in the bureau, taking from the open top drawer a pair of modern horn-rimmed glasses, which he shined on a dissociated argyle and placed, after removing his hat, over his striking bald crown, a rectilinear ridge ending at the back in a depression, a scallop filled with baby's down. Ready at last, he pulled the cord on the multi-bladed fan and sat down at the table, wincing at the compromise of an unscholarly cushioned chair, but at age seventy-four, with a gross of piles, unable to withstand its privileges.

Time passed. The sun snaked over the wooden sashes, the air in the shaftway cooled, scallions and blueberries rode the convection currents to spectacular heights, and departing trucks ground their gears at Horatio Street and blew low, shiplike horns. Within the room on the fifth floor, everything was still. No odor penetrated the vibrating blades of the fan, no sound overcame its powerful motor. The scholar sat with his chin on the backs of his bony wrists, his face blank and very white. The row of books sagged listlessly in late-afternoon detumescence. A sheet of notebook paper rose at the corner and fell. In contrast, the caraway seeds jumped in their dish like a hill of ants. Now and then the old man's hand would fall among them; he would pinch two or three between finger and thumb, dip them in the glass of water, and force them between his teeth, while the survivors danced in outrage and the light drained imperceptibly off the walls.

Hochbrucker was drifting back to Rumania, where he passed most of his working hours. The nearer his life's work came to completion, the more he returned to the Cincinnyati, a notorious, even radical, nightspot where, in the winter of 1915, it had had its origin. His first memory of the back hall—no member of the All-Bucharest Sons of the Enlightenment was allowed in the front, where the Rumanians drank slivowitz and slapped on the tables be-

tween the arias of Sophia Parados, the well-known Thessalonikan alto—in fact, the first memory he possessed of anything, was of the water glasses lined up on the Directors'
table. This table stretched across the back of the raised
platform at the front of the hall. Another, smaller platform,
or podium, rested on this one and supported a wooden
speaker's lectern. The rest of the room was divided left
and right into benches, with an aisle down the center and
a doorway in the back which led to the nightclub area.
Another door at the side—a private entrance—led outdoors.
From his seat at one of the rear benches, sitting on an
intellectual cousin's knee, Hochbrucker had watched the
tumblers shining through the haze of cigar smoke like the
stars of a particularly orderly constellation, studs on Orion's
belt.

He remembered, too, how a few years later he had
studied the glittering glass-beaded curtain that hung like
a rainbow between the drawling solecisms of Block's lecture on dirigibles (or Rosen's on the importance of corn,
or Lieberman's on Japan) and the clear, sunny flight of the
transposed song:

> *Vedrai, carino,*
> *Se sei buonino,*
> *Che bel rimedio*
> *Ti voglio dar.*

Sometimes the curtain would half-part and Sophia would
lean against the door jamb, clutching the elbow of one
downcast arm, while Posner, the speaker, swayed from side
to side as he described salmon leaping upward over fresh-
water falls. She was near enough for Hochbrucker—at the
turn of the century, still perched on the bony knee—to
touch, close enough to startle him with her dark, close-set
eyes suspended between black cradles below and thick
brows arched like angry caterpillars in confrontation above.
Tiny ladders of black hair climbed up her temples and reappeared mysteriously at the corners of her mouth. If she
moved at all strands of light ran up and down her body,
and there was always the surprise of white teeth glimpsed
between her full, pursed lips. Every Son of the Enlightenment knew she was there (Hochbrucker's cousin pivoted
his left boot back and forth, as if grinding out a cigarette),

though none turned to acknowledge her. She would simply remain among the dazzling beads, her mouth slowly falling open, seeming to listen with her long, serious nose, until the slapping sounds in the front room called her back to herself and, releasing the arm she held pinned to her side, with a faint ringing of the crystal bells that hung from her ears, she would slip away. Bernhardt, manufacturer of magnesium antacids and owner of a French autocar, formed an anemone with his fingers, kissed them, and said, "Like every Thessalonikan woman, she has the soul of a scholar." Hochbrucker turned his already slightly pointed head, caught the light rippling on the curtain, and grew older. Posner's spectacles flashed as he dwelt upon the bitter irony of the spawning grounds.

Hochbrucker fumbled among the last prostrate caraways with the hand of an Aztec god. Through the red and black exhaust over the Jersey Palisades, as once above the overcast Carpathians, the Directors' tumblers continued to shine in his eye. He knew each face behind the rims. Bearded, elegant Saffron, who won the Chairmanship and a reputation for suavity by having once attended the Russian Ballet ("Léon Bakst: Heresy or Heritage?", the scandalous lecture of 1906, was still much admired almost a decade later); Aaron Popovitz (called "the despotic Aaron" to his face, in reference to the sixteenth-century Semitic tyrant who exiled his own race from Rumania, and to his habit of shouting "Out of order!") was succeeded in the Vice-Chairmanship by Bernhardt, who was in turn replaced (his autocar having been immobilized late in 1914 by the embargo on parts) by Guttman, whose American brother knew, firsthand, Traianu Kolotescu, the son of the owner of the Cincinnyati. Kelpman and Karp, both from Tergu Frumas, alternated in the office of Treasurer, though each stood accused by the other of sympathy with Zionism; and old Silbersheim, whose distinction sprang not so much from his having, as he said, "carried the banner in '48," as from his childhood spent in Vienna, read the opening credo through a series of strokes: "By our rights under Article XLIV of the Treaty of Berlin, and in the spirit of Disraeli, who won them!" He had become so deaf that the name, Disraeli, shouted at the top of his lungs, overcame for a moment every sound from the frivolous front room.

That left, Hochbrucker knew, two glasses unaccounted for. The face behind one was not often present at the table, for it belonged to Moses Levai, the Emeritus, one of only eighty Jewish citizens of Rumania and hence, unlike the "protectees," entitled to remain in the front of the club, a privilege of which he availed himself. He also, it was later rumored, had saved Sophia Parados from the general deportation during the Greco-Rumanian disputes of 1920–1924. The other belonged to Posner, holder of the Scholar's Chair. Originally, that place at the Directors' table was filled by the particular lecturer for the evening; but by common consent it came to be increasingly, and then exclusively, occupied by this brilliant young academician who spoke so movingly of the lives of simple creatures that some among the Sons of the Enlightenment who had never seen a live animal save a cat or a dog wept openly at the catastrophe of the tusked boar in the folds of enormous green snakes or the flight of an Arctic tern, and even Sophia was forced to press her long wet lashes against her cheeks. Posner it was who stood on the podium that cold, windy evening in 1915 when, contrary to all precedent, young Hochbrucker strode into the room and announced in a strong, steady voice that W. A. Mozart was a Jew.

The silence that fell was so complete—you could hear the wind gasp in astonishment outdoors—that the Zuckerman brothers woke spontaneously, and Silbersheim, having opened his mouth to ask what was going on, shut it again and wondered to himself why everyone held so still. Up at the lectern Posner froze slightly to the right, his spectacles gone suddenly blank, his arms supporting an aquarium of newts, like the statue of a Commandant handing over his weathered sword. Even the Rumanians were unnaturally quiet: the scrape of a chair, the giggling of a waiter, then a long and, to Hochbrucker, reverent hush as he prepared to stitch up this gash in history.

Suddenly Popovitz stabbed a finger at Hochbrucker and cried from invulnerable habit, "Out of order!" but before the words were out of his mouth Guttman was on his feet.

"*You* are out of order!" bellowed the new Vice-Chairman authoritatively, while seeking to catch the eye of his immediate predecessor for a nod of support.

"The subject is salamanders," Popovitz piped, also get-

ting to his feet and reading off the printed agenda for that
week: "'Third piece of business—Lecture, *The Urodelan
Amphibian and the Struggle for Life.* Full Professor N. Posner.' Unless Mozart had a tail," concluded the despotic
Aaron, with a flash of that wit under which so many Sons
had smarted, "the young man is out of order." From the
benches on both sides of the hall cries for recognition rang
out, and at the rear of the room an old gentleman threw his
cap into the air. A knot of disputants formed in the center
aisle, and amid their raised voices and metronomic index
fingers a man wearing suspenders over a sweater began
playing the piano part of K. 564 upon a clarinet. In the
next room palms began to strike the tabletops. Guttman
wavered in the growing tumult, while Bernhardt studiously
unwrapped the cellophane from a pastille. Suddenly the
ungainly Karp dove for the Vice-Chairman's gavel and
began pounding on the Directors' table so strenuously that
he sent Silbersheim's glass of water spilling.

"I beg to differ with the former Vice-Chairman upon the
parliamentary question," he shouted. "Article XXII of our
constitution provides that in certain extraordinary circumstances, and at the discretion of the Chairman, the usual
rules of order may be suspended."

"And what, I would like to know, is so extraordinary
about W. A. Mozart or his religion?" shot back Kelpman
from his place on the floor. "Fifteen years ago, during a
meeting of the Tergu Frumas Council of Citizens and
Jews, we disposed of precisely this question, which, I might
add"—and here, as if from nowhere, a toothpick appeared
in his mouth—"is not at all extraordinary but is instead
extremely banal."

"Just a moment. Just a moment," said Karp, pounding
over his own glass. "That question was not 'disposed,' to
use our colleague's word for it, but was kept in abeyance
until such time as the report that W. A. Mozart named his
son for a Jew could be verified. That is not quite disposal,
my dear Kelpman."

"That, Karp, is neither here nor is it there," Kelpman
replied. "This rumor was *not* verified, and that is what the
point is. Its foolishness should be obvious to any but a wish-
ful thinker, and I suggest, I *move,* that we resume our pro-

ceedings where they were interrupted and not indulge in any further displays of Zionist ethnocentrism."

"I believe we were discussing the gills of the new-hatched newt," Popovitz interjected between the present and former Treasurers.

"What's going on?" asked Silbersheim, dabbing at his soaked pants with one hand and cupping his ear toward Guttman with the other. The latter, grateful for something to do, shouted, "W. A. Mozart named his son for a Jew," into the old man's face.

"His firstborn son," replied Silbersheim in a voice for all to hear. "It was well known in Vienna."

"This," snickered Kelpman, "is a maneuver typical of Herzl and his crowd," but his warning went unheard in the renewed shouts for recognition and the outburst of isolated debates, as assimilationist left met ethnic right and the meeting fell to disorder—just as Popovitz, hugging his shoulders now in a caustic X, had predicted.

Chairman Saffron at last stifled the sneeze that had been undermining his suavity ("What is more ludicrous," he thought, "than a bearded man with a cold?") and, less fearful now for his own reputation than for that of Bakst—threatened by this pale young man who stood with a handful of papers rock-fast in the center of the aisle—he took the gavel from Karp. Such was his authority still, that after only a few strokes the uproar was stilled and he leaned forward to address Hochbrucker in a surprisingly soft voice.

"Young man, you are perhaps too naïve to appreciate that our *raison d'être* as a learned society of savants depends upon the integrity of our scholarship, scholarship based solely upon the methodology of the Enlightenment, that is to say, the inductive technique originated by Diderot and Bacon and perfected by the Vilnar Gaon and Voltaire. There is simply no room in Bucharest for rumor, innuendo, or appeals to the emotions." Hochbrucker was not listening. As the dealer in a game of Klob will suddenly collapse the deck and look about the table before asking that all wagers be completed, so Hochbrucker folded his sheaf of notes under his arm, turned left and right to see the occupants of both sets of benches, and spoke.

"Mister Chairman," he began, "honored Directors, Distinguished Members and guests. W. A. Mozart's son, his first son, his son of sons, was born 17 June, 1783, and was named—the word 'christened' is not appropriate—Raimund Leopold, after Baron Raimund Wetzlar von Plankenstern, son of Karl Abraham Wetzlar von Plankenstern, wholesale merchant, banker, Baron of the Realm. This Raimund Wetzlar von Plankenstern, whom da Ponte (whose real name, as I need hardly tell you, was not Lorenzo but Emmanuele, son of Geremia) called W. A. Mozart's 'great adviser and friend' (*Memorie*, Second edition, three volumes, Strasbourg, 1829–1830), was not only the infant Raimund's namesake, he was—and the significance of this must not escape you—his godfather as well. The details of the ceremony are on record still at the Church Am Hof in Vienna. I submit this fact, not to your emotion, but to your faculty of reason, and ask that I may be allowed to elucidate further the inherent logic of my findings."

"Please continue," stammered Saffron, distraught at the nasal tones that crept into his voice and reverberated in the muted room. There was no need for Hochbrucker to spread out his notes again. Three years of surreptitious research were arranged in an orderly file in his head. He was amazed how he could remember not only the location of a passage or stray sentence on the page, but the color of the binding, the type face, even the smell of the dust that blew across his shaking fingers. (Thus Goethe's, "I can remember the little fellow with his wig and his sword," was printed by Eckermann toward the top of the right-hand page dealing with February 3, 1830, a page that ran a crease down its center, ironically cutting the sword, *Degen*, in two. And how sat that wig, it occurred to him all at once. With ringlets and curls? The Helbling portrait of 1767 was infuriatingly obscure precisely at the eleven-year-old's ears. Could it be the chiaroscuro was deliberate? A way of emphasizing what it covered up?) These thoughts darted through his mind as he spun the thread of red-leather facts and mottled logic about the entranced and hardly-breathing Sons.

"On 19 August, 1783, R. L. Mozart, just two months old, died of an intestinal cramp, the German *Gedärmfrais*. What more may we say of the infant's godfather? That he was W. A. Mozart's admirer and friend we have already established. That he was his patron, his landlord, his benefactor and hidden coreligionist must be deductively pried from the few facts history has vouchsafed us. In December of 1782 the composer and his wife moved to a new apartment in Vienna, on the Hohe Brücke, number forty-two, third floor, the so-called Little Herberstein House. There were two rooms, an anteroom and kitchen. The landlord was Raimund Wetzlar, Baron Plankenstern. A month later a private ball was held for Mozart there, the space for which was provided by the Baron. A month after that, February, 1783, our subject moved out, and again the expenses were undertaken by the good Wetzlar. We know tragically little else, save that the Baron was named godfather in June, gave a quartet evening in early April which Mozart attended and for which he undoubtedly performed, subscribed to Mozart's concerts and occasional publications (a subscription list that included, by the way, Regine Josepha Aichelburg, née Wetzlar, old Karl Abraham himself, one Nathan Adam von Arnstein, and various Binnenfelds, Jacobis, Levanaus and Schwabs—Schwab, Phillip, and Schwab, Ignaz, wholesale merchants), and that the two friends occasionally dined together.

"These facts by themselves reveal little. It is in the juxtaposition of details, the addition of two of this and of that, that we shall reach the four of historical truth. Thus, when, *precisely*, did the two friends dine? The only date that has come down to us is the 27th of March, 1785, when W. A. Mozart supped at the home of the Baron. And why is that date significant? Because, in the first place, it is a Sunday, and in the second place it is Easter Sunday. Father and godfather quietly breaking bread on such a day, altogether apart from the rest of the world—just the gesture of sarcastic bravado we would expect from the creator of the fantastical Don, who also, we might add, was given to symbolic dinner invitations.

"Furthermore, we must ask precisely *where* did Mozart finally settle with the help of his devoted follower and friend? Fortunately we know the answer. On the 24th of April, 1783, W. A. Mozart moved to a first-floor apartment in the Inner City, and to be yet more rigorous, more meticulous, more *exact*"—and here Hochbrucker allowed himself a triumphant glance at the podium, where Posner, to whose porcupines and hibernating bears he had been forced to listen for week after week, year after year, all the while his idea swelling in his head like a melon, remained paralyzed with shock, his eyes peering senselessly through dead lenses over the heads of his lost audience, toward the blank wall at the back of the room—"to be more scientific in every way, W. A. Mozart's address was number two-forty-four, number two-forty-four *Judenplatz!*"

There was no calming the tumult now. Each faction united in crying, "Up front! Up front!" and even before Saffron rose and crooked a finger at him, Hochbrucker was shouldering his way through a crowd that had given itself up to pandemonium, a crowd in which some men were pulling a handkerchief to tatters in a dance none of them knew, in which an unknown man stood up and slapped Lieberman, the expert on Japan, across the face, and in which a few of the older members, the spirit of Disraeli to the contrary notwithstanding, began to rock shyly in prayer and a few others to weep. Meanwhile, above it all, the old gentleman's cap flew like an albatross, an omen, thought Hochbrucker as he mounted the steps to the platform, of imminent success.

He was greeted by Guttman, who shook his hand in both of his own and offered him, "in my capacity as Vice-Chairman," the floor. At last the meeting was his, to lead, to illuminate, to shape however he wished. There would be no more displays of the sort of shallow logic the Chairman so admired and over which the crowd was now making so much *noise* (from the corner of his eye he saw the clarinetist's face go red over a cadenza written for the violin), the sort of scholarship any industrious clown could produce after a few hours in a book. The idea of lecturing him, from the beginning a disciple of Bacon, about the inductive method! He would show them how to use that method creatively, and at the same time with the utmost rigor. His argument would be based solely on internal grounds, upon the deepest understanding of the works themselves, and then, using the purest inductive technique, he would apply the evidence of art to the circumstances of life. An excited Karp was wringing his hand and yelling in his ear, "Mozart, Mendelssohn, Meyerbeer, the three M's, eh, my dear fellow? What an achievement!" Yet something—perhaps the way the boy's scalp showed delicately through his soft, black, close-cropped hair—stopped the large man from clapping him on the back, and he watched with an odd feeling of bafflement and even sadness as the prodigy turned from him and walked toward Saffron and Silbersheim, who waited like congregation officials to shake his hand.

As Hochbrucker went through these formalities and then walked toward the podium, he thought of how there would be no need to dwell upon his more commonplace researches —such as his lengthy compilation of correspondences between the Masonic ritual of *Die Zauberflöte* and the theosophy of the Zohar, or his discovery that the Greek setting of *Idomeneo* (conspicuously, Mozart's favorite among all his works) was nothing but a clever disguise for the Biblical tale of Jeptha, who, like his surrogate, the King of Crete, vows to sacrifice to God the first person he meets on his return from the wars and encounters his daughter. No, he would plunge his audience directly into his interpretation of K. 118, W. A. Mozart's oratorio based on Metastasio's *Betulia Liberata* (undertaken when the composer was just fourteen, and hence much concerned with religious matters). The opera, far from being the usual celebration of the beleaguered Jews or the traditional depiction of Judith's desperate heroism in freeing them from Holofernes' grasp, concentrates instead on Achion, an Ammonite Prince who is won over to the Hebrew cause and eventually to their religion. Why, we must ask, this focus upon a hero who, when living among the gentiles is described as a prisoner (*"prigionier"*) trapped in horrid night (*"orrori"*), and who, arriving safely in the Jewish camp, is said to receive the splendor (*"lo splendor"*) of daylight (*"i lumi d'rai del giorno"*), unless the composer was in fact transposing into harmonic terms his own isolation within a society of night, trapped in the *"orrori"* of silence and dissembling, unable to express his thoughts save to himself, to declare himself—except in his art, in his music? Thus the conversion of Achion—

> *Giuditta, Ozia, Popoli, Amici, io credo.*
> *Vinto so io. Prende un novello aspetto*
> *Ogni cosa per me. Tutto son pieno,*

> *Tutto del vostro Dio. Grande, infinito,*
> *Unico lo confesso . . .*

must be understood as W. A. Mozart's only recorded testament of faith:

> Judith, Ozia, People, Friends, I believe.
> I am convinced. Behold, everything
> Takes on a new aspect for me. I am full,
> Full of your God. Great, infinite,
> One, I acknowledge him.

Mentally rehearsing his disclosure thus, Hochbrucker crashed into Posner on the rostrum and spilled his notes to the floor. He started to retrieve them, then thought better of it. Had he not, this moment, gone over—and without error—the very speech he had prepared to deliver? He was becoming infected with the enthusiasm of the crowd, now growing restless and excited behind his back. Its eagerness seemed to embrace him, to lift him out of himself and propel him again to the lectern, behind which Posner stood unmoved. There was no time to be magnanimous. "There has been a change in the agenda," Hochbrucker announced to him, knowing full well that the change would be permanent, that they had heard the last of grunion thrashing on the beaches and of tortoises who lived one hundred years, that the reign of the Full Professor in the Scholar's Chair was over. But why wouldn't he go down the podium steps? It was as if the shock of being interrupted by an unknown adversary had struck him numb; even the newts seemed paralyzed with their arms against the glass, like children frozen to an icy window.

With the clamor at his back, Hochbrucker grabbed the bottom of the speaker's coat, but before he could give it the tug he intended, he inadvertently glanced through the rims of Posner's spectacles and directly into his dark, set, almost pupil-less eyes. It was impossible not to follow their unblinking gaze out over the heads of the audience (which fell into rapt, expectant silence the moment Hochbrucker turned toward it), through the portraits cigar smoke formed in the air, into the back of the hall where Sophia glistened like a mermaid in the beads. And there, his fingers on her downy neck, his white thumb against the swarthy hollow of her throat, stood Moses Levai. He saw how her breasts hove, how a shiver ran down her body in a sparkle of light, and how, with that sigh, she cast toward Posner a look of despair and undivided regret. Suddenly understanding cuffed Hochbrucker over the head. The great zoologist was not paralyzed by his challenge—had not perhaps even heard it—but by the sight of the Emeritus who, drawn from his table by the uproar in the hall, lay his fingers so naturally, so familiarly, like a strand of plump pearls, about Sophia's neck. The crowd, mute, motionless, full of faith, was completely forgotten as Hochbrucker struggled with the wave of pain that swamped him. Did it mean that Posner and Sophia were lovers? Or did that look—she dared not repeat it—encompass them both, or more than they, did it include the whole world of disinterested scholarship and inductive logic which they represented and which the grasp of one of Rumania's chief citizens now denied her? He remembered, as clearly as if it had been said at the last meeting and not fifteen years before, the former Vice-Chairman's maxim about the intellectual souls of Thessalonikan women, and took heart.

After all, perhaps everything could be recouped. With a brilliant performance, he could shatter Levai's—and perhaps even Posner's—hold upon her. He imagined the fat hand wither away, crinkling like ash before the bright fire of his revelation. "The Zohar speaks of the marriage of day and night, light and dark," he began. No, not *Die Zauber-flöte*, the Masonic parallel had already been demolished by Hernski's publications. "The King of Crete, Distinguished Members, while walking on the beach—" Metastasio! He meant to speak of Metastasio! How did it go? "*Betulia Liberata*, far from being the usual celebration of the beleaguered Jews or the traditional depiction of Judith's desperate courage . . ." When, over the years, he had happened to see Sophia, it had been from his seat on the bench, from below, the slight projection of upper lip over lower, the round, thoughtful tip of her nose, the edge of her brows, the brilliant black crown of hair only partly deflecting the bundled light that pulsed from her earrings. She sighed again and again her breasts pressed against the stiff sequined front of her dress and then fell away again, so that it was possible to follow them downward into endless shadow. Once more, desperately, he tried to pierce the thunderous silence with the words of the Ammonite Prince, but once more Sophia breathed, taking his own breath away as her breasts threatened to hurl themselves over the rim of her dress and then fell back, at once exposed and obscured, like the hot springs he had seen in the Transylvanian Alps which one moment bubble over their craters and the next withdraw to the center of all mystery. His tongue rattled against, and then clove, to the roof of his mouth.

At that moment Silbersheim, his crotch thoroughly chilled by the draft leaking through the walls, sneezed, which was as dangerous for him, a man with four strokes, as it was disastrous for Saffron, who broke into a fit of sympathetic sneezing before the eyes of the spellbound Sons. All at once the room was filled with a sizzling sound as the audience, with one vast simultaneous exhalation, let go its suspended breath. It was as if someone had taken the lid from a pan of frying food, releasing the smell of fraud into the air. They muttered, shrugged, and wrapped long, disenchanted mufflers about their necks. No one looked at the dumb Messiah on the podium, mere adolescent, a boy of twenty-two. Sophia and Levai had disappeared, leaving only a plash of excited light among the curtain's beads. Icy air swept through the banging door like a broom, pushing the smoke before it. Hochbrucker did not feel it, nor did he see his audience file away. He was insulated by the moment, which he knew to be crucial to his life, a moment not of defeat or despair but of triumph and dedication.

It was not that he felt no deprivation but that, like the loss of virginity, it was a gain. It was the moment in which the ripple of light about her body, the darkness between her breasts, the regret in her eyes, became inextricably and forever part of his own being, the source of all his future power, the sustainer of his life's work, augury of fame, his illuminator, destroyer, upholder, inspirer. Posner had lost a mistress, while he, Hochbrucker, had won a Muse. Former Treasurer Kelpman was the only member who turned at the doorway to look back, and then only for an instant, just long enough to turn his toothpick laterally with his tongue, so that it pricked both sides of his mouth. The two men remained on the podium, tied to each other umbilically, the one's coat in the other's hand. The clear light of the Directors' bulb struck off them as if they were stone, while the scholar's notes rustled near their feet like stray paper about the base of a heroic figure in the park.

THE SUN FELL off the bottom pane and, with the suddenness of electricity, the remaining light rushed from the room. The white patch of paper continued to reverberate a moment on the table, like the retinal impression of a lamp after it has been switched off. Two bloated seeds lay beneath an inch of water, whose surface was hardly ruffled by the whirling fan. The *Nifluot Maharal* ("Miracles of the Maharal") and Giovanni Bertati's *Il Convitato di Pietra* ("The Stone Guest") rested on the center of the table, unopened. A sway-backed fedora with a wide band and brim drooped on top of the bureau like a beached man-of-war. Hochbrucker groaned in the dismal light. It was an agony beyond bearing that on this day dedicated to the relationship between the Commendatore theme of *Don Giovanni* and the myth of the Golem he should remember not the evidence he needed but Posner's silly lecture on the Portuguese jellyfish, down to the guppies in the hanging tentacles and the inflated sail above the waves. He plucked a pencil from the glass, pulled the lower edge of the notebook against his chest, but before his eyes the swatch of paper faded further, a forgotten sheet on a nighttime line.

Hochbrucker pushed himself from the table, stood, and pulled the cord that stopped the fan. Heavy trucks were idling in the streets and a Chilean freighter blew its horn, mistaking the dusk for fog. From somewhere in the building a baby howled, feet rang on the metal edges of the staircase, and at the end of the hall the toilet, faithful as a thermal geyser, began its two-minute cascade. Hochbrucker felt his way through the barking of an excited dog to the closed doors of the phonograph player, which he opened outward, as if uncovering an ark. It was an old-fashioned Capehart which held a thick pile of twenty-two records in the crook of a black mechanical arm. As each record finished, the arm descended over the spindle, picked up the exhausted disk, and added it to the bottom of its stack. Then it withdrew from the spindle, turned upside down, centered itself once again, and dropped a fresh record onto the revolving platform, after which it moved aside, trembling slightly from its contortions and steeling itself for fresh demands. In this way, the machine played both sides of an entire work before, through some inbred intelligence of its own, it rested on the last side of the last record, which turned until an outside power shut it off.

Against a pale blue, flaking sky a cloud in the pompadour fashion shot golden rays over the most illustrious central European artists of the Twenties, Hanna Hrùsková and Jiri Cermak, while two angels on either side of the label aimed twin bows at the manufacturer's name in darker blue, PRAHA. Hochbrucker engaged the changing mechanism and returned to the table; but as he was sitting down again, the Commendatore knocked seven times at the door—just as Isaac ben Shimshon circled the homunculus of the Maharal seven times in order to make its clay eyes glow with the fire of life.

"*Apri, apri ti dico*," Giovanni ordered his dumbstruck servant, and the music swelled with what was meant to be terror, but was now the shrill laboring of an orchestra grown tiny and sour. Nevertheless, the Commendatore entered on two magnificent chords which retained something of their original ominousness, the very notes, Hochbrucker mused, that Rabbi Yehuda Loew blew upon the shofar when he created the famous Golem of Prague. "You have invited me to dinner," the stone guest announced, "*e son venuto*." The Don ordered his servant to set another place at table, but the Commendatore stopped him with the words, "*Non si pasce di cibo mortale*."

"Exactly," Hochbrucker shouted out loud in Rumanian, for he knew that the best way to unmask a suspected monster is to offer it food, which, lacking an alimentary canal, it will be forced to reject.

"*Chi si pasce di cibo celeste*," the statue continued, in what could only be a reference to the tetragrammaton, the "celestial food" of God's Ineffable Name, the Shem-Hamforesh. After getting around Don Giovanni's offer, the Commendatore explained that he had more important ("*più gravi*") matters to discuss. The Don asked him what it was, then, he wished ("*Che chiedi? Che vuoi?*"). The Commendatore's voice dropped an octave as he asked his host to listen with care since he had little time left to speak.

(Thus, too, the Golem's span on earth is limited and he hastens through all his tasks.)

"Parla, parla: ascoltando ti sto," Giovanni replied bravely, and the orchestra carried the Commendatore back to his previous words, *"più tempo non ho"*; to which Giovanni again replied, though more impatiently, "Speak, speak, I am listening to you."

At which point the record ended and the Great Dane in the next apartment barked without accompaniment. Hochbrucker looked toward the open cupboard of the Capehart, which seemed, in the half-light of the room, to be filled with an enormous beetle furiously working over the empty spindle shaft. When at last a new disk dropped into place, instead of the Commendatore's return invitation to Don Giovanni (*"Verrai tu a cenar meco?"*) he had expected, Hochbrucker heard the plucking of a mandolin and recognized instantly the Serenade from Act Two, scene one. He was powerless to change the scrambled order of the opera once it was set in motion; moreover, he found himself fascinated by the Don's flattery, his talk of honeyed mouths and sugar at the heart, and when Cermak, employing his celebrated "liquid tones," went into the reprise, it was he, Hochbrucker, who stood beneath the casement and sang of his passionate desire, *"O gioia mia,"* to see his beloved appear before him there.

The reply to his plea came—and Hochbrucker's heart pounded while the robot bumbled through its routine—on the next record that was dropped, not the next in sequence as it turned out, but the one which closed the scene, Zerlina's remedy for the wounds of her betrothed:

> *Vedrai, carino,*
> *Se sei buonino,*
> *Che bel rimedio*
> *Ti voglio dar.*

Though sung in the original, untransposed key and by an artist undoubtedly dead, impressed upon a disk shellacked to shine, the tune was perfectly familiar to Hochbrucker's ears. Decades burst around him, the curtain began to shimmer through the entire spectrum, as he listened once more to Sophia's lullaby, the Muse's song, the salve of his afflictions. For it was he, not Masetto, who had been beaten, had suffered shame, scorn, humiliation, the laughter of the academies, the musicologists' neglect, and, the deepest gash of all, the disgrace of self-doubt. Thus it was to him that Hrùsková offered her wondrous balm (*"un certo balsamo"*), the ministration no druggist knows but which every woman possesses in a secret place, the poultice for his disrepute.

> *Dare te'l posso*
> *Se'l vuoi provar.*
> *Saper vorresti*
> *Dove mi stà . . .*

"If you want to try it, I can give it to you. Do you want to know where it is?" sang the siren, the inspirer, the uplifter, the coquette. Hochbrucker squirmed in his seat. Zerlina took Masetto's hand, as Hrùsková took an unknown basso's, and as Sophia now her scholarly admirer's, and placed it beneath her dress and over her heart.

> *Sentilo battere,*
> *Toccami qua*

"Hear it beating, touch me here," here at the shadow's end, here, here at the unraveling of the mystery. Without warning, beneath the shiny sharkskin, his pointless anachronism began to stir. The soprano had repeated her closing phrase four times and Leporello was already figuring out a way of escaping Donna Elvira by the time Hochbrucker, his hat pulled down over his ears, stood in the street, surrounded by pineapples.

The warehouse over which Hochbrucker lived on the 100 block of Horatio Street was an island of vegetarianism in a sea of meat. Only four steps east were the packing houses of Friend and Monahan, as well as W. 11th Street Poultry, Inc. He passed them at a near-trot, dodged the water that always dripped from the railway bridge, turned left on Washington Street, and lost the looming funnels of the hawsered ships. He was accompanied, as always, from Gansevort, past Little West 12th to 13th Street, by a stretch of wall whose stenciled signs he had never mastered, launched into the world by a litany of organs he could not recite or read:

Beef Fabrications, Inc.

Our Specialty

Rounds	Strip Loins
Top Rounds	Sirloin Butts
Bottom Rounds	Top Butts
Knuckle Faces	Fillets

All above items bone in and bone out
Loew Ave. Beef Co.

Livers	Brains
Hearts	Tripe
Kidneys	Tongue

Seiler's Phila. Scrapple

Gooseneck Liverwurst   Dried Beef   Lebanon Bologna

He was forced to slow down as he turned the corner of 14th Street, and then to stop and start as he picked his way through the wet, stained sawdust and wrapping paper, and the ubiquitous abandoned gloves. Even at this hour the central packing area was crowded. Meat-eating pigeons flopped over his shoes. Trucks, oddly mammalian, mounted the curbs with their carriages and forced the old man into the street. Hooks hung like medieval weaponry among the conveyor belts and scales, all stamped: Cincinnati Butchers' Supply Co., 98 Forsyth St. Recognizing the word despite its misspelling, Hochbrucker thought of Guttman, his defender, and kept his eyes off the barrels of white fat, the pools of blood at the bottom of suspended plastic sacks. He clung to the words he could not decipher ("Fresh and frozen eviscerated turkeys") or to those, Dorato and Cerutti, Inc., NY Loin Corp., Meichman, Seligman, Hoffman and Mayer, which seemed more innocent.

A yellow helicopter hovered over the Port Authority, a boy stood in the cleft of a cement whale's tail and beat his belly, and Hochbrucker turned left on Ninth Avenue into residential, meatless Chelsea. Eight blocks ahead, past the Negroes playing basketball, the question marks and labyrinths chalked on the pavement, the seminary students wrestling with a rug, was a colored girl who flicked a pink ribbon at him and asked, "Where you headin', Daddy?" whenever he went by. He always walked quickly past and turned at 23rd Street without explaining that he was going for a bath at the Y. Now, however, he simply stood and stared at her while she rolled her ribbon, which lay like a rose between them, about her finger; when she opened her coat to him, he stepped without hesitation into her arms.

No one paid any attention. The men in the tavern across the street kept on drinking, women skirted them with shopping bags, and two policemen in a parked patrol car continued a serious conversation. Hochbrucker, lost in the folds of her coat, smelled the brilliantine of her hair, saw the dark skin, and the darker creases, of her neck. "Like a harem beauty in *Die Entführung*," he thought and leaned against her, catching his breath when he felt her lean back. He thought, in his horrid English, of something to say. Constanze, Dorabella, Zaide, the Queen of the Night; "Vot's de name, honey?" he blurted at last, but a merciful bus drowned him in a blast of exhaust, and they remained pressed to each other on the sidewalk, slightly swaying, the gold lettering of the Wm. Gong Laundry behind her back, a tricolored barber pole spiraling from the top of his head.

Hochbrucker heard her say, "We gonna fiddle 'round here all night, or are you gonna come upstairs with me?" and the streetlights snapped on. Blinded by the incandescent arc, he reeled back from her and fumbled his way across the intersection. Outside the bar he found two empty liquor bottles and a gallon jug once filled with wine. Scooping them up, he headed downtown, but stopped soon in front of an antique store, where he discovered half of a discarded chandelier. From a wire trash basket he plucked the pane from a broken picture frame. At a novelty shop on 14th Street he bought three dollars worth of beads, bottles, trinkets, and mirrors. With his pockets overflowing, gathering into his loaded arms all the stray light from shopfronts and headlight beams, he retraced his steps, running. And as he ran, past the nearly deserted packing center, past the arcane writing on the walls, and up the scented stairwell, the crystal lozenges of the chandelier struck against each other, tinkling at his knees like bells. In his pitch-black room, with three free fingers, he managed to pick up from the table the two glasses and the ashtray. He crossed to the window and nudged it partway up with his shoulder, then pushed it fully open with his elbow and hurled out his armfuls of glass. Then he groped his way to the sofa and lay down, his shoes on, spent. The fan was motionless above him. The books, breached by his entrance, lay collapsed about the room. The edge of the paper rose once, like a pale flag of surrender. The needle scraped back and forth over the black, grooveless center of the record, asking for silence. From the faint luminescence that swam over the walls, Hochbrucker knew that outside, over the airshaft, embedded in the sky like an auspicious birthmark, the moon shone down on the mountain of shards.

Three Poems

James Welch

The Versatile Historian

I CAME through autumn forests needing
wind that needed fire. Sun on larch,
fir, the ponderosa told me to forget
the friends I needed years ago.
Sky is all the rage in country steeped
in lore, the troubled Indians wise within
their graves. The chanting clouds
crowded against the lowest peak. I sang
of trouble to the north. Sleeping weasels robbed
my song of real words. Everywhere, rhythm raged.
Sun beneath my feet, I became
the statue needing friends in wind
that needed fire, mountains to bang against.

In My Lifetime

THIS DAY the children of Speakthunder
run the wrong man, a saint unable
to love a weasel way, able only to smile
and drink the wind that makes the others
go away. Trees are ancient in his breath.
His bleeding feet tell a story of run
the sacred way, chase the antelope naked
till it drops, the odor of run
quiet in his blood. He watches cactus
jump against the moon. Moon is speaking
woman to the ancient fire. Always woman.

His sins were numerous, this wrong man.
Buttes were good to listen from. With thunder-
hands, his father shaped the dust, circled
fire, tumbled up the wind to make a fool.

Now the fool is dead. His bones go back
so scarred in time, the buttes are young to look
for signs that say a man could love his fate,
that winter in the blood is one sad thing.

His sins—I don't explain. Desperate in my song,
I run these woman hills, translate wind
to mean a kind of life, the children of Speakthunder
are never wrong and I am rhythm to strong medicine.

There Are Silent Legends

Y ou might be bucking bales or hazing strays
and get a bug in your ear, some meaningless
tapping on the wind. You'd look up,
relax your stare until you saw a willow shift
or a hasty pheasant flushed. He'd be there,
watching your eyes jump to the black hair hung
against the ditch bank. Deafy knew he was a legend,
could see it in your face. Drunk, just enough beard,
a mad Mongol sniffing a few feet ahead
of your downwind fear. Dusk and birdsongs
banged against his drum-tight ear and you could yell
until his thin body turned to stone.

Though he never heard your stories, never heard the ones
you told about the crazy Indian, the slick black hair
dangling at his belt, his ears lost mysterious
in St. Louis in that alley no one quite recalls—
though wind has shut his ears for good, he squats
for hours at the slough, skipping stones, dreaming
of a moon, the quiet nights and a not quite done
love affair with a high lady in costly red shoes.

The True and Only Crisis
of the Theater

NOTES FOR A SCENARIO ON
DRAMA, MOVIES, ACTING,
ILLUSION, AND REALITY

Richard Gilman

1. An Admission

FOR THE PAST YEAR I have been teaching a seminar in
playwriting at the Yale School of Drama. It's a famous
course, Playwriting 47, which has been given continuously
for over forty years, or ever since it was started at the
school by George Pierce Baker, who was as famous as a
professor of playwriting can be. Eugene O'Neill was one
of his students and Thomas Wolfe another (both at
Harvard, where the course started; on the wings of it
Baker was wafted to Yale, where he was given a whole new
department as well as a large Schubert-type theater to play
with), along with a good many other lesser dramatists and
writers. So it's a pretty formidable tradition I inherited,
and I felt my responsibility. I think I have discharged it,
too: the only thing that might bother an inspection board
being the fact that during thirty weeks of interesting,
often useful discussions with nine or ten young playwrights
we talked at least as much about movies as about drama.

2. The Shortest Possible History of Modern Drama

WHEN Nora kept on going after she'd slammed the door on her husband, she did something more than disconcert and bewilder audiences, who sat waiting for *A Doll's House* really, *properly*, to end, and discomfit critics, who wrote that Ibsen had surely turned freedom into libertinism. She set the idea of dramatic "characters" back on its heels, not by being an unpleasant kind of heroine, one who acted against accepted moral and social values (this was what we might call the manifest content of the dream), but by stepping outside the accepted framework in which all stage characters were supposed to be contained. That is to say, her chief dramatic reality, her final presence in the imagination, was established at one stroke by absence, by her decision to take off, to refuse physically to support the dramatic situation (a very different matter from not supporting the moral one) or bring it to a resolution. Onlookers were not to find out—fatal condition for the old easygoing entente between playwright and spectator—what happened to her, what she was *now*, what she'd been brought to; the play hadn't fulfilled drama's traditional task: to bring characters from one known place to another. The demand was heavy for some time that Ibsen bring her back in a new play that would fill up the hole at the end of the first one. (It was plugged at a number of performances by new endings written by local theatrical types.)

But the holes kept opening up. August Strindberg was responsible for some very large ones. "Time and space do not exist," he wrote in the preface to *A Dream Play*. "On a slight groundwork of reality, imagination spins and weaves new patterns made up of memories, experiences, unfettered fantasies, absurdities, and improvisations." (Isn't that a concise vocabulary for almost everything we think of as modern in drama?) "The characters split, double, and multiply," he went on, "they evaporate, crystallize, and converge." And they also fly out of reach of logic, conventional psychology, history, the reigning spirit of entertainment, and all structures of morality.

Almost all the interesting drama of our century has taken shape under Strindberg's auspices, or those of Alfred Jarry his contemporary, or at least in the atmosphere they made inescapable. Strindberg, the larger figure, was, like Mallarmé for poetry, a writer in whose wake drama had to change; a source of freedom, a new direction, or a bulky impediment, his work meant that a principle of *doing things differently* had sovereignty now. What chiefly had been overthrown, what couldn't be restored to the hegemony it had had in nineteenth-century drama was the idea of stage characters as coherent, consistent, orderly; as simulacra of our own presumedly coherent existences; as substitute, enacted biographies. The dismantling of plot accompanied this destruction of character, an event in dramatic history parallel to activities in fiction, music, and painting designed to bring about the end of heroes, melodies, and subjects. We were no longer to be taken from one place to another in the course of the evening, made to feel that we'd been on a journey from darkness to light, problem to solution, unmeaning to meaning. From Chekhov down to Beckett, characters go nowhere, or struggle against being propelled (the secret of Chekhov's purported "static" quality), just as they struggle with their remaining life as stage personages against easy recognition, against being "identified" with. Who of us has met in the street Gogo, Azdak, Ubu, Enrico IV, or the Police Chief in *The Balcony?*

Strindberg again, in the preface to *Miss Julie:*

The word "character" has, over the years, frequently changed its meaning. Originally it meant the dominant feature in a person's psyche, and was synonymous with temperament. Then it became the middle-class euphemism for an automaton; so that an individual who had stopped developing, or who had molded himself to a fixed role in life . . . came to be called a "character"—whereas the man who goes on developing, the skillful navigator of life's river, who does not sail with a fixed sheet but rides before the wind to luff again, was stigmatized as "characterless" (in, of course, a derogatory sense) because he was so difficult to catch, classify, and keep tabs on. This bourgeois conception of the immutability of the soul became transferred to the stage, which had always been bourgeois-dominated. A character, there, became a man fixed in a mold, who always appeared to be drunk, or comic, or pathetic, and to establish whom it was only necessary to equip with some physical defect, such as a clubfoot, a wooden leg, or a red nose, or else some oft-repeated phrase. . . . I do not believe in theatrical "characters." And these summary judgments that authors pronounce upon people—"He is stupid, he is brutal, he is jealous, he is mean," etc.— ought to be challenged. . . . My souls (or characters) are agglomerations of past and present cultures, scraps from books and newspapers, fragments of humanity, torn shreds of once-fine clothing that has become rags, in just the way that a human soul is patched together.

Some other parts of the story: Pirandello gave his stage characters connections with life outside the theater, and called attention to the artificiality of dramas; Brecht told his audiences they weren't watching characters but actors impersonating characters; the Surrealists cut all strings to recognizable behavior; at the Bauhaus they tried to make dramas out of abstractions, inhuman figments. Beckett came along to present the histories of history-less men, and Ionesco to detach language from personage and make speech the *dramatis personae.* To bring things down to the very moment: large dolls with actors *inside* them are the best things about *America Hurrah;* and mixed media events, which use only the barest of scripts and in which nobody "acts," are where the action is.

3. Footnote and Correction to the Shortest Possible History

CERTAIN PLAYWRIGHTS persisted in behaving as though characters were still alive and plausible, and audiences persisted gamely with them. Certain critics went on writing essays about how character and plot are instrumentalities of exhibiting man's fate in action. Naturalism didn't die away as a category or a practice, though under dogged attack by other critics and by lyric types, experimentalists, and madmen like Antonin Artaud. Arthur Miller wrote *Death of a Salesman* and many persons were brought to tears by a process we have to call identification. Forms in art are never wholly superseded. Painters have gone on painting portraits decades after Picasso blew up the genre with those three noses; novelists continue to write books about men in society as Balzac taught them to do, never dreaming that a Proust or a Joyce has supervened; there are still Imagist poems coming out of Iowa. And people still go to the theater to identify with characters, not having been apprised of their death.

4. Some Clichés about the Theater

The theater is eternal.

Conflict is of the essence of drama. So is character. So is plot.

Dramatic illusion is what makes the theater work; suspension of disbelief is the key to its operation.

The theater, being "live," is a deeper, more basic, more important, and more "human" art than the film.

Being a directly communal activity, the theater has the power to bind us together the way no other art can.

We like theater because we feel our own lives to be dramas, or would like to feel that they were.

The "crisis" of the theater is almost wholly a physical and economic matter.

5. A Question

WHY ARE MOST intelligent people, most people who are interested in art in general, most bright young people, most young people with ambitions to create works in the area of performance, most good literary critics, most good teachers, and most philosophers much more drawn to the films today than to the theater?

6. On Boredom

THAT WE ARE bored by most plays today is unquestionable. Is this a matter of there being so many bad plays around, or so little good acting in the good ones? But we're bored by Shakespeare, too, and Molière and Greek tragedy (young people have never before been so bored by classics), by Shaw and Pirandello and Brecht. Even by Ionesco and Genet. Tinkering with the classics, throwing out all the old pieties of production are measures of our boredom.

When we say that we want to make a Shakespeare play "work for our time," we don't mean that we want to make it "relevant" so much as that we want to make it stop boring us. The Royal Shakespeare Company's *King Lear* and Joseph Papp's *Hamlet*—the former a brilliant, steady feat of skill, the other a clumsy ragged affair—are united by a common, admirable decision not to add to the stock of boring objects. And both have been decried by people who expostulate: "Where's the old passion, the old dignity, where's Shakespeare?" By which is meant, where's the lack of surprise, the predictability, the train that's been down the same track a hundred thousand times?

We're bored by actors, too, perhaps most by the best ones. By Sir Laurence Olivier, for example, who is a truly great actor, which is what enabled Joan Littlewood, a theater person as bored by "normal" theater as anyone could be, to say of him: " 'Look at me! Look at me!' That's what this bloody chap and all the rest of these bloody nineteenth-century bastards keep saying up on that bloody stage!" This egotism, even when it's not exploited directly or even when it's entirely jettisoned, is what makes us bored —because it's of the nature of the stage—with Sir Laurence and Sir John Gielgud, Sir Alec Guinness and Sir Michael Redgrave, heirs of the nineteenth century.

Ionesco wrote, to explain his own boredom with the stage in the years before he decided to try to relieve it with a few plays of his own: "It was as though there were present two levels of reality, the concrete reality, impoverished, empty, limited, of these banal living men, moving and speaking upon the stage, and the reality of the imagination." He wasn't talking only about naturalism or drawing-room comedy; from a certain perspective, one that has freedom from convention, anyone on a stage in any traditional kind of performance appears impoverished and empty, a no longer useful lie. We find it hard to believe in "characters" anymore: banal impersonations, jerry-built replicas of ourselves, surrogates who ask our indulgence and solicit our credence—to what end?

It's a commonplace now that boredom of a certain kind operates as an intention in much recent aesthetic practice. But what kind? I've always taken this boredom to mean that in certain new paintings, the films of Antonioni or

Andy Warhol, the novels of Robbe-Grillet or Claude Simon, to take only some examples, we are deliberately prevented from having what we might call "enthusiasms," from having emotions and undergoing excitements whose corrupted origins lie in the aesthetic *habit of mind,* and which therefore prevent us from seeing the strangeness and actuality of the work in front of us. It's rather like that earlier revolution in which "beauty" was dethroned as the aim of art, or in which at least the definition of the beautiful was enormously expanded. The truth is that art has continually to overthrow expectations about itself, to move over and over again out of reach of the *aesthetic.* In this new boredom (which is never wholly that; intimations of new kinds of pleasure stir around its edges), we are deprived of what the artist considers false pleasures. And a habit of liking art for its confirmation of previous satisfactions, its repetitions, is one of the conditions in reaction to which new art is made in every age.

Elements of a boredom which prevents us from jumping to conclusive delight, which keeps us from repetition and complacency, are present in some of the most irrefutable plays of recent years: Gelber's *The Connection,* Pinter's *The Homecoming,* Lowell's *Benito Cereno,* above all Beckett's static dramas. But these works have managed to overcome the other kind of tedium, that which we feel in the face of the blandishments of drama generally. For our boredom with the theater has to do with its very procedures, its declared and sanctified intentions, not with its failures, however numerous these may be. What we have found increasingly uninteresting as forms, the kinds of creations drama traditionally makes, are its hitherto unquestioned means of conducting its business: illusion, impersonation, pretense, the stage as justified ruse.

We don't trust "live" replicas of ourselves, we don't wish for surrogates to exhibit, through a series of inexorably limited gestures, our "meanings," we're turned off by people who *right in front of our noses* pretend to be *someone else.* And we find it harder than ever to think of the expression or representation of emotion as having very much to do with any art at all; banality lies not in the quality or kind of emotion but in the superannuated impulse to bestow it on others. As though we couldn't have obtained it by ourselves.

7. On Dramatic Illusion

THE IDEA OF the stage as a magic place, a scene of prestidigitation, was never seriously challenged until this century. Through all the theater's vicissitudes of style, manner, and subject, throughout all historical changes in dramaturgy, there persisted a belief in the efficacy of and necessity for dramatic illusion. By a mysterious process of sympathy and analogy, faith is engendered in the reality of what is taking place; false identities are accepted as true ones, invented acts as natural, arbitrary sequences and connections as inevitable. Acting is impersonation, imposture, the creation of beings—characters—whose "lives" (for this brief space of time) are accepted, deferred to, followed with passion or at least interest . . . or else rejected as not being of a worthy kind. Quarrels about acting, the classic one having to do with whether it's better for the actor actually to feel the emotions he's representing or be detached from them as pure instrument, never question the necessity of illusion but only the means of establishing it.

But then self-consciousness sets in. This sublime trick, dramatic illusion, is seen to have been flourishing in the void, for what is being conjured into existence is what has already existed: the illusions of the stage are the common-places of everyday life. It is felt, as Strindberg says, that bourgeois life, a life of strict *appearances*, is nearly coter-minous with the uses of the theater. This is what lies behind the ensuing assault on naturalism and the recourse to dream, fantasy, the surreal and the unlifelike, as well as to poetry (unavailing as it's proved) as means of rein-vigorating the life of the stage.

Mirror images, reflections, resemblances, human *fixtures* with which the era of naturalism replaced pumped-up typologies—villains, heroes, eccentrics, fathers, lovers, suf-ferers, understanders—such is what these "banal living men," actors, have been offering behind the magic circle of illusion. So effort after effort is made to strike at them, at their expectedness, predictability, familiarity, their recapitulations of what we have already experienced, at their presumptuous narrowing of possibility, their fixing of traits, ideas, attitudes, gestures, appearances, human rhythms, moods, emotions—singly or in packages of twos and threes —into incarnations, stiff, presumptuous, *completed* beings. The history of the theater since 1880 is a record of attempts to work free from the morass of illusion.

8. *Three Quotations*

Psychology, which works relentlessly to reduce the unknown to the known, to the quotidian and the ordinary, is the cause of the theater's abasement and its fearful loss of energy. —Antonin Artaud

. . . the theater often does not portray the changes of man and of the world but rather gives an image of an unchanging man in an unchanging universe. Yet we all know that the world changes, that it changes man and that man changes the world. And if this is not what ought to be the profound subject of any play, then the theater no longer has a subject. —Jean-Paul Sartre

The aim of the theater as a whole is to restore its art, and it should commence by banishing . . . this idea of impersonation, this idea of reproducing nature . . . that frantic desire to put "life" into their work . . . no longer would there be a living figure to confuse us into connecting actuality and art; no longer a living figure in which the weaknesses and tremors of the flesh were perceptible. The actor must go and in his place comes the inanimate figure—the ueber-marionette we may call him.—Edward Gordon Craig

9. *On Theaters of Non-Actors*

GORDON CRAIG'S IDEA has been tried, but masks, puppets, marionettes, inanimate figures of many kinds haven't proved the answer to the problem of the stage. Belief is always possible to reawaken, and in some ways it's easier to believe in marionettes, who don't try to convince us that they're flesh and blood, easier to believe in their task —to create artificial, *aesthetic* life—than in actors, who have to try to *be* the thing whose existence has come about by fiat of the imagination. But marionettes and puppets remove only one dimension of the problem; derived inevitably from human models, they can ultimately repeat only human gestures and attitudes, even though they've stripped away the tight sheathings of personality and character as we have been defining them. They are still pretenses, whereas the problem is more and more how to make real occasions.

Etienne Gilson writes: "There is no point in adding to reality images of natural beings, which, precisely because they are but its images, add nothing to reality. What matters is to turn out, not an image, but a thing; not to add an image to reality, but a reality to reality." The central procedures of contemporary poetry, fiction, music, dance, painting, and sculpture are obedient to this dictum; the theater has struggled in the grip of image-making.

In America, where we've produced no significant body of formal dramatic works, there is an increasing interest in theaters of improvisation and games, testimony to the dissatisfaction with the stage as a place for the conjuring up of images. The desire that it become an arena for new, original gestures, performed by actors who are no longer executors, *stand-ins*, but instigators and makers, lies behind the growing repudiation of formal texts, as well as the increasing currency of words like "ritual," "myth," and "play" (the verb). A vocabulary with a potential for self-deception and indulgence of adolescent ambitions, it nevertheless also expresses an appetite for theater as an actuality rather than a reflection, an original gesture rather than an interpretive one—for theater, in other words, to stop being illusion.

The movement away from formal, *preexisting* texts has been gathering speed for some time. "Why not conceive of a play composed directly on the stage, realized on the stage?" Artaud asked more than thirty years ago. Though he would most likely consider Happenings to be not quite the thing he had in mind, Artaud doubtless would have been sympathetic to their intention. The great decrier of psychology and rationalism in the theater saw the supremacy of language as drama's widest curse, and Happenings reduce verbal elements to a minimum. He hated the use of drama as a means of giving "information," ideas, or even perceptions about the world, since its proper function, he felt, was to provide visions—new and "terrible" myths. And Happenings, while entirely scorning the "artistic" implications of words like "vision" and "myth" and having no traffic with emotions, terrible or otherwise, are theatrical actions rooted in a refusal to impart information and in a wish to be "about" nothing but themselves.

The central point about Happenings, Environments, mixed-media events, and the like is that they've emerged out of an impulse to blot out as much as possible of the remaining distance between theater and life, to destroy the artificiality of drama, its inherent tendency to fix human actions and qualities and its reign as illusion. For there is nothing illusory about Happenings; they are real events, distinguishable from the events of ordinary life only by a thin line (there will always be some line of demarcation; as long as we have the word "Happening" we are in the presence of something different from what takes place in our everyday lives, an increment and an analogy to it). Happenings are meant to indicate by their having been instituted at all that things do happen, that the world is to be looked at and seen freshly again and again.

A remark of John Cage, the philosopher of new theater if anyone is, illustrates what I mean to say: "Theater takes place all the time wherever one is, and art simply facilitates persuading one this is the case." The central implication here for the crisis of the theater is that as long as we think of drama as something to *go to*, rather than as something that's a sign of everything else, as long as we regard it as illusion instead of a form of reality, we will go on being bored with it as we are bored, ultimately, with all illusions. The new movement to replace formal, textual, illusionist drama may not triumph soon or ever, but it isn't likely to fade quietly away.

10. Meanwhile, Back at the Art Theaters . . .

THE NOTION THAT film is a rival and alternative to theater arose with the movies' origins and is to this day a commonplace idea. Whole eras of film history would seem to buttress such thinking; in the archives are thousands of movies that are nothing but filmed plays. Yet even when movies go outdoors, away from sets and props and walls, they clearly employ many of the materials of plays: actors, scripts, dramatic conflict, etc. It was André Malraux who I think first pointed out that only a misuse and misunderstanding of film art could lead to the conclusion that it was an art resembling that of drama; it resembled more nearly, he said, that of fiction. Yet while this is surely true aesthetically, film remains linked in a great many minds—and properly so—with drama: as alternative fields of practice, as alternative magnets for energies, as alternative ways of looking at and dealing with the world.

11. An Anthology of Comments on Film by Students of Drama at Yale

It's a more clandestine experience, darker than the theater.

Actors *perform* on a stage; that's very different from people *living* on a screen.

The camera can give a sense of greater reality than the stage, even in highly "unrealistic" movies.

Films are more responsive to the world around them than theater.

Movies add a new dimension by being open-ended; their techniques expand the imagination . . . they are a great jumping-off point for stimulating immediate thought: they present ideas visually which trigger emotional and intellectual responses much more rapidly than in the theater.

Film transcends reality much more easily than theater.

Movies are technical poetry. You have the potential of a totally controlled environment as opposed to the live quality of the theater.

Movies have the same advantage as the mind has—not being limited in space. There's an immediacy of transition that can't be achieved on the stage.

Films are inhuman, though they pretend not to be; that's a great attraction.

They concentrate and focus for you. It's easier to be

involved and also not involved, depending on which you want to be.

Movies handle internals better than any other medium because they have a total range of vision.

Films always give the illusion of the First Time.

Movies have the possibility of all the speed of living without the time wasted—in the bathroom or sitting in a doctor's office. Godard can edit out the three or four frames it takes Belmondo to go from opening the car door in *Breathless* to stepping out.

Anything can happen in the movies.

Anything can happen in the movies. Like theater or any art, film, from one point of view, is also an illusion, but an illusion which doesn't pretend to be anything else. This is its source and ground of freedom: that unlike the theater it has no need to solicit our belief against the evidence of our senses. People "living" in that strange new habitat, a screen; actors "performing" on a stage . . . the difference is that a reality is being created in the former but in the latter merely an imitation. By being physically "unreal," something that doesn't exist except through an imaginative fiat, the aesthetic reality of film is all the more convincing, all the more supple and responsive. The traditional theater is locked into the physical world, wedded to bodies and language, and has to struggle perpetually against their clichés, against the inexorable exhaustion of possibility; film, on the other hand, extends possibility by being, in the most liberating sense, *abstract*, a series of planes, an arrangement of visual modalities, a juxtaposition and continuity of images which together do not mount up to a new image but a new thing. This is what the theater has found it so hard to achieve and this is why its future, far from being a matter of local, contingent considerations, or a question of gaining a new redoubtableness or revived élan, is, in this era of the death of sacred cows, an absolute issue of survival.

Wordlessly

Marilyn Coffey

WORDLESSLY he took me
pasting red labels on each breast
pressing air mail stickers on my buttocks
leaving me to do the rest which I did
quite willingly RUSH along the inside
of each thigh PRESS HERE where ever there
was room TOUCH ME on each eyeball

When the labels fell off
the glue remained behind
forming a sort of thin translucent shell
which didn't hurt at first (it fit quite
well, actually, covering each and every pore
crack & crevice)   it was just
as good as skin being quite thin
& adhering to my eyelids despite repeated blinking
preventing me from seeing too well
or thinking much about it. The tragedy:
I fell from a very high cliff being
unable to see where I was going, (1),
and, (2), being too stiff to clamber up again
All I could do was stammer for help
on my way down. Unfortunately,
my tongue was dry (repeated lickings)
and, anyway, the glue adhered to my jaws.
I broke both arms, thinking about him.
Did I do it well?

Lines from the Quick

George Stiles

Dear One,

I am here in this big lonesome awfull place and I think about you nights (Smile) and days. Days we keep busy here. I mean all kind of things are done to us. Only not what you Think. I guess I know what you think. If that was so it wouldnt be to bad. (Smile) I mean like we get taken out too the showers every two days. Every two days we take a shower in lots, you know? Three of us girls or four at one time and howd you like a sight like That? You would I bet. But we aint that way so we all clean ourselves like Good (Smile) girls and get out of there and let in the next lot of girls. But it does feel allright soaping ourselvs everywhere and having the hot and cold water shower down over us, it sure feels awfull, good allright, the water good and warm, we all soaping ourselvs and maybe each another. Maybe one girl soaps another. She scrub me and I scrub her, like that. You know? I guess your thinking, she must be really that way sure only, you know different and better and if not you (Smile) who does?

The way I got here—Im committed. They caught me committing something and here I am, wham, for just only walking in the Park. I was lonesome. Not in the way Im lonesome in this place, like I am but, that night I was just trying too walk this—You know—out of myself, in the Park. You been with me there. You know.

There I was walking in the Park alone and lonesome and thinking, about You maybe, I *mean* it, when two or three come on me. Got the time, asks One. Time for what, I ask back. (Smile) Because, you know me. Their young and maybe their lonesome like me. I laugh, *you* know, and they laugh back. Laugh and smile and they keep coming on. Smoke? Sure. You know me. You looking for something maybe? May be, I say. I look at them again, three of them, their young and not to bad, you know? Three are safe, Im thinking, their three and I wanting company, jesus. It was the heat in my room. I been turned off four months now you know and how much days and nights I dont even count. No drinks. No (Smile) You know. You know. Thats what got too me, I guess. Thinking, about It. Dont you think about It, I say too me. Then I dream about It.

I dreamed about you all one night—that you made me pregnant. Jesus, in a dream. Did I shake when I woke up in the morning. Did I. Really thought, jesus, I'll pass my Period this time.

Im walking in the Park and sweating, under my dress, my arms, I feel sweat all down me, Im wet and hot every where, there (Smile) and all over. If youd been through what I had to come through—but your a Man, so you cant imagine I bet. Thats how I took on the three Boys. Three Boys, their lonesome, Im lonesome, they made me laugh and smile and, you know me thats, all I want, you know? Thats all I want, I tell them that committed me here. A laugh and some smokes. I cant drink, never could and thats my mistake. My mistake No. 2, I got in the back seat with two boys. Want a ride, Lonesome, they ask me. Thats me. Lonesome. I need too laugh, thats what I went for. I love too laugh and smile. It wasnt the Car ride and three Boys that might never be Men, they wont live that long. Thats all we committed all night—ride. You know. (Smile) In the back seat. Thats allright. I shut my eyes and make believe their all You. They were just Boys with plenty laughs in them and thats how I took the drive and got committed again. Because their car was a stolen car and a crime. That and my history. They read up my history and that Id been committed and they mail me right back here to this place. Their all Fiends here, alky and dope and Sex. But dont You worry. I wont be unfaithful like *that*. (Smile)

In this place we all sleep together in one big Ward. They put us all too bed early and I cant sleep that early and jesus, just what do you think I think about in my lonesome bed in the dark after a hot and cold shower and my skin shooting off electric sparks almost and my blood coming on like a flood and a storm. Almighty jesus, if thats not Torture and a torment, well. I know youd do something about It. If you could. Where are you anyway? Well just sos your alive some where.

The other night the girl sleeping next too me couldnt sleep either. Shes afraid, shes scared of the Mouse, she says, this girl and, when she hears Mouse going for a walk under our beds she asks me too let her come in. She begs me too. Shes allright but a Fiend, you know? Alky she tells me and she has a darling little shape and darling little breasts and a sweet little tail, a Model, which is what she was, I hear, as long as she could control her alky intake. Im afraid of Mice too but you cant even imagine why shes so frightened of a Mouse. Because she thinks that one is going too climb up into her. You know? Did you ever hear that before? I know I never did before and Ive been around some Fiends. So thats why she wanted too get in with me and so I let her, naturally knowing Im allright, to. She gets out of bed into mine and shes shivering like its winter and I put my arms around her and she puts hers around me, like lovers. Thinking about it now its a laugh but when the attendant comes by with her flash light she takes one fast look at that empty bed standing and guesses there must be a breakout or a kidnap and she goes right for the phone. And before either of us can make a move or tell her anything the Ward is full of keepers and attendants and guards and nurses and all the Fiends are up and howling. When they looked and find her in with me you can imagine what they think and accuse us of doing together under the covers. They had too almost operate on the both of us too get her out of my bed, she was so scared of them and afraid of the Mouse. It was a laugh that what I kept thinking when we were laying like that right up against each other, here we are, I kept thinking, both grown women, the both of us Have had It, believe us, and theres nothing between us two that can do each other a bit of good. You know. Two girls, their practically useless too each other and here their imagining us actually doing any thing, and that we could.

In Isolation everything is taken away from you, everything. All they leave you with is some covering, a nightshirt and nothing else. Not even a toothbrush or a postage stamp and no smokes. They want too drive you crazy, I guess. There was a girl in Isolation before me. I heard about *her* and her writing on the walls, in the can, in the showerroom, in the halls and even on the bed sheets. You can still read it but its fading. This girl wrote it with one finger.

They took every thing away from her and she wrote it anyway, one word or almost one word. This girl had bleeding piles and she used her one finger, like a pen and red ink and it came out a little brown, to. She ran all through the Ward writing in red and brown that one word until they caught her and tied her down. She was trying to spell H E L P, I guess. It reads H E L and it is.

The Doctor just came by. He wants to look me over, he says, after he comes back in here. I have to take every thing off, so he can look me over. (Smile) He looks cute, especially all in white and like he knows a lot more than sticking something like a needle into you. You know. But I *wish* it was You. (Smile)

Faithfully,
L

P.S.   Im sending this to the last address Ive got down for you, only I know that your not in that place. I hope you arranged about forwarding. Next time write me what your doing and where. I pray your not in some place like this, god.

The Heir

Irving Feldman

He is a surgeon resectioning the heart.
Confessedly dead, yet the corpse
Sits up and shouts at him, "You idiot,
Do you know how to do anything right?"
And tries to grab the knife or the dream itself.
It seems to him they are struggling over
The very nature of reality.

On the bed awaking, he who was the doctor
Is now the patient. So short the life, so long
The convalescence! Sad, square, and aching,
He accepts his father's dead heart, commonplace,
Appalling, and the old man's misery and maiming
Return in the son's chest to their brutal beating.
Devoted and good, his normality resurrects
In dull parody that bitterness and failure.

Unloaded, held to the head,
That catastrophic life clicks repeatedly
In the empty chambers.

Sitting in our room now
And carried away for a moment, he says, as if
Repeating an important lesson, earnestly,
With yearning and with pride, "Actually,
Dad and I have the same sense of humor."

Colloquy

Irving Feldman

I HAVE questioned myself aloud
At night in a voice I did not
Recognize, hurried and
Disobedient, hardly brighter.
What have I kept? Nothing.
Not bread or the bread-word.
What have I offered? Rebel
In the kingdom, my gift
Has wanted a grace. I am crazy
With the brutality of it.
What have I said? I
Have not spoken clearly,
Not what must be said,
Failed in using, in blessing.
I have wanted long to confess
But do not know to whom
I must speak, and cannot
Spend a life on my knees.
Nonetheless, I have always
Meant to write in joy.

Where's the Relevance?

Ronald Steel

Wʜɪʟᴇ ᴛʜᴇ ɴᴇᴡsᴘᴀᴘᴇʀs and television tell us of students rioting in Paris and New York, of devastation in Vietnam and armies clashing in the Middle East, of people massacred in Biafra, the Sudan, and Indonesia, of colonels seizing power in Greece and Latin America, of a Stalinist regime overthrown in Czechoslovakia and a neo-Nazi party rising in Germany, of American cities burning and American society destroying itself over the question of the tint of American skin, the movies have been busily conducting us into outer space, back to the Old Frontier, and into the minds of adolescents who fall prey to older women.

It is hard to remember a time when the movies have been more irrelevant to what is happening in our society. Americans have become involuntarily politicalized, even traumatized, by the imperial war in Vietnam and the race war at home. But, with a couple of exceptions, the movies have been totally out of it. The great success of the past season, Mike Nichols' *The Graduate*, is an updated version of Andy Hardy. Although the latter part of the film takes place at Berkeley, a center of the new morality to which *The Graduate* pays tribute, we see nothing of its atmosphere of alienation and dissent. This is a movie that could have been, in fact should have been, made ten years ago. Like the equally slick and diverting *Bonnie and Clyde*, it is an exercise in nostalgia with a vinyl veneer.

We are always being told how the movies are *the* art form of our age, superseding such outdated forms as plays and books. But where is the movie that tells us as much about our changing attitudes toward sex, race, and authority, a movie that grooves like the rock musical *Hair?* Where is the movie that tells us as much about the ghetto as Claude Brown's *Manchild in the Promised Land,* about the black-white chasm as Eldridge Cleaver's *Soul on Ice?* Where is the movie as switched-on to the modern idiom as the Joffrey Ballet's *Astarte* or, for that matter, Mart Crowley's comedy, *The Boys in the Band?* When is the avant-garde art form of the twentieth century going to catch up with the world we live in and the way we think about it?

For the most part, the world has been creeping in through the back door: a mixed marriage in *Guess Who's Coming to Dinner* (would Sidney Poitier want to marry such a ninny?), reconciliation with yesterday's enemy in *The Russians Are Coming!,* and the end of the Cold War mentality in Len Deighton's superior spy thriller, *Billion Dollar Brain,* in which a demented Texas Fascist tries to "liberate" Latvia with a deadly virus, a talking computer, and a mercenary army. Otherwise, Hollywood has been mute, and there has scarcely been a political film worthy of the name since Frankenheimer's dated but still chilling *The Manchurian Candidate.* It is only through documentaries, the underground cinema, and a few European imports that the movies seem aware that something is going on out there—in the American empire, in the ghettos, in the universities.

There have been surprisingly few documentaries on the war: Felix Greene's propagandistic *Vietnam,* which is mainly an idyllic account of life under Ho Chi Minh; *The Anderson Platoon,* originally produced for television; and the French-made *Far from Vietnam,* a joint effort of protest by Alain Resnais, William Klein, Joris Ivens, Agnès Varda, Claude Lelouch, and Jean-Luc Godard. By far the most successful of the lot is the devastatingly immediate *A Face of War.* Filmed in combat by Eugene Jones, who was twice wounded, and three brave assistants, it tells the story of this tragic, brutal, corrupting colonial war exactly the way it is. There are no heroes and there are no villains —only victims. We never see a live Vietcong, but we watch a child die from shrapnel in its brain, an old woman sobbing as her house is consumed in flames by Americans trying to flush out "the enemy," a young Marine with his leg blown off crying to be taken home, and a baby being born amid the chaos and fury of modern war.

There is no sermonizing, no attempt to romanticize the Vietcong or point a finger of accusation at young Americans who have been sent halfway around the world to die for a cause they do not understand and to fight an enemy they often cannot see. There are moments of beauty, as when a flare slowly descends through the night sky behind an abstract thicket of barbed wire; moments of understated social comment, as when Marines wrestle in the mud during a game of football, all a single mud color, and then, after dousing themselves in a pond, slowly emerge, one by one, black separated from white; and moments of the sudden blind fatality of war, as when a truck strikes a land mine, gravely wounding some of the Marines. A Face of War is not the whole story about Vietnam. It explores none of the political issues and seeks to do no more than record what is happening, what Americans are doing to themselves and to others in a distant country among uncomprehending people. By keeping his camera sensitively trained on the open faces of these young Americans, only a few of whom are over 21, and half of whom were killed or wounded during the filming, Jones presents the special anguish of this war in a point-blank way.

A number of underground filmmakers have also been trying to make sense of contemporary political experience: Robert Kramer in his study of unfulfilled radicalism, The Edge; Robert Machover and Norman Fruchter in Troublemakers, a documentary of community organizing in Newark; and Adolfas Mekas in his portrait of a draft-dodger, Windflowers. In addition, there is the recently organized series known as the Newsreel, founded last December by a group of independent filmmakers as a "radical news service whose purpose is to provide an alternative to the limited and biased coverage of television news." Dealing with such topics as the Pentagon demonstration, draft resistance, and riot-control weapons, it proposes a "process of liberation" from many of the more conventional assumptions of American society. These underground films may form an important stage in the development of a politically engaged American cinema. But for the most part they have not developed an artistry that matches their ambitions, nor have they begun to reach an audience beyond those who are already committed. Their standards are lax, their technical means necessarily limited, and their points are blunted by the knowledge that they are preaching to the converted and cannot expect to reach the general public.

PERHAPS ONE REASON why the commercial cinema has dealt so trivially, if at all, with current political themes is that the Hollywood director does not have the kind of control over his material that his European counterpart enjoys. Except for Hitchcock, we have almost no *auteurs,* and certainly none who seems inclined to take on a political theme without giving it the Stanley Kramer treatment. This is an old situation, but until it changes we shall have to rely mostly on European imports for political themes of any complexity. Europeans are not any wiser about politics than Americans, and, until recently at least, their situation seemed almost bucolic by comparison. But filmmaking there is still more of a one-man undertaking than it is a corporate enterprise. This, among other reasons, is why European films usually have the director's name on the marquee, while American films don't. Everybody knows who directed *Open City,* but only the buffs remember who made *The Quiet American* or *A Lion Is in the Streets.*

Alain Resnais' *Hiroshima, Mon Amour* was basically a Marguerite Duras love story wrapped in antiwar tinsel. His latest effort, *La Guerre est Finie,* takes on the theme of political commitment, but is really more concerned with the decaying illusions and the sadness of middle age. While the political treatment is weak, the film has its *auteur's* signature stamped on every reel. The same kind of strongly emphasized point of view marks young Bernardo Bertolucci's *Before the Revolution,* a sensitive yet unsentimental portrayal of a young Marxist who loses his best friend, his innocence and finally his ideals. Made several years ago, but only spottily released in this country, it probes the conscience of a fashionably alienated bourgeois who has neither the courage nor the intensity to live up to his values, who blindly uses others just as he is used by them, and who ends up like Fabrizio in *The Charterhouse of Parma,* from which the script is loosely patterned, a prisoner of his own fantasies and intellectual limitations.

A comic version of a similar theme is deftly handled in *China Is Near,* a second film by the young Italian director who made such a remarkable debut in *Fist in the Pockets* (later released in America). In his first film, Bellocchio viewed both murder and politics as equally farcical, but gave his scene of social alienation a Dostoevskian tone by emphasizing the epilepsy of his assassination-prone teen-age hero. In *China Is Near,* he expands this framework to include all of life as politics. The vocabulary is Maoist; the action involves a seventeen-year-old militant hero who threatens to assassinate the local Socialist party hacks, including his ludicrous brother who has bought himself a place on the electoral ticket. But the mood is black comedy and the antics straight out of *commedia dell'arte.* The capitalists are not vicious but pathetically ineffectual, the workers are not noble but ambitious and unscrupulous. Political idealism is real and important, but somehow lost in such intricacies of life as seducing girls, revenging insults, and improving one's social position. Politics is life, and therefore absurd. This is Bellocchio's message, verging on cynicism, but delivered with a virtuosity and wit that makes it all the more telling.

Where Bellocchio sees politics as farce, Jean-Luc Godard tends to see it as intellectual abstraction, which may be the difference between the French and the Italian view of the world. Still, Godard's treatment of politics is topical and tendentious—which probably accounts for a good deal of his not always merited esteem on college campuses and in second-run art houses. In *Les Carabiniers,* a film several years old but only recently released in this country, the master turns his hand to the inanities of war, or rather of those who conduct it. Two simple farm louts, Michelangelo and Ulysses (let it not be said that Jean-Luc is unfamiliar with the classics), receive an invitation from the king to join the army, see the world, stab old people in the back, and leave restaurants without paying. They go off to war, commit numerous atrocities without ever being aware of what they are doing, shoot a tiresome Barbarella-type partisan who shouts bad verses from Mayakovski at the firing squad, and return to their sluttish girlfriends with nothing to show for their exploits but a sheaf of postcards of the Parthenon and the stockyards. This is Pop art war, and offers a splendid opportunity for some clever camera work. Its intellectual content is celluloid deep, which is par for the Godard course, but it has a stylish veneer that attracts the with-it crowd. Managing to suggest the presence of Profound Ideas while avoiding engagement with them, the master cleverly flatters his audiences without ever challenging their assumptions. It is really a pity that Godard has so little in his head, for he always says his piece quite imaginatively. As the David Bailey of the art houses, he has found a secure place for himself in the annals of French intellectual *chinoiserie*.

Always keeping a half-step ahead of the latest fad, Godard has more recently turned his attention directly to Maoism and the student rebellion. *La Chinoise*, his most recent film, recounts the exploits of a Maoist cell group under the leadership of the current Madame Godard, an actress of limited ability and remarkable ugliness. Well-brought-up *fils de papa* every one of them, the young Maoists plot the downfall of bourgeois civilization as they munch *croissants* and chant maxims to one another from the Little Red Book. It is all good clean fun—Red Guard calisthenics on the balcony, self-criticism classes, communal living with occasional tumbles into sexual therapy, and pamphleteering in the streets—until the young revolutionaries draw straws to murder a visiting Russian diplomat (Russians, of course, being worse than Americans since they have betrayed the faith). Suddenly it is all for real. The self-styled young *chinoise* of the title walks into a hotel, assassinates a man, later discovers she has killed the wrong one, and calmly returns for another murder. The assassinations take place offscreen, and thus the violence is kept abstract, even symbolic, more of an *acte gratuit* in André Gide's sense than part of a coherent political program. Anyway, Godard seems glibly to be saying, this is the way it is. Take it or leave it.

Except that you can't leave it when it involves assassinations, barricades in the streets, and bloody battles with the police. And it is hard to know how to take it when the revolutionaries themselves don't know quite what they want, other than to get rid of the whole rotten system and replace it with one which may well turn out to be equally rotten, but which will at least be different. Perhaps the best scene in the film is where the young assassin tries to explain her rambling, confused thoughts to a sympathetic but baffled Francis Jeanson, Sartre's disciple and a former spokesman for Algerian independence. Godard doesn't know what these romantic revolutionaries want, and doesn't even seem to be sure what he thinks of them, if indeed he thinks about them at all other than as objects to be manipulated on a screen. He never quite takes them seriously, and was himself, like the rest of French society, caught flatfooted during the student-triggered uprising in France last May.

Godard shows little understanding of the difference between a play-acting revolution directed against mendacious elders and cramping social restrictions, and a real revolution designed to overthrow a government and replace it with a new social order. It is the difference between being a poodle-clipper and a butcher. Gillo Pontecorvo, director of *The Battle of Algiers*, understands this very well. What makes this semi-documentary so thrilling and disturbing is precisely that quality of participating in a real event for real causes, not an intellectual fantasy about abstract ideas. We are pulled into the film by the documentary technique, locked into an Algiers where the sound of the discothèque in the French quarter is as real as the smoke of *kif* in the Casbah, and held there by a dramatic power that transcends the limitations of the pure documentary.

Pontecorvo's camera is harsh, unyielding, implacable, never surrendering to sentiment or poetic effects, never romanticizing the rebels, who are killers of the innocent as well as victims, and always retaining a distance from the protagonists as though it were recording a Greek tragedy whose outcome it was powerless to affect and whose horror it was unable to escape. A remarkable feat of historical reconstruction (Pontecorvo uses only his own footage), *The Battle of Algiers* possesses the versimilitude of the observed event, without any of the monotony or superficiality that can easily stultify an ordinary documentary. He avoids banality by superb cutting, by focusing on morally ambiguous figures—the illiterate terrorist, the French commander who had himself served in the Resistance.

Keeping tight control over his material at all times, subordinating the action to an explicit and inexorable dramatic end, Pontecorvo never allows the film to turn into a catalog of atrocities and counteratrocities, to descend to the simplistic level of preaching that war is hell, or that colonial rebellions are so morally justified that they permit immoral means. Terror may be necessary, but it is never excused, and the massacre of innocent French teen-agers is just as appalling as the murder of the nationalist rebels.

This, then, is not simply the story of a colonial rebellion, one that deserves to be consigned to the pile of yard-goods documentaries that are the specialty of *cinema-verité*. Its theme of urban, anticolonial rebellion has a special message for America today. But the film transcends such narrow application, just as it transcends the Algerian war, an event that becomes the context of a probing account of human cruelty, degradation, courage, and dedication. *The Battle of Algiers* is the most articulate expression we have yet seen on a screen of the philosophy of Frantz Fanon—of the rage of the oppressed against their oppressors, of the rape of the colonial mind by the colonizers, and the final corruption that sees the colonized become morally no better than their oppressors, of the victims changing place with the victimizers, and the two becoming indistinguishable in a bottomless pit of frustration and revenge. At the end, the battle for Algiers has been won, the colonial oppressors have departed, the people surge through the streets in exaltation. Yet the triumph is also a tragedy, and the revolution only another beginning.

Films like this are precious, as is any work of art that manages to capture a sense of the immediate and fuse it with an intellectual conception of general import. It requires artistic skill, discipline, and sensibility of the highest order. This doesn't happen very often, but when it does we are reminded of what Hollywood seems never to have learned: that politics is not a stranger to art, but at the very center of man's struggle with himself and his society.

Fluxation and Slurrage

William Weintraub

UNTIL RECENTLY, the New Cinema knew Ron Chaffinch only for his "proems" (*Basilisk One, Basilisk Two, Basilisk Three*, etc.). These films run from seventy to ninety seconds each, and in terms of their avowed intention —"to fragment the instant"—I have found them moderately successful. But I have never been able to share the unreserved enthusiasm of most critics, as each succeeding proem (there have been twenty-three so far) has left me with a nagging feeling of promise unfulfilled.

In the *Basilisks*, Chaffinch never fully exploits the opportunities for ambiguity inherent in his subject matter, although I admit that the effects of this are mitigated by the very brevity of the films. Also, there is a troubling lack of fluidity-within-the-frame, and without Chaffinch's highly personal use of the hand-held projector we would probably never feel the full impact of his granitic images.

There was, therefore, considerable surprise at the recent premiere of his latest film when Chaffinch entered the hall and conspicuously took a seat among the audience. Obviously he would not be handling the projection himself. This added to the air of anticipation, for there had been much rumor of a radical change in Chaffinch's style, and Chaffinch had been uncharacteristically secretive about his new project. Thus none of us had the slightest idea of what to expect when the lights were dimmed for this first showing of *Dig My Holocaust*.

Four hours later, when the lights went up again, one thing was stunningly apparent: Ron Chaffinch had abandoned the short form.

But beyond this stark fact lay a richly ambiguous texture of filmic intent and effect. This was reflected in the hubbub from the audience as voices rose to exclaim about this or that aspect of the *oeuvre*. Had anyone since Antonioni so completely captured the bone-crushing boredom of life? Had anyone since Godard so adumbrated the random nature of perception? Had anyone *ever* superimposed the Hiroshima mushroom on the female breast so courageously often?

Despite varying interpretations of the nature of Chaffinch's accomplishment, there was complete agreement that he had now thrown off any vestige of *retardataire* shackles. Here was a truly subversive film. In its evisceration of the middle-class ethos, no entrail had been left unturned.

But what interested me most were *Holocaust*'s frequent ventures into the narrative form. This, of course, was not "plot" in the Pauline Kaelic sense, nor even in the Robbe-Grilletian sense; there was no sacrifice here of the aleatory for "story line." It was, rather, narrative of the sort that fully expresses the film-maker's contempt for the chloroform that Hollywood distills from literature.

In this vein, Chaffinch's nonprofessional actors (so free of sophistic gloss!) gave us moments that will not easily be forgotten. One that keeps returning to my mind is that climactic scene in the fourteenth reel of *Holocaust*. Surely it must be one of the most electrifying Pregnancy Announcement Sequences screened in recent months. Suffice to say that when Chaffinch's high-school heroine, Immolata, said, "Gregory, I've got something to tell you," a choking sound ran through the audience.

Some viewers thought that Chaffinch's impact derived from the fact that he had symbolically buried Immolata up to her neck in sand for this scene, but credit must also go to Gregory's unconventional rejoinder to the dread phrase, "I am with child." (All dialogue, of course, was improvised by the actors.)

Unlike Mario, in Bognor's *Negation 17*, Gregory does not say, "Are you sure?" And unlike Hubert, in Trent's *Bitter Elixir*, he does not say, "Ya sure?" No, Gregory's reply, which promises to become a byword on the nation's campuses, gets its effect by being far more mosaic than linear.

It seems to me that the Pregnancy Announcement, by its climactic nature, frequently throws into sharp focus the film-maker's efforts to break new ground in the narrative form, often through a painterly approach. One therefore immediately compares Chaffinch's masterstroke in *Holocaust* with the Announcements in earlier films, like Kretschmer's pioneer work *Lydia* (1965). One recalls that Lydia, wishing to impart the news of her parturient state, tugs at Ludwig's beard and says, "Ludwig, I've got something to tell you." But Ludwig, absorbed with his yo-yo, affects not to hear. In order to attract his attention, Lydia dances on the beach and turns from positive to negative every eight frames. Though this may appear primitive today, it was epochal for its time (since then, of course, Kretschmer has grown enormously, thanks to his unique technical innovations like focus-mangling, fluxation, and slurrage).

In later works by "Kretsch" (as the film-makers call him), what is probably the best Pregnancy Announcement comes in *Medusa* (1967). One recalls how Medusa, tugging at Harold's Iron Cross, cries, "Harold, I've got something to tell you." This, naturally, causes Harold to crash the motorcycle, and Medusa's next remark ("I'm five weeks late"), uttered as she staggers from the wreckage, is surely a landmark in the Expanded Cinema. The fact that Medusa addresses this observation to a tree stump has been attributed by some critics to a parallax problem that dogged Kretschmer's viewfinder throughout the shooting, but the *cinéaste* himself assures me that Harold was *meant* to be out-of-frame, and that the tree stump embodies a symbolism that will not be lost on Suburbia.

Bligh, on the other hand, has chosen a more documentary approach in *Black Forceps* (1966). In this film, one recalls that when Jocko says, "Are you sure?" Althea goes to her chiffonier and produces a calendar, a table of logarithms, and a sundial. As the young couple sit down to do their arithmetic, one is spared any *longueurs* in the ensuing twenty-minute obstetrical discussion thanks to the haunting overlay of song and guitar by Dow Jones and the Industrials.

Though Bligh's somewhat archaic, sequential logic has a curious power, the full use of irrelevance is still probably the film-maker's most cunning sledgehammer. And in this *genre*, of course, Porchester has no peer.

In *A Chick Too Groovy* (1966), where we see one of the few non-dream sequences Porchester has ever attempted, he shows us his heroine, Rosamund, on the telephone. She is about to make her Announcement when her parents saunter into the room. Rosamund's abrupt switch to four hours of small talk, on the phone, is surely Porchester at his most savage. As she speaks her monologue, the parents' continuous performance of Swedish calisthenics, in the foreground, heightens the effect of Porchester's bold refusal to compress time. And the father's callous remark ("If you ask me, that girl's got one in the oven") must surely be one of the underground's most searing comments on middle-class values.

But probably the most impactful of all will be *Orpheus Nacreant,* which Ruttenberg is making in multi-screen and Fujichrome color for the World Youth Pavilion at the Osaka World's Fair in 1970. "Rut" has just vouchsafed me a peek at the draft script, and I can only say that as an experience the film will probably compare with Chaffinch at his uttermost.

In *Orpheus,* Ruttenberg puts the Announcement Sequence at the very end of the *oeuvre.* The sequence begins with Screens 2 and 3 dark. On Screen 1, Lisa is dialing a number. She is a swinging young item from Prince Edward Island, a hostess at the Pulp and Paper Pavilion at Expo '67.

The gigantic Screen 3 lights up as Kevin answers. Kevin is assistant manager of the maple-syrup boutique in the State of Vermont Pavilion.

"Kevin, I've got something to tell you," says Lisa.

"What makes you think it was me, my little doxy," says Kevin. "I haven't seen you since the Youthfest at the Katanga Pavilion. If you're preggers, it could have been any one of those wops, coons, kikes, krauts, pepsis, gyppos, greasers, squareheads, micks, hunkies, limeys, frogs, spicks, japs, chinks, or reds from the other pavilions. So it's strictly *your* problem, baby."

As Kevin hangs up on Screen 3, Lisa dissolves in tears on Screen 1, and, for the first time, Screen 2 lights up, in the middle. On it, from its cushion of flame, a Saturn rocket lifts hissingly off its pad at Cape Kennedy. As we follow it up into space, the Narrator says, "The Family of Man . . . Earth . . . One planet in the heavens . . . Childbirth, death . . . Beauty, terror, as World Youth wanders through the Ying in search of its Yang." (The words "United States" stenciled on the rocket will not be lost on audiences at Osaka.)

Ruttenberg, of course, is able to paint on a massive canvas, thanks to sponsorship by the Kyoto Specie Bank, but today equally pungent statements are being made by the shoestring film-maker. One immediately thinks of Rakor's mini-film *Hudibras Spangled* (1968).

Hudibras opens with the telephone ringing in a young man's pad. The young man picks up the phone, listens for a moment, puts down the receiver, and shoots himself. End titles, credits. The audience has not heard a single word; there has been no whisper, even, of an Announcement. Yet everyone understands. For such is the grammar of the New Cinema.

No I Am Not

Sidney Goldfarb

No I am not the skies of Paris!
It is not my blue. I
See it, I
am astounded, but it is not my
geometric garden that is
divided into six perfect hexagons,
six perfect hexagons,
and in the center
a well-planned city,

and in the center
of the well-planned city,
a garden more perfect
than any garden, and in the garden,
a man, walking.
No I am not the man
walking in the perfect garden!
Who do you think I am
with my English pants
and Russian sensibility?
I have been many times to Oregon also,
but they are not my meadows:
juniper, tumbleweed,
gas station, sage,
the high desert, the higher desert,
and suddenly a sea of green grass,
arbitrary, beautiful, inhabited
by cattle.
Who has the right
to claim such places?
Look at me making my bed anywhere,
stretched out on the sidewalk,
under a blanket of sand.
No I am not the surface of the earth!
I am astounded, the arrangement
is astonishing, and when you
compare it to society,
well then!
Actually I'm under
a certain kind of cover.
Description is loneliness.
Why should I lie?

Deep Art and Shallow Art

Amy Goldin

War is simpler than revolution. It is very tempting to believe that war is efficient, and that it really does offer final solutions. But does it? Suppose we decide to wipe out that insidious system whereby the green world diverts the power of the sun from human to vegetable purposes. Down with photosynthesis! In such a war, defoliation, chemical weaponry, fire, and sword will avail us nothing. As the last leaf withers, we may still wonder if we have eliminated the system of photosynthesis, or only leaves. All the men and material in the world can obliterate only bodies. Systems are hardier, including those systems of feeling, thought, and value that we call culture.

Whatever man makes of the world—mythology, art, science—any system of meaning he creates *is* culture. We traditionally approach meaning in terms of form and content, ignoring its systematic character. We treat cultural situations, from modern dance to urban renewal, as if they were physical situations that contained nonmaterial meanings—as if the leaves contained photosynthesis. This is a frame of mind that encourages schematic violence as a technique for engendering new cultural values. As long as we reach for meaning as if it came in form-and-content bits, the way letters come in envelopes, we preserve our stupidity and guarantee the inefficacy of culture. Culture is the human form of existence. An unusable culture condemns us to enduring life rather than living it, and we in America are the world's pioneers in the experience of humanly unusable culture.

The last world war stimulated technological and political developments that accelerated the tempo of cultural change. During the same period, new approaches to the problem of meaning arose in connection with developments in analytic philosophy, in Chomsky's linguistics, and in Levi-Strauss's cultural anthropology. The concept of meaning became more available to investigation, but for the most part, those gains have remained within the special disciplines. The theories that have appeared to account for new situations owe almost nothing to recent work in philosophy or science.

At first glance this seems surprising. Most people assume that new ideas travel in a single direction, like water. We suppose that the fountainhead of thought is high culture, and that it flows downwards, picking up reality as it goes. Popular culture supposedly represents what is left of high culture after it has been brought down to earth, popularized, and debased. High culture is the good stuff, the crystal stream of theoretical knowledge and truth, while low culture is full of colorful oversimplifications. Middlebrow culture is supposed to be in the middle, closer to pure, clear thought in essence, but less precise and more concrete in expression. I doubt if this was ever wholly true; it is certainly not true today. Middlebrow theorizing is unlikely to borrow much from specialized investigations aside from rhetorical details. Their popularity depends on the delight of finding that what everybody knows can be used to explain what they don't know.

In a very dynamic society, however, what everybody knows is not uncommonly wrong. By the time everybody has learned something, new questions and new answers have superseded. Theoreticians are probably formulating the most pressing questions in other terms or in relation to other matters. By updating and extending popular assumptions, middlebrow culture often reinforces old-fashioned and false ideas. We cannot simply assume that theoretical elaboration represents intellectual growth or refinement. It may be flatly reactionary, inhibiting the spread of genuinely new ideas and making their acceptance more difficult.

At the same time that the form-and-content organization of meaning has been under scrutiny in literary criticism, philosophy, and the social sciences, popular theories have multiplied, based on the very assumptions that are so painfully being questioned elsewhere. Popular or middlebrow theories win power, like politicians, by being fundamentally banal, and they gain plausibility by being vague. McLuhan is a notable case in point. Although he uses the rhetoric of information theory, in which meaning *is* system-bound, he does not take into account the problem of noise—that is, the possibility of meaninglessness. So he is free to identify media with messages, and the forms of communication become "contents." McLuhan's is not the only recent cultural theory that struggles with the old form-and-content problem and ends by embracing it. Negritude or Negro culture is characterized by "soul," a formless content, and theories of modern art try to account for the significance of abstract form.

The difficulties of the form-and-content structure are notorious. They were obvious thirty years ago, when people hunted false dichotomies all over the place, the way we go after flying saucers today. Why does it persist? Form-and-content is a beguiling explanatory device because it allows us to interpret appearances any way we like, attributing importance to them or withdrawing it as we please. We can assure ourselves of the permanence of something desired, like love or creativity, by saying that the form has changed but the content remains the same. Conversely, we can claim that something unwanted, such as anti-Semitism, is changing despite appearances, and that new attitudes are concealed by the persistence of rigid forms. The important thing to notice is that "content" in these theories cannot be inferred from material evidence and must always be intuited. Form-and-content acknowledges a theoretical complexity but allows us to act simplistically. If we divide a complex situation into an important aspect and a trivial one, we can neglect its complexity with perfect righteousness. And either form or content can be considered beside the point, according to taste.

Form-and-content is so shoddy a framework for thought that it is most often found in off-the-cuff, informal theorizing. In the arts, however, the form-and-content scheme is entrenched. Art theory has steadily stumped along on these twin pillars, holding beauty in the appropriate place, between them. Style is considered to be roughly equivalent to form, and subject matter to be the ultimate source of content. The meaning of a landscape, for example, might be summed up as "the artist's interpretation of nature." This is not a very satisfactory explanation, but the problem of accounting for pictorial meaning did not become acute until the advent of art without subject matter. In the past the

confusions of traditional aesthetics were eased by the satis-
factoriness of art. Today art itself looks meaningless. My
fundamental argument is that what is difficult and problem-
atic about modern art has little to do with style. It depends
on the complex nature of artistic meaning itself.

I

EXPLANATIONS OF modern art usually proceed historically. Beginning with the Impressionists, art history is read
as a series of revolutions, a quasi-Hegelian sequence of
styles and theories that followed each other so rapidly that
meaning got lost in the shuffle. There is a suggestion that
each "historical factor" walks onstage, plays its part, and
disappears into the wings. We get a narrative in which the
decline of the French Academy is linked to social change,
the Dada movement to moral protest, and the appearance
of Cubism to abstraction. The present state of art is explained away as the outcome of social and cultural forces.
Indeed, it no longer exists as an opaque situation at all. It
is hardly more than the accumulation of cultural debris left
behind by the march of time.

Because many people continue to find contemporary art
opaque, I propose to deal only with the present. Neither
historical explanations nor persistent exposure to art is
likely to reduce the frustration aroused by finding modern
art meaningless. Some of that meaninglessness is built in.
Unfamiliar kinds of meaning go unrecognized. However,
regardless of the reasons for the experience of meaninglessness, the attendant cultural malaise is not trivial. Primitive
societies define the human condition by locating themselves
within and over against nature; more dynamic societies
define themselves historically. To be old-fashioned is to be
lost, a stranger in one's own time. Bombarded by the culture explosion, it is easy to be seized by a metaphysical
nostalgia for feeling at home in one's own culture. Such
nostalgia leaves one especially vulnerable to traditionalist
theories that rationalize and harden alienation.

Beginning with the artistic situation at present, I shall
begin, too, with a description of what I take to be common
assumptions about that situation. Although popular culture

has grown more respectable, most people still believe that art can be divided into its nearer and farther reaches: into deep art and shallow art, or high art and low. This division does not simply correspond to good art and bad, but represents different levels of artistic aspiration. We acknowledge that commercial posters or carpets can be judged artistically, as good or bad examples of their kind. It is in high art, "serious" painting and sculpture, that we expect meaning.

Low art, we feel, tends to be easy to take, decorative, and at times old-fashioned or conservative. We don't expect low art to mean much; it's shallow. High art, on the other hand, is supposed to mean a great deal. That's how it got so high, by having all those layers of meaning piled up on each other. It may be difficult to untangle the layers of meaning, but we imagine that its ultimate decipherability can be intuitively felt. The presence of meaning seems almost tangible, even though we can't say what it is.

The difficulty of modern art, whatever experimental complexities of form the artist has chosen to get involved in, is stubbornly approached as a problem in locating meaning. We "intuitively" set up a list that looks like this:

Deep Art	Shallow Art
meaningful	decorative
hard	easy
abstract	representational
radical	conservative

Having assumed that high art is meaningful, we expect certain personal and social consequences to follow. We expect to have to struggle to grasp that meaning. We expect to find ideas in art, we expect the art to have cultural importance, we expect high prices, critical attention—the whole bit falls into line. And in fact, the social trappings and the theoretical claims of high art have remained stable and recognizable. It seems as if the only thing that's changed is the art. Or, if the art is still high art and the artists are playing their "traditional" roles as cultural innovators, the elite audience has somehow become stuck, somewhere around Picasso's *Guernica*.

The trouble is that high art, nowadays, is not deep at all. It's shallow. To equip yourself with aqualungs and flippers to penetrate its depths of meaning becomes ludicrous. Yet people will not tell you that meaning has been displaced.

Why not? Because nobody is quite sure what's happened to it. Moreover, now that it seems to be gone, nobody remembers what it looked like. Cultural conservatives say it looked like subject matter and was consequently incompatible with abstract art. People who are culturally with-it say that meaning looked like artistic quality and it's still there, only you have to be terribly sensitive to recognize it because styles have changed so. The question of meaning in art has become a matter of faith, a dogma separating the believers from the unbelievers. The hostiles say that contemporary art is meaningless and empty; the defenders claim that art is still meaningful, and that nothing has changed but style.

WHAT IS MEANING? For most people, most of the time, meaning is something moral. It has to do with behavior. In daily life, meaning in the lexical, definitional sense of the term rarely becomes an issue. When it does, the "problem" of meaning can usually be cleared up quickly, and the issue is felt to be trivial. But when the verbal meaning is clear and we ask someone, "What do you mean by that?" we are asking him to clarify his intentions or his attitude, so that we can know if he is well- or ill-disposed toward something. If we ask of a theatrical performance or a piece of writing, "What does it really *mean?*"—we initially try to find whether the author wants us to respect the thesis or situation presented and find it worthy of serious attention, or whether we are supposed to laugh and repudiate or deplore it. It is the author's attitude toward his subject matter that we are trying to locate, so that we have a norm with which we can agree or disagree.

Whatever it may have experienced or felt, an audience deprived of moral orientation feels deprived of meaning. Uncertain of its own role in the artistic situation, the audience is likely to deny that it has felt anything, for lack of a position from which shades of feeling can be identified. Regardless of the grounds offered for admiration or disapproval, people want to know what moral attitudes are aesthetically appropriate. An audience torn between approval and disapproval is an unhappy audience.

Abstract Expressionism was given an aura of approval when it was baptized "Action Painting." "Action," with its connotations of personal heroism and social significance, is clearly a Good Thing, so Abstract Expressionism became the latest member of a series of icons celebrating the identity of the Good, the True, and the Beautiful. Abstract art was saved for moral idealism. Almost as soon as the style was thoroughly accepted by the artistic establishment, however, it was abandoned by a new artistic generation.

The artists of Pop, Op, and Happenings, and the sculptors grouped around Minimal art *all* made gestures and verbal statements repudiating the idea of cultural heroism. Whatever their work looked like, the artists talked as if they had something against art. Anti-art statements from artists and writers, however, only make sense as a notice to the audience that the artists are shifting their artistic intentions. What intention could be expressed in such a range of styles?

The one element common to all recent art is the insistence that the audience's approval is irrelevant to the meaning of the work. This art wishes to disengage itself from appeals to strong, morally unconflicted emotion. It makes no appeal to feelings of human tenderness and admiration. Our habitual attempt to interpret art as a pleasant form of moral propaganda while enjoying and approving of our own feelings is deliberately flouted or evaded.

Those artists appear most up-to-date who, with greater or lesser steadfastness, refuse to participate in things that encourage public love. Stylistic developments allied to Pop—Funk art and various forms of theater—actively reject it by incorporating repulsive and scatological materials. Abstract sculpture and modernist painting withdraw from being lovable by insisting on an impersonal *look,* which is reinforced by a critical theory that makes it appropriate to react to those works as morally indeterminate objects.

Although Pop is presently not a widely used style, I wish to discuss it briefly because it uses subject matter, and uses it in a manner that neutralizes and complicates our emotional reactions to it. As soon as the element of emotional uncommittedness or complexity is lost and affectionate nostalgia is allowed to dominate, Pop shades off into Camp.

Pop is most ambitious when it manages to preserve its bite. How does it do this?

By treating advertising, pornography, and news photos as artistic subject matter, Pop began as an in-joke at the expense of art's pretensions to spiritual elevation. Largely as a result of the genius of Claes Oldenburg and the intelligence of Rosenquist and Lichtenstein, Pop has been able to extend its range of reference while maintaining a precarious suspension of moral commitment. Reproducing the materials of the commercial world, it presents the businessman's Garden of Eden, the Good Life as deep feeling, fun, and gracious living without either affirming or denying the value of these things. Unharmonized color, weightlessness, and relatively broad scale help to keep the viewer at a public, nonintimate aesthetic distance. The style functions to separate the picture's meaning from that of its subject matter, the way quotation marks do in isolating the tone of jargon or colloquial expressions from the tone of the surrounding sentence. "Task Force Oregon announced that it had killed . . . 3300 enemy soldiers and 'detained' five thousand people." The inner quotation marks report a specific situation and call attention to the reporter's withdrawal from full acceptance of the official point of view—"They said it, I didn't"—while refraining from taking any direct issue with it. It's a neat trick, but difficult. Pop can sustain its ironical good humor and its consequent emotional complexity only by being extremely careful about keeping its subjects of reference highly charged while emphasizing its own formal cool. When this tension is lost, it can easily fall into Campy chic (Lichtenstein is particularly liable to this) or dramatic gesture (Oldenburg's midnight "burial" in Central Park).

Contemporary abstract art is so thorough about repudiating human involvement that it looks like the result of industrial processes even when it's handmade. Canvases seem stained rather than painted, sculptural forms are bland and regular, and variations of surface and form are everywhere limited or suppressed.

Work in monumental size avoids "aggressiveness" or strong movement, suggesting the simultaneous assertion of the presence of power and the fact of its being sealed off, so that the viewer is left unthreatened. Other sculptural styles present the audience with unfocused sequences of industrially defined spaces or forms as "environments," "fields," or "progressions" which make a point of leaving the spectator disengaged from anything but a vaguely architectural situation. This work presents itself as pure artifact, unusable and inhuman, a sort of simplified maze in which you cannot lose yourself or a circular supply room with an entrance but no exit.

None of this stuff means anything. The artist's message to the viewer is: "I have no intention of charming you or frightening you. I don't intend to do anything to you. I just make things. What you see is what you see." Feelings of density, awareness of stasis or unfocused movement, the experience of unwilled, inorganic, but rational repetition— these are complexes of sensation that are not easily available to ordinary consciousness. Nor are they feelings that are likely to strike us as being noteworthy or interesting, lacking as they do any special moral orientation. That is, they seem neither particularly desirable nor undesirable. Yet it cannot be denied that these feelings, now made available for the first time in art, seem to be particularly insistent in a mass industrial society. Our art forces us to acknowledge them and refuses to judge them. It also refuses us the commonplace humanistic reassurances, leaving us uncertain whether their absence is to be taken as warning, prophecy, or mere observation. Our art only says, "Notice it. Maybe it means something."

The artistic problem involved in making the repudiation of meaning and emotion explicit in Minimal art lies in the quasi-involuntary beauty of simple orderliness and smooth industrial finishes. In terms of artistic form, this work, which effaces itself as anything beyond a physical presence, cannot easily avoid being assimilated to architectural or interior decoration. The artists' denial of any extra-aesthetic intention does not succeed in creating a moral Switzerland for them to work in. They are still pitifully vulnerable to being loved *anyway*, and being accepted as purveyors of depth and beauty.

It is interesting to observe how difficult it is to formalize and develop a style that will evade implications of moral commitment. It seems as if the audience is determined to find art uplifting, no matter how strenuously artists try to discourage them. Be that as it may, the point remains that the evasion from passionate approval is sought, and that this evasion constitutes the deliberate "meaninglessness" of modern art.

II

I HAVE INSISTED on the primacy of treating artistic meaning as a moral concept although the idea that the plastic arts carry moral connotations was generally banished from criticism a long time ago. It was revived only for special styles: the social protest art of the thirties and for the Existentialist message of Abstract Expressionism. In general, art criticism has tended to proceed as if the content or meaning of modern art were intellectual rather than moral.

I assure you that this idea is ludicrous. Intelligence is common, among artists as elsewhere, but original ideas of any sort are very rare indeed. There are few artists with original ideas, and those they have are likely to be bad. In this they resemble chemists, engineers, teachers, doctors, and lawyers.

I suggest that ideas in art are, like beauty, to be found chiefly in the eye of the beholder. No matter how thoroughly abstract a picture is, critics can always be found to tell you what it's about. Pictures that are smudged or airy-looking are often supposed to be about moods, feelings related to nature, or images of one or another state of the inner man. (Since nobody knows what the inner man looks like, who can deny it?) Abstract paintings with fewer and more decisive marks have recently been interpreted as being "about" art. Sometimes it's art materials or elements—what critics call the pure *fact* of paint, or of color, or of space. But more often it's style. The implication is that art history or aesthetics is somehow the work's implicit subject matter, and that if you don't know anything about those subjects you can't expect to understand the work. Assertions that abstract art is *about* anything, and particularly about abstractions like time, science, or Cubism, are nonsense—desperate attempts to preserve the old form-and-content structure of artistic meaning. Artistic meaning cannot be created by fiat. Even if the artist says that he wants his work to be interpreted in some particular way, his expressed intentions do not constitute a rule that establishes meaning.

The Formalist thesis that artistic meaning corresponds, at any particular moment, to the essential formal conventions of a given style is simply obscurantism. Formal conventions may be the focus of interest for a hard-working art critic, but he has no reason to suppose that the entire world of art is a gigantic conspiracy to provide him with professional puzzles. The suggestion that extensive study of aesthetics and art history is necessary in order to understand contemporary art is utterly false. Our art is so far from being a privileged message, a game intelligible only to highly trained players, that it is truer to say that the less you know about art the better. Irrelevant expectations of meaning will not distract you from the essentially simple-minded, sensuous pleasure to be derived from it. It even seems as if a high degree of literary culture can be positively inhibiting. Certainly some very refined and artistically well-educated people—Bernard Berenson, for one—have found themselves unable to tolerate modern art at all.

Before the end of the nineteenth century, it was possible to understand art without particularly concerning yourself with artistic ideas. On the other hand, in order to grasp an artist's meaning you usually did have to know what vices and virtues were considered important. Consequently you needed a rather firm grasp of Christian and pagan myths and symbols, but you knew where to look for artistic meaning. The same habits don't work for modern art. Today the range of experience relevant to art has shifted, and it is narrower, not wider than it used to be.

BUT IF ART today is so simple, and requires neither enthusiasm nor high intelligence, what is it that *seems* so difficult? We have to change our habits, and look for artistic meaning in new places. "Meaning" is here a lamentably imprecise term, but it lies close to "moral," at the intersection of the personal and the social, and it unites elements of thought and feeling. We would expect art to have something to do with these matters. The discussion that follows is primitive, but in a field as intricate as art, a firm hold on the obvious may be worth as much as ingenuity.

We are commonly liable to feel that anything unfamiliar

and large is intellectually challenging. The most complex structures and phenomena, as long as they are familiar, seem easy. Nobody thinks of his monetary or kinship system as presenting intellectual difficulty; they seem natural. In fact, they *are* natural, in the same way that art is. They isolate and structure the pervasive social values, and we can scarcely conceive of "money" or "relatives" or "art" apart from the structures with which we are familiar. Ideas about art, however simple, are characteristically hard to grasp, abrasive, and indigestible.

The shift in art away from the traditional moral location of meaning is a major idea, one of the sort I described as very rare. Although it is an old idea by now, it has become commonplace without being thoroughly grasped. Nor have the appropriate revisions of art criticism or aesthetic theory been made. Meanwhile, most (not all) of the developments in painting and sculpture of the last eighty years or so have been statements, variations, and investigations of nonmoral artistic ideas.

Most artistic ideas are not the sort of things we usually call ideas at all. They are fragments or clots of feeling-about-something, intrinsically complex, like ordinary experience. It is because new artistic ideas *are* in part new feelings that we don't know what to do with them. They can interrupt old patterns of feeling and demand a place for themselves while we are still uncertain about whether we want them. A novelty or a commercial gimmick is always welcome, because it brings an air of freshness without disturbing anything. We are offered something that we can react to in a familiar way, with only the slightest shift of nuances. But new feelings, like new ideas, can disrupt the psychic economy.

A "new" feeling, of course, is not a heretofore unexperienced emotion. It is a new complex, a new feeling-about-something. If we are suddenly presented with the fact that we are reacting to A in a way that we had always supposed was appropriate only to B, we seem to get something we can call either a new feeling or a new idea. Suppose you suddenly found yourself feeling about a boy in a way you had always supposed you could feel only in relation to girls. You can see that a new feeling in this sense could require at least as much psychic reorganization as a new idea of what the relationship between the sexes should be. Because new artistic ideas are feelings-about-something, they can be presented either with or without familiar subject matter. Pop art offers an example of the first; Cubism an example of the second.

Artistic ideas are the particles of artistic meaning, and it is as difficult to define them outside the context of art as it is to define a word outside the context of language. A sound becomes a word by entering the mainstream of language usage in a regular and structured way. Artistic ideas enter the public world in the same manner, by becoming discriminable regularities in the experience of art.

The most blatant characteristic of art is the one it shares with language: both are structures of meaning. At this point, however, we must stop talking about meaning as if moral meanings were the only sort there are. Moreover, meaning is not a physical characteristic, like weight; understanding meaning is something people *do*. Similarly, art objects are not a special class of things. Our museums are full of things that became art after respectable careers as pots or illustrations or ornaments. "Art" is not a physical category like "plant life"; it is a social construct, like marriage or the church. Art is a part of culture, a part of the human world, and artistic meaning is integrative and synthetic, a gathering together of ideas, sensations, and attitudes initially learned in nonartistic experiences.

Art is also cheap, exactly as life itself is cheap. Art always means something, but it needn't mean much. Creativity is absurdly overrated nowadays—it's what is created that counts. In folk art, for example, meaning is usually so banal that we hardly notice it. Advertising is the folk art of industrial societies, and it is usually pretty dull, too. Because so many kinds of artistic meaning are repetitive and trivial, the pleasure we get from art, as opposed to any knowledge or profit, becomes very important. And because modern communication techniques make the repetition of sounds, images, and ideas ubiquitous, we are frenziedly grateful for variation and novelty.

At the same time, artistic meanings are extremely varied; the feelings and ideas art carries range from the picayune to the exalted. Therefore it is possible to conceive of art as a melting pot of the sacred and the profane, an alembic for the clarification and redefinition of what men consider important. Both rejection and celebration are necessary to this process: Pop art can be read as raising the fallen world. That is, the squalid, fragmented world of contemporary disorder becomes a part of the iconic, highly ordered structure of fine art, thus creating the possibility of a jollier, more unified existence.

THE IMPORTANCE of art lies in its effect on extra-artistic meaning, for it inevitably *has* effects, quite indepedently of whether it is high art or low, good art or bad. A work of art that satisfies us binds us to the world and, by doing so, reinforces some of society's established values. A work of art that repels us exacerbates our sense of social and personal incoherence and facilitates the dissolution of social conventions into new attitudes and new ways of appraising experience.

I would like to suggest that artistic meaning can best be understood as arising from three interacting levels of experience, *none of which ever occurs in isolation.* At any point in time we *are* physical, social, and moral beings, and although most of our experience calls on us to make a highly discriminated response, art stops us. It characteristically blots out extra-artistic discriminations and unifies experience into a closed, focused system.

For instance, a sudden loud noise is primarily a physical experience; our response is to jump and look around to see if we are in physical danger. An ordinary question addressed to us ("What time is it, please?") requires a social response: an answer offered in an appropriate language and manner. A problem or a confrontation can call for an act or a moral decision. If the question addressed to us is an indecent proposal, we have to decide whether to accept it, ignore it, walk away, or maybe call a cop.

The important thing to notice is the way these classes of experience nest into each other. The social implies the physical, the moral implies the social. The formal level of experience—the range of choices and behavior appropriate to a class of experience—can shift swiftly and easily, even though the physical components remain stable.

A work of art always addresses us in terms of sensuous, physical experience. This is the primary level of artistic form, the formal level of art, and it corresponds to the physical level of experience. All art sustains formal analysis, although confused or undeveloped methods of analysis can make such procedures trivial. Abstract art tends to stress this level of response.

A work of art also engages us on the level of conventional social communication: the level of genre. A genre defines the social function of art, and generic distinctions allow us to discriminate advertising art, political cartoons, or religious art as providing special, highly specific kinds of meaning. Religious, literary, and other sorts of social symbolism are established on this level. Sometimes a stable iconography developed in one genre spreads to others.

Any response more lively than flat indifference engages us morally. If we find a work attractive, we want to keep on looking; if we are repelled, we want to escape or attack it. The fact that art can spark behavior, sometimes in very direct ways, is probably the reason most people get interested in it. We first learn to respect art on the basis of its brute power to move us, to make us cry with pity, burn with indignation, squirm with concupiscence. Pornography, propaganda, and advertising—art that sets out to affect behavior without stopping at "Go" to pay its respects to aesthetic values—have repeatedly been disowned as not belonging to the category of art at all. This is silly. It is merely a sign of the authoritarian temperament that would like to bind all power to the service of a selected slate of attitudes. The fact that art stimulates such sanctions and judgments is merely further evidence of its ability to engage us on this level of behavior.

The moral level of response includes more innocuous reactions: seeing a still life can make us decide to buy it or resolve to go home and bake a cherry pie. Art can also affect us as demanding an urgent, overt response, yet it is a mistake, I believe, to equate this vividness with the apogee of artistic power. Ultimately more far-reaching is the tendency of works of art to bind and coagulate feelings, values, and meanings, the tendency to become iconic, stabilizing our sense of what is ideally true, good, and beautiful. Most people assume that all artists want to move them morally above all, for this is the way in which they most want to be moved: vividly, emotionally, and in familiar directions.

MODERN ART rarely aims at this response. It focuses on the first level of experience, emphasizing body feelings of openness or closure, and avoiding, as far as possible, suggestions that any state is ideal or deplorable. This is likely to strike most people as surprising, indeed, barely intelligible as an artistic intention. (I think that the artists themselves have found it difficult to keep from idealizing and embellishing their work, turning boxes into icons of the private, inner-directed man. The unprofessional public is not alone in its habit of interpreting works of high art as microcosmic or macrocosmic emblems.) Perhaps we should see the will to make art that inhibits easy moral responses and tries to engage directly with "reality" as itself embodying a moral intention. It looks like one to me, a proto-ethic of a highly rationalistic sort that places great importance on not lying or overstating anything. The emotional austerity of Pop and Minimal styles tends to create a low-pressure experience for the audience at the opposite pole from appetite-oriented advertising. The moral suggestion lies in the implication that dispassion is valuable.

Probably the most serious question posed by the withdrawal of our best artists from a willingness to mean anything in the usual sense of artistic meaning is the problem of accounting for the prestige of high art, the respect it receives and demands. It is reverence for art that seems to be called into question when we have serious art that insists on fooling around and making jokes, the way some Pop does, or when, like Minimal sculpture, it solemnly renounces the status of art in favor of object-hood. Perhaps the fine arts are still "high" because they still imply the artist's impersonal seriousness, his attention to the implications and moral consequences of attending to artistic meaning. Of course, this sort of seriousness doesn't necessarily produce great art. It can encourage an owlish solemnity that is hilarious to an unsympathetic audience—Neo-Classicism provides many examples. Moreover, we should not forget that the connection between moral or religious intentions and art of high formal coherence may simply be a sometimes thing, a matter of historical fact.

What does it mean to say that a picture is intelligible, or that we understand a work of art? We have been so sentimentally eager to "appreciate" art that the question has barely been raised. We have tried to settle for love, without regard to the complex transactions of meaning that actually take place in all experiences of art. If critics were less eager to see themselves as defenders of the cultural faith, they might have something useful to tell us. In this age of mass communication we are an audience longer and more thoroughly than we are citizens. The arts are charged with social power, and the Victorian assumption that culture is intrinsically polite is a twentieth-century joke.

Letter to an Absent Son

Sister Madeline De Frees

It's RIGHT to call you son. That cursing alcoholic
is the god I married early before I really knew him:
spiked to his crossbeam bed, I've lasted thirty years.
Nails are my habit now. Without them I'm afraid.

At night I spider up the wall to hide in crevices
deeper than guilt. His hot breath smokes me out.
I fall and fall into the arms I bargained for,
sifting them cool as rain. A flower touch could tame me.
Bring me down that giant beam to lie submissive
in his fumbling clutch. One touch. Bad weather
moves indoors: a cyclone takes me.

How shall I find a shelter in the clouds, driven by
gods, gold breaking out of them everywhere?
Nothing is what it pretends. It gathers to a loss
of leaves and graves. Winter in the breath.
Your father looked like you, his dying proportioned
oddly to my breast. I boxed him in my plain pine
arms and let him take his ease just for a minute.

Of Our Time

Alan Lelchuk

Look, i can't talk on the phone. It bugs me. You know that, gorgeous. Come on over. Screw your work."

"Okay," he answered, begrudgingly, thinking about that work. "See you."

"Wait, wait, wait! Can you get me some radishes . . . bananas, apples, chived cottage cheese. No, no, no— *chivier* cottage cheese. Come on, don't put up a fuss. I know I'm a drag. Just remember—I'll have to be the fucking housewife one day, not you, lover. Thanks." She planted three small kisses on the telephone, then hung up.

All right, he said to himself, all right. No use fighting about it. Don't think, just get dressed, get the provisions, take a nice drive. At eleven at night, shopping. Christ!

Leavitt picked up her most recent note. Written in her small sloping handwriting, legible, neat. (The clarity a good sign, he had said from the first.)

> My dear Professor,
> I want to tell you that your company was most enjoyable yesterday evening. I was not in a very good mood, as I told you, and you could see for yourself that my manners were more deficient than usual. But you mustn't take my ill-placed words of anger or sullen disagreeableness in the *wrong* way. You know this, I am sure. If it were another age, please be assured that this (and similar notes) would be deeply and painfully apologetic. As it is—you will forgive me any possible impudence and misreadings, but I believe that I am, to use a phrase, of our time. I thoroughly agree with you as to its abrasive nature.
> Yours,
> Miss S. Sorotkin

The usual mixture of warmth and bewilderment rose in him. Her character—he preferred that word to personality —never ceased performing cartwheels. That was its one predictable trait. Hard to take, but exhilarating. He took up his coat, a worn pea-green duffel purchased at a second-hand shop. From scattered piles of paper and books, strewn on chairs, mantelpieces, windowsills, occasional tables, he put together his lecture notes for the next day and left the apartment.

November had turned cold. His '59 Ford whined and whined, then caught. Leavitt drove to Cahaley's on Mount Auburn (faithful till midnight seven days a week), purchased the food amid the late evening rush of Harvard students, and headed back East on Massachusetts Avenue toward Central Square. Despite himself he felt curiously relaxed driving alone in the night. As he was approaching Tech Square, small squares of yellow light shone asymmetrically from the four concrete and glass skyscrapers, transforming them into giant electronic punchboards, blinking brilliantly in the blackness.

Leavitt parked on Ames, a street of grubby brick tenements and clapboard houses. Twenty-seven was a four-story walk-up, notable for the large graffiti scrawled in white chalk above the cellar entrance.

An odor of fried fish hung in the air as he ascended the wooden steps. Sarah lived on the third floor, above the Valdespinos, a Puerto Rican family, and Ellen Walters, a blond divorcée with two kids and a Negro boyfriend, a policeman who worked the graveyard shift. Sarah made it a point to introduce her neighbors to him. ("Hi, Ellen," she would say. "This is, uh, Cliffie, a very dear friend.")

He knocked at the door.

"It's open."

A combination of rock music and TV narrative blared from the living room. He made his way to the kitchen and placed the parcel on the round table. No one appeared. Puzzled, he began removing the food.

"Hi," she called. "Could you bring the radishes? And hurry in here." Said sweetly.

She was settled in her green vinyl chair, her legs on a hassock.

"Mmmm. Come here you—no no, don't take off that damn coat—just drop here." She held her arms out to him and he found himself jerked onto her lap. And almost over it.

"Hey!"

She kissed him hard, mouth closed, on the lips, then nipped at his nose. "Now sit still," she commanded, and guided his head toward the TV.

"The radishes, you fool—"

"Ssshhhh!" She put her hand over his mouth. He tore it away and tried to reach for the radishes, which were being crushed between the cushion and the seat.

"Will you stop it?" she wailed, and tugged at him. "You're *preventing* me from watching Mrs. HICKS!" Angrily he tried to disentangle himself from her lap, but the balance was hers and she gripped his waist vigorously.

"I just like to test you," he offered, and relaxed.

Mrs. Hicks, dimpling her soft puffy cheeks, was speaking in a high squeal with long Boston A's. Simultaneously, a female singer was good-naturedly rocking the room from a portable stereo.

"Look, do you need the phonograph? Why don't—"

Her palm covered his mouth, and she pointed at the TV screen. He removed her hand and tried to follow Mrs. Hicks.

Again I say to you, people of Boston, my Boston: *Here is where I stand*. I feel that the racial imbalance law violates one of the basic American rights—freedom of choice. And that is why I am against it. I am against bussing of children to different parts of the city, and breaking up neighborhood schools. That is why I would repeal this *unjust* law if I were mayor of Boston. (Pause.) This is Louise Day Hicks. Here is where I stand. (Takes glasses off, smiles.)

"Her voice sounds like what, at the end—that last sentence?"

"Could you turn that record off?"

"Like what?" she repeated, addressing a small schoolboy.

He shook his head. She pinched his ear.

He thought. "A cow, chewing."

"Chewing what?"

"Marshmallow."

"Better . . ." She reached for his ear.

He caught her hand, "Will you—"

"Taffy. Cud. Fodder. Dummy."

He moved to get up.

She eyed him with a tilted head, strands of hair falling over one eye. Calmly she gestured his freedom.

He rose, annoyed by his send-off, and went to hang his coat in the hall closet.

A song called "Take It Like You Give It" was erupting from the phonograph. He picked up the record jacket: someone named Aretha Franklin. The television prattled on. Looking around in vain for a safe refuge, he decided on the worn Morris chair, which faced a blank wall. He slipped his loose-leaf lecture notes from the manila envelope . . . Idealism in *Middlemarch*. Perfectly appropriate to his present surroundings, he reflected. He read for a bit, then looked up. His eye was caught by a small oil landscape tucked away in a far corner. She had painted it while still an undergraduate. It was modest but clearly talented in its colors (muted ochres and greens) and strokes (the effect of the wind on the trees and grass). He remembered the brutal fight she had put up after he had fished it out from amid a jungle of worn baby clothing that they were preparing for Goodwill. Never a word about drawing or painting until that discovery in the musty closet, where other canvases lay buried and crumpled. Her marriage had put an end to all that. . . . He returned to Dorothea Brooke and tried to concentrate.

After a futile few minutes he asked, peacefully, "Do we need Johnny Carson?"

She looked up from her book. "Uh, huh! He's so soothing for research, don't you think? I mean alongside the right music." She returned to her book, with Vermeer's "Lady with a Red Hat" on the cover. There was little use mentioning the sociology paper that was due. She despised sociology. That's why she was a graduate student in it, she had explained. . . .

He fought with Aretha Franklin, Johnny Carson, and the radiator pipes, and the temptation to study her.

Her legs were flung across the arm of the chair, her old-fashioned pleated skirt tossed up across her thighs. Exposing soft creamy flesh. She was popping large strawberries into her mouth from a bowl which now held the radishes as well. Nearby stood a pint of Ballantine's Scotch, which she was drinking with water. Her hair, the color of wheat, was piled high and intricately. ("I'm dying to be a city planner!" she would argue, flaunting her ingenious hairdos.) Over a striped turtleneck jersey she wore a loose army fatigue shirt, with a corporal's insignia on the arm. As she read, her forehead was burdened by two deep creases.

He drank in her tousled childishness, her careless costume that masked the inner turmoil ("Casual—dress for city—stress" she would say, assuming the stance of a fashion model.) Occasionally during the night he'd awake, look at her sleeping face and turn over on his back, thinking about her through endless gulfs of time (an hour or more by his watch). It was a favored period, lying next to her that way, her foot entwined about his, her hand settled on his chest. (Prolonged ecstasies of ordered intimacy, so different from the moments of slipping passion.) Later, when driving, he recalled them—in a slow sweet wash of contentment that mingled with the passing whispering cars and the disappearing dashes of the road.

"Jerk! Who do you think you're staring at?" And the book was flung at him, which he just managed to deflect. "You absolute fool! I'm not one of your students to peek at." She glared at him.

"You're out of your mind."

"That's right. That's what I've been telling you. Shove off, mate, if you don't like it. Shove off. I keep giving it to you straight. I'm freaked out," she said, "get it? freaked out?" She leaned across to him. "In my head, baby, that's where I spend my time. I don't like it *out there*, with you people. My *head's* better." More strands of hair had come loose.

Then from afar, "Mom . . . Momma."

The boy's voice stifled her grating rant. The anger and resentment remained momentarily in her eyes before giving way submissively. . . . There was a moment of pounding silence. He had been hating her, but the boy's voice and her changed look shifted his emotion.

"Mom?"

"Coming, Joshua." She sprang quickly from the chair, moving in her bare feet.

Leavitt sat there. The voice of a popular singer bore in upon him from the television. He got up and took a perverse pleasure in turning off only the sound. Then the scratching of the phonograph record raced across the room in the new silence, and he edged anxiously around the cumbersome portable TV and picked up the phonograph arm. He found himself sweating. He was furious again. He hated her fierce bursts of irrationality, the geysers of enraged venom that suddenly sprouted from nowhere, without cause. If she couldn't act *civilized* he shouldn't see her. When he was twenty, it was all right; not now. Why was he doing it? Why was he in a position like this? Why? He thought of the many girls who had flitted through his life, of the endless variety to be found everywhere—in the streets, in classrooms, in supermarkets . . . why her? So she was *interesting*, so what? Was it worth his book remaining undone . . . his concentration shattered . . . his discipline interrupted? For what? For *love?* Foolish nonsense. A disease that afflicts children and failures. He walked quickly to the hallway and got his coat from the closet. But as he was on the verge of slipping out the door he overheard voices. He stopped and listened, though he couldn't make out the words. Ambivalent again, he walked back to the living room, dumped his coat on the chair, and went back toward the children's bedroom.

The door was ajar. A small hurricane lamp threw light on Sarah and Joshua, sitting on his bed. In the other Katie lay sound asleep, finger in her mouth. Drawings of Kimba, the UHF white lion, and Babar, the kindly French elephant, adorned the walls.

He stood at the door, leaning. He wanted badly to go in.

"Leavitt!" Joshua said, looking dreamily over his mother's shoulder. "Hi, Leavitt. I didn't know you were here."

Sarah turned about, came to the door, and closed it without looking at him.

The bitch! A strong desire rose in him to burst in and smack her in the mouth.

But he kept himself in check, waited, then walked away. He felt shaken, drawn out, foolish. He collected his notes and again took up his coat. But then, standing there in the middle of the living room, he again wasn't sure what he wanted to do. Or how he felt. She had battered his ego all right, but there was an objective point to it. The kids already had a shitty betrayed existence from one man; Sarah was doing what he would do, keeping a stern guard over possible future betrayers. . . . Especially for Joshua, the boy. He was a real problem. Leavitt had seen that from the first. He had built very slowly with the boy, who seemed to trust him so easily. Too easily to be real. Leavitt put him out of his mind. More important was the problem of Sarah.

Then he stopped trying to understand his feelings. Tough, he decided.

But as he started to leave again, the creaking floor announced her approach. He waited, motionless, a figure of uncertainty, a guest who doesn't know whether he's suffering from injury or from guilt. She walked by into the living room, unmindful of him. Then she turned toward the silent phonograph and the stupid soundless TV picture. They stood a few feet from each other, the silence a torment.

Finally, she turned back, walked past him, and switched off the floor lamp. She sat down in her green monstrosity, her hands on the arms, her legs uncrossed, not speaking or moving.

He waited. The television showed two women hanging up their wash, smiling, and holding up a box of Fab. The next was a cigarette commercial, with a couple walking at the oceanfront. Then Johnny Carson reappeared.

There was nothing for him to do. He wanted to say something to her to break the awful silence but couldn't think of anything. He felt drained. He also didn't know what was going through her mind. Finally he turned and walked out. He found himself counting the steps as he descended them.

At the twelfth, the last one on the landing, he suddenly paused, then sat down. Cigarette butts lay on the floor in the dim light. He lit a cigarette and threw his head back, massaging the back of his neck. The pounding in his head eased somewhat. He was relieved to be out of the apartment. It was as if, upstairs there, the battery charging his emotions and thoughts was constantly being used up and run down, leaving him unable to generate any energy, leaving him empty.

Now, apart, he was returning to himself. But even as he revived, his sympathy and passion strangely subdued his anger and rose into an overwhelming desire to be near her. The feeling gained in him lucidly and firmly, yet he hated and resisted it, mocking himself for his weakness. He thought of her sitting in that green chair in that idiot flickering darkness, thinking who knows what in that head. No, there was no point. Not under those conditions. He fought his impulses and stood up, resolved.

He was startled, however, by the sense of a solitary figure, somewhere above him on the landing. He turned, frightened. Sarah was sitting quietly on the top step, watching. She poured in upon his plans and resolutions and washed them away.

He mounted the steps, not looking up. Near her, he sensed her about to rise, and touched her shoulder. He laid the back of his hand on the girlish cheek, caressing it. He leaned over and kissed her hair.

"Move it, baby," said John Williams, in his policeman's uniform. "I'm already late. Ain't you got an apartment to do that stuff in?"

They arose and moved the few steps into the apartment. Immediately inside the door she kissed his cheek slightly, then his lips. Her hand ran inside his shirt along his back. The sheaf of notes floated featherly south, and he was caught up by the whirlpool of her pleading intensity. Pressed against the wall they whipped their bodies in coupling turbulence. Then the flat hard linoleum rose to jolt his knees and bruise his knuckles. In a moment tongues had reunited with ears and mouths, drawing gasps and quick moans. She rolled upon him, then over, somehow releasing his arms from oceans of wool. "Pudgy thing," she uttered, and took his lips hard between her teeth before he could reply. Here full body angled across him, but now he grew playful and spinned her in his strength. Above her, he applied a cool hand to a patch of tenderwarm belly. She squealed. Then said, tutorially, "you're burning me," indicating the radiator pipes, exposed and pulsing, near her arm. His weight on straining fingertips, he reached for the radiator valve and unleashed a gush of steam. Under the camouflage of sound he jerked their bodies a few feet and dove back to that delicious mocking face.

An explosion of clothes. Shirts and sweaters flew apart, hooks burst, straps and zippers unloosened. The lovely pleated skirt was a hoop around her waist as she drew his head down to her soft pears of pink, browned deeply at the tips. The salty wetness careened wantonly through his body, teasing his poor senses (the floor shooting pricks of pain into his elbows and knees). He sought clumsily to arrange his coat underneath her but managed only a head pillow. A nudge of thigh sent crazy shivers up his spine and propelled him into full stiffness.

"Sweet professor, good professor, handsome professor, my luscious historian, my Disraeli, brave, brave Disraeli!" she moaned and mocked back and forth into his gluttonous ear. He sank helpless and delirious into her gelatin softness. Her musky scent drifted upward and drove on his beating blood. Far far away a cacophony of bells and machine-grunts continued their mad echoing. Quickly she was taking him with her into some sweet slipping space. Sliding feathery with hurtling force toward the point where the ground started breaking, shifting, separating, and they dropped and swallowed, bobbing together (and she was soon saying his name, naming his name, naming him) . . .

LATER, SHE WAS talking: "I'm scattered, Professor, got it? Scattered. Ten different directions at once. That's the way it is. It tears me up. Too bad, huh? Well, I live with it . . ." She reached for his hand. "Come here, sweets, let me show you." And led him to the window. "Look at it. Just look. That's why I moved here. Just so I could be near MIT. Near all that *certainty*. Straight tall buildings, great vertical absolutes. No ambiguities." She leaned over and tenderly kissed his cheek, still looking at the buildings. She drew back, then walked off a few steps. "Ten directions. At least ten. Not much I can do, is there?"

He didn't answer, and walked to the Morris chair and leaned his elbows on the back.

She fixed his gaze and spoke with driving deliberateness. "Now you've got the right look on your face. Just hold it—wonder, bewilderment. You're not kidding, love. You know what you see, all right. Splitting apart. Nervous and schizy. My only focus—the kids in there and now you, sort of—and both of you get so easily swarmed over! Like I want to write about the Puerto Rican migrants in Concord. But I get a call about Vietnam canvassing. Or sit down and think about a thesis. But then 'Lawyer' wants to see me about child support. Or write my congressman about my slum landlord who lives in Newton and has a posh law office in Boston but won't fix the lousy leaking oil furnace downstairs . . ." She paused, then started up again in a smaller voice. "And then I want to figure out what the hell I'm doing with you. How you fit in with me. Or with the kids. Or with yourself. I don't even know what I'm doing with you. I know you six months and you've never asked me to live with you. Why not? It means one of two things: you're unsure of me. Or you're unsure of you." She lit a cigarette. "Well, I amend position 'A.' You should be unsure of me—my position as a *mom* and all that. . . . Who knows—you might be the wrong father figure for me—It would be *untherapeutic*." She took a step closer and crossed her arms. "What do you think?"

A minute passed.

"I think maybe you want to talk more."

Her teeth slowly nudged her lower lip. She nodded, her concentration elsewhere.

She turned around, her back to him, continuing to nod. "Yeah, talk more . . . Sorry, Cliff—no, stay there, right where you are, behind me by that chair. You see I've stood here so often like this, facing this lousy cracking wall. Alone. And I'd permit myself to think of you—somewhere here with me. Only you weren't. There was nothing. Except my futile fantasies. So this is quite a luxury—imagining you, and knowing that I can turn and see you." She remained with her back to him.

Some few minutes passed, a silence building slowly and powerfully, in which he thought of her thinking of him, just now, and at other times, alone, looking at the broken plaster.

Then she turned and walked close to him. "Don't mind me too much, you know. I love you, but I can do without you. So don't worry. And forget this bullshit existentializing . . ." She slapped him playfully on the arm, like a male schoolmate. Then she said, "Can I whisper something to you, very private?"

He looked at her grave face.

She leaned close to his ear and said, mournfully, "Do you love me more than you love Susan Sontag?"

It took him a moment to recover and shift moods. By that time she had backed away, into the doorway, where she stood and stared.

"Brute," she said quietly, and wandered away.

He moved to the window and looked out at the twinkling lights from MIT amid the moonless night. From the kitchen came the familiar sounds of dishes clattering and water running.

He was disturbed and exhilarated by her. All peaks and valleys, no plateaus. The thought of living with her had been a dilemma. He liked the kids; more, he luxuriated in them. And he liked her, though at times he could smash dinner plates over her head. If only they had lived in another time, she would have been perfect. Or near-perfect. It was not that another age didn't have its vulgarity. Not at all. It was that it didn't have the resources to *multiply* its vulgarities so, to spread them around at every level of life, to cheapen and debase every crevice of society and culture. The truth was, everything was topsy-turvy. Dirty words were heralded as the new literacy. And the defenders of dirty words, from nice Jewish girls from the Bronx to fashionable academics, were proclaimed as major critics and in demand everywhere. Movies intended for children were being palmed off as a subtle art. Art galleries had become supermarkets, furniture stores (to buy stacks of soup cans or bedroom-set replicas) or aboriginal caves, where mindless blobs of paint netted staggering sums (there's the ticket, son—the more primitive, the more cash!). And politically, things were never worse. The new menace of the world was the red, white, and blue banner. We supplied money and troops to back all dictators, in the name of anti-Communism. We destroyed cities in order to protect them, killed citizens in order to set them free. Our language was Orwellian. Civil war was external aggression; extermination was pacification; LBJ was a peace president. And at home, equality-and-justice-for-all was being set ablaze, burning, baby, by those who hadn't been let in on the bargain. And the fires would be put out by the new doctors, the new cures: the police, the troops, the National Guard, bringing their tanks, their Mace, their Stoner rifles. Peace, Sanity, Health, Justice, step this way.

So here was poor Sarah—(and poor Leavitt!)—tossed and tormented by the proliferation of viruses that was the contemporary. Hardy's Sue Bridehead had become Sarah Sorotkin, he mused. Well, who was he to turn back the clock? If he liked Sue, in spite of (and because of) her imperfections, why not Sarah? How easy it all was!

He ran to tell her his conclusion, but she threw him a towel and turned up the water. He dried slowly and meticulously, confident in his new wisdom. Visions of a pastoral hearth—mod-style, if necessary—floated through his head.

AND MUCH LATER: he was climbing a wire fence, somewhere in his childhood, when he heard a voice from far off . . . He wished it would go away.

"Did you hear me? I think you better go."

He opened his eyes and saw Sarah sitting by the window, wrapped in her woolen robe and smoking.

"What time is it?"

"Four, four-fifteen. So, out. Beat it. Scram."

His mouth felt like an empty garbage pail. His stomach ached.

"Yeah, I know." She puffed on her cigarette, still looking out into the darkness. "It's not the proper time to be waking people. And I'm being perverse. But I got a paper to write. Or have you forgotten?"

She was talking very straight, and he knew it. No wit, no irony, no play now. Just like that.

Still covered with sleepiness, he tossed his legs wearily to the ground. He groped for his socks.

"Rough, huh? On me too. But I got work to do. And when I feel the impulse, I gotta get to it. You know what I mean—you were *impulsive* once."

He was getting into his trousers. He kept silent.

"Atta boy. Get into the clothes and get out. And keep your cool. That's what you've learned to do. Formula for troubled females: silence. And when they turn hysterical: departure. You fellows are amusing creatures, luv. But you bore me. Why *are* men so boring, huh, Cliffie? Maybe it's your preoccupation with immortality. The fear of dying like the rest of us. Boring and brutal. That would account for it." She took a long puff. "You're so interested in what's right, what's good, what's noble. Well, nothing's good, nothing's right, nothing's *noble,* sweetie. And stop aching after virtue. It's a pain in the neck. It's out of date. You're all out of date, you're all children—you believe the world should be perfect, and permanent. Men, ha!" She moved closer. "Do me a favor—try another planet."

"Why don't you shut up?" he muttered, low. Even that took an effort. He wanted to dress and get out without the effort of thinking or talking.

"And don't go moping for yourself, because you got a class to teach at nine. My kids are up at seven-thirty, every morning. If I can do it without sleep, you can."

"You have a rough life," he finally said.

She stood and walked to him, as he got his suit jacket. Her hand caught his cheek, stinging. She stood there without flinching. He slapped her back. The burst of satisfaction embarrassed him. Her face softened, then she turned and walked back to the window. A slim girl in a cheap robe —it hurt him.

He was at the front door when she called out, "Do you have your notes?"

She was right, he had forgotten them. He returned to the living room, gathered them up, grateful to her for the gesture. But he was too angry, too anxious, too sleepy, to sort out the rest of his feelings.

Driving back, he thought for a moment of her sitting in the dark bedroom, and he missed her terribly. Then he closed off his feelings and promised to write himself a memorandum when he got home: *That's the end. No more. Young Miss Sorotkin takes up too much time.* UPSETS WORK.

Driving the Mass Pike in the morning he was sure the case was closed: the end of Sarah Sorotkin. No use pursuing it whatsoever.

Leavitt was grateful for the notes in class, for he found, surprisingly, that his mind wandered . . . toward the bare maples and birches out the window, and the slow gathering clouds. He lectured on idealism in Eliot, pointing out how her attachment to Dorothea Brooke blinded her to the larger questions of social and political reform raised in the novel. He was answering the question of a particularly earnest, well-dressed co-ed, when the faint figure of Sarah, in a disheveled nightgown, appeared in the corner of the room. He barely caught himself from moving to hold her. "Yes," he stuttered, toward his student, "yes, that's true, there is that element in her work."

The student frowned with puzzlement.

"Uh, perhaps I didn't understand you well. Could you repeat your question?"

She babbled something innocuous, he answered something credible, and soon the bell was ringing.

He got back to his snug brick-walled office, guilty about the class, but still distracted. Students came by to talk about term papers, then two colleagues led him to coffee in the student lounge. They were joined there by two graduate students. Pleading papers to grade, he finally escaped.

At a Howard Johnson's by Fresh Pond, he sat in a booth and opened the Boston *Globe*. A waitress took his order for a hamburger and coffee. The room swam with early Xmas tinsel and slabs of chromed formica. Cash registers fidgeted and clanged. Babies squealed. Scrubbed suburban mothers chatted and touched their hair. Muzak coated the room. He stared at the finned fish, black and white, gliding in and out of the parking lot.

She was a lovely girl, we all know that (Could you speak up louder, sir?). Had a hard time, fought it alone. Parentless, husbandless, with two little hostages to Fortune. All right: medal for contemporary bravery. Even educated, somewhere down deep. Liked to read books, though she hated to admit it ("an antique habit," she explained). Pulling through . . . is that what she's doing? The point is, why now, when she's thirty, with two kids? Why didn't she "pull through" ten years ago? He would give her up. . . .

He sipped his coffee. He would turn his attention to one of those things the graduate schools turn out. Something safe, tidy, prudent: one of those earnest Mary Marvels stamped "ready to produce" by Harvard or Yale, guaranteed to weather the crises, to scribble articles, to process infants, to memorize Emily Dickinson, to wear tweeds, warm the milk, shovel the snow, read the journals. And bring in a steady income. Why, it was just like having another man around the house . . . Sarah's face floated softly toward the window. He pushed his hand out, to push it all away, to remove the vulnerable face and the dark eyes . . . How absurd, how absolutely absurd!

"Something wrong, Mister?"

He looked up at the bleached face of the waitress. "Uh, no. No. What do I owe you?"

"You've caused quite a mess there." He looked at the pool of spilled coffee. She eyed him strangely as she wrote out the check, and told him to pay on the way out.

Sweaty and jumpy, he paid and left. The cool air slapped at him refreshingly, and he found himself wandering around the back of the restaurant, into a vacant dirty lot. He turned a milk crate on its side and sat down. His eye sighted an old rusty chain; he took it in his hand and stared at the varying pimples of rust on the links.

It was absurd that he couldn't give her up, simply and cleanly. It was not as if he hadn't done it before. Hadn't he learned well enough that it didn't make much of a difference which female you mated with? You adapted and adjusted and got used to it. You remained alone ultimately, regardless. To think otherwise was to comfort yourself with an illusion. If only he could believe that she was just another indulgent narcissist, whose main source of chaos sprouted from the *self*. Or that she was one of those temporary hooky players from the middle class—skin-deep a swinging hippie but underneath as radical as George Romney. But she was neither. Nor was she arrogant. There was no pretentious mystique about having suffered, or had lovers, or painted pictures, or visited shrinks. Those absurd delusions of status or irritating puffs of vanity that characterized a certain type of vulgarly educated female posed no temptations for her. Her scars and, especially, her merits were her own private affair. He admitted that so far as cultural diseases were concerned she had a clean bill of health.

The kitchen door from the restaurant opened and a lanky Negro, wearing a rubber apron and a sanitary hat, rolled out a garbage can. He was slightly startled by Leavitt, sitting smoking there, holding the chain. His step slowed as he approached the door.

Leavitt kept his eyes down.

"You lookin' for work?"

He shook his head.

"Hungry?"

He shook his head again.

"Cold out here." He went in.

Leavitt waited another few minutes, staring vacantly at the cars passing a few hundred yards away. Then he got up and wandered away.

Back in the car he realized embarrassedly that he had carried the chain with him. He dropped it on the floor in back.

BACK IN HIS apartment he tried to sleep but found he was overtired. He smoked, drank coffee, walked back and forth, and watched a cowboy serial on television. When he passed the phone on the wall he would stop and stare at it, as if it were some magic totem. Time moved along a track of memories and fantasies as if in a dream. He felt almost like an addict sweating it out. Once the phone rang. He waited, then answered. A colleague chatting. He cut him off politely after a few minutes.

He got to sleep about three.

The next morning brought shafts of sunlight, and he felt a bit better. He drove with eagerness to school and, for the first time in a long while, gave a good class. Especially when he set down his notes and began improvising. After the hour, when a student came up and praised the lecture, he realized painfully what a lousy teacher he had become. He went back to his office and promised himself that he would turn over a new leaf.

And when Miss Cordoran came by, he suddenly looked at her approvingly. He invited her for coffee and was surprised to hear, in the upstairs lounge, that she had spent a summer teaching at a CORE school in Roxbury. Though she belabored the point, she was much more sensible than he had remembered, and her legs were shapelier. He offered to meet her some evening soon.

When he got home there was a letter. No return address,

the familiar small handwriting in black ink. He took it upstairs, holding it fearfully, like a live bomb. He laid it on the kitchen table and walked into the bedroom. Changing his clothes, he thought at first that he would keep it without opening it. Then he decided to destroy it. He wondered how. Ripping it up seemed out of the question. So did tossing it into the garbage. When he got to the idea of burning it he realized his madness. He returned to the kitchen and stared at the envelope while buttoning his shirt. He lifted it, trying to feel whether it was a long letter or simply a note. There was only one five-cent stamp posted on it.

He sat down, and tore the envelope corner.

Dear Friend,

I am glad that you've opened this, although I realize that your doubts are well founded. I was pretty awful the other night, wasn't I?

I've just come from McDermott Court at MIT. (Do you remember, I took you there once?) I went to the 20th floor lounge, and looked down at the dark Calder sculpture, and watched the dots of people strolling and stopping. From there it looked like some elegant bird, with a labyrinth of dark wings, ready for flight. But when I got down and stood under it, it seemed very different. It was already soaring and hurtling into space. I liked it.

Across from it is the Green building—you know, that stupid pillar of concrete that rises forty stories or so. Full of function, they say. Like all the young men who are incubated inside of it . . . So I walk about my sweeping bird, occasionally running my hand across a smooth wing. I have an urge to climb inside one of the lovely dark curves, and be cradled by one of its smooth steel bellies. Like being born into the troposphere (another long-seated wish: to sit and watch the clouds form!). Then I stroll around the outer layer of the court, to get a fuller sense of my bird. I've renamed the court: "Court no. 22072." Lovely name, don't you think? It's my own Piazza di Campidoglio, where I'll take you one day if you remain well-behaved. MIT and Michelangelo. Calder and Marcus Aurelius (he's on a horse in the center of that square). You can see I have all that I'll ever want in life.

Which brings me to my father.

He had wanted to be a mathematician, but instead he wound up teaching math in a high school (Samuel J. Tilden, East Flatbush, Brooklyn). When I knew him he was already beaten and defeated. By the failure of his ambitions, by the abject taunts of my mother, that dear woman. She was vulgar, vain, selfish, what else? Anti-intellectual. But shrewd. Cunning. I don't know what turned her into all those things. Maybe coming from a German Jewish background and marrying an East European *stetl* Jew (whose father was a tailor). Maybe having no son but just a daughter. Too much competition. She hated my father's closeness to me. I remember when I would be dragged off to some horrible Catskill house-keeping cottage, where I was forced to remain all week alone with her, till father came up, for weekends. (He was urged to teach during the summer so we could enjoy the luxury of a holiday!) Sometimes, he'd kidnap me for the entire day—that is, my mother would sit around and play cards and gossip, and we would take walks or trips to Liberty. The evening meal would be brutal. She'd punish us mercilessly. From vile accusation to tearful self-injury. And she'd always manage to carry on a flirtation with some male in front of my father, as a joke. (I used to leave the room to cry, but of course never let on to him.) I never knew if she was ever really unfaithful. Now, I think not: it wouldn't have been as satisfying as her own masochism/sadism . . . He also taught Hebrew in school in the late afternoons. He loved Sholem Aleichem. His greatest joy was when I got to read Yiddish. . . . He had a heart attack on the subway and died on the platform of the Utica Avenue station. They called us, and my mother's words to me, as I was setting the Friday night table, were: "You better come with me. Your father's had a heart attack. He's probably dead by now anyway. What can you expect, from the way that man smoked?" And she took me with her to the station, a few blocks from our house . . . I remember his double-breasted blue serge suit, his flopping fedora with a black band, his high black shoes. And his eyes. And the way he used to pinch my cheek affectionately.

All right, enough, just now.

Yes, I've felt guilty about never having been able to protect him from her, from the world. Yes, I can understand my difficulties "clinically" (but that's so dull and limiting once you understand it). No, I'm not sorry for having gone through it. Yes, I do regret errors. Yes, I do regret regret. Yes, I do hope to change. No, I probably won't.

Now be a good boy and let me continue kicking my heels in the air.

Your physical proximity and old-fashioned solicitude are, as usual, gratefully acknowledged and duly appreciated.

I'm a tough one to ride and stay on, though, as you can see. I understand perfectly if you choose to leave. Prudence is a much-maligned virtue these days. Don't you malign it any more.

> Yours,
> S. Sorotkin

He waited five minutes, by the clock. Then he phoned. She was in the middle of fixing dinner. Why didn't he pick her up about eight, she said matter-of-factly. They might take a walk along the Charles. Wasn't it a bit chilly for that, he muttered. A bit chilly, but not for that, she replied.

THE AIR WAS cold and windless, and nipped at their faces as they walked along the dirt path, away from Boston. Cars speeded along Memorial Drive. The river, on their left, rippled quietly and darkly. She soon led him off the path and onto the boggy turf closer to the water.

She gripped his arm and spoke solemnly. "You've liberated me from the chains of the kitchen. You're my savior."

He nodded appreciatively and reached for her hand. "Could you hold me a little easier, now that you're free?"

"Of course." She looked up, eyes mischievous, grip firm. "Just a few more moments, my dear Professor. Just a few more moments. Then you can return to your office and your work."

He looked at her skeptically.

"Now it's about this girl, this raunchy Pygmalion type, who claims to know you. Could you tell me your connection with her?" She jerked him to the side of a jutting rock. "Your connection?"

"Well, I knew her in Rangoon, to begin with. Yes.

Actually it was her father. I had known him in Classics at Yale, and then there he was: on a holiday from Hong Kong, a self-made man, retired at the age of thirty-eight. And do you know on what? On storm windows, of all things."

"The girl?"

"Oh yes, the girl. Eurasian bone structure, French sensibility, Russian passion. Luscious, in a remote sort of way. If you know what I mean."

"No, I don't."

"Yes. Yes, of course. Now, as I was saying—"

"Divorced with two children, I think you said. And chaotic and intractable."

"Well, you might put it that way," he answered calmly, wishing he carried a pouch of tobacco so he could empty it on her. "Wait—where the hell are you taking me?—the road's up this way!"

"Ssshh. Your manners. There are creatures sleeping here. This way," she whispered, looking about with mock fear and suspicion. "Come along, my good sir, come along! To here—the cave of confessions!"

He grimaced privately as she led him down beneath the arch of the footbridge.

"Christ!" He slipped on the muddy bank but she caught him. It was very dark under the bridge, and the water gurgled in among the rocks only a few feet away.

"A delightful place you have here," he said.

"Yes. We like it . . . We find that the people who are most capable of disguising the truth, of keeping it out of sight, come clean here. It's . . . the surroundings perhaps. Now, about the girl." She placed her hands on his shoulders. She was smiling, dimly.

"Oh, yes. Well, I couldn't abandon her, you see. Out of respect for the father, on one level. Left Yale and Homer for aluminum sash, sills, panes. If you can't respect *that,* what can you respect?"

"True . . . and another level?"

"Well, I had taken a liking to the youngest child. She was full of sores and rickets. A manic depressive at seven. Nervous with ideas. Her hands used to shake so, she would have to leave her drawing board. Was strangely soothed when I read her Yvor Winters' poetry. Nothing else would do."

"He's not an easy one to crack, Vassily," she muttered back over her shoulder. "But ve vill, ve vill, von't ve?" She put her question to him. "Now think. Why, Professor, did you stick with her?"

"I give up."

"You can't. You haven't answered yet. He's shrewd, Comrade."

He listened to the trickling water, the far-away sounds of the traffic. He sighed heavily.

"Passion."

"Say it again, louder," she said sweetly.

"Passion."

"Very good Professor. Very good. Noble. Heroic. Forthright. But wrong! You do very well with words, but you have a limited ability for what we call *content analysis*. Not passion. *Responsibility*. Yes. Now you try it."

He was puzzled.

She indulged her habit with his ear. "Go ahead, please. Re-spon-si-bil-i-ty. Six syllables."

He waited, then repeated.

"Responsibility."

"All right. I'll accept that . . . Now, more precisely: responsibility . . . in an age of technology. How does that sound? Appropriately phenomenological?"

"Pretentiously accurate."

"Only wrong again. You see, it's *misguided* responsibility. The girl *is not worth it*." She waited for an answer, but he said nothing. "Do you understand? Is it clear?"

"It's clear."

"Good. Now the court enjoins you from continuing your pursuit under false pretenses. It warns you that such pursuit will force the court to impose severe penalties in consequence of such action. A prudent man, it goes without saying, will do well to heed such wisdom. . . . Do you have anything to say, sir?"

"Only this—that your court's reputation for myopic judgment and well-intentioned self-deception is rather well known."

She posed her forefinger at her cheek.

"The defendant's a fool, and impertinent."

"The judge is a jerk, but solicitous."

236 NEW AMERICAN REVIEW

"Mmmm . . ."

She raised her hand to his face and caressed his cheek. It seemed to take forever.

Then her tone shifted. "All right, buster, follow me. And don't try to cut out." She locked his hand, and began leading him across the jutting rocks and up the grassy bank. In the darkness he was struck momentarily by the soft whiteness of her forearm.

"Look," she said, looking down at the water as they reached the dirt path. "A river without ships. Not much good, is it?"

He gazed at the Charles, winding its dark peaceful path toward Boston. Beyond, on the far side, the red brick Georgian buildings of the Harvard Business School were stacked in neat rows. Just before them ran Storrow Drive, where endless autos darted forward with little puffs of energy, looking like a model racing game. The glimmering blue-black water was a painter's delight, attracting the yellow and red lights of the cars, merging and blending them on its liquid canvas. The series of hanging highway lamps were distorted into uneven golden verticals, shimmering skyscrapers. And in midstream, the watery cradle of the moon was rocking gently back and forth like a child's sailboat. His heart reached out for the girl next to him, for the pageant of muted colors and changing shapes. . . .

She crashed in upon his mood. "C'mon, moonstruck. You're getting too comfortable with my river. You can come back on your own time and introspect." She jerked him away with an appreciative glint in her eye.

SATURDAY EVENING brought two parties, one in retaliation for the other.

"All right, honeybunch," her voice mischievous on the phone, "we'll go to Academia. Then, we'll make the mod scene."

"What do you mean?"

"We'll go to one of *my* necessary engagements. Fair enough? Brattle Street first, high society, then Central Square and the workers. Don't be frightened; it'll be good for you. The quick change of sets will keep you from getting jaded. Or mannered. Or com-pla-cent. Saturday at eight."

Kiss.

Click.

Helpless.

On arrival they were led into the spacious rectangular living room, with alcoves in various places. Well-dressed groups of twos and threes stood and talked, drinks in their hands. He recognized a few colleagues from his school, others from the university. From a pair of wooden speakers, skillfully tucked into a side wall-shelf, a Brandenburg Concerto was being distributed about the room. The general décor was contemporary and affluent. The upholstered chairs were modern versions of Byzantine decoration: tall, straight-backed, ornamented by spindle finials and meticulous filigree. The couch, unpainted pine and studiously cracked black leather, sucked you down into its luxury. A huge abstract oil painting, of protruding blisters and textures of charcoal grays and dark blues, emerged from one of the white walls. Clifford noticed a man reading an art book in a butterfly chair, which was encircled by an elongated black metal tube, with a rubbery neck and a lightbulb encased in a black cylinder for a head. In front of the bay windows, placed on a pedestal, a potted asparagus fern, with acid-green leaves and frizzy tendrils, groped about aggressively.

They stopped near the deserted fireplace and were immediately surrounded by two couples. Clifford knew one of the men. A crew-cut college boy took their orders for drinks. While introductions were being served and returned, Clifford noticed Edward Eggleston's quick furtive glance at Sarah's legs. He wanted to grab Eggleston by the collar and make him eat his bow tie. Still, there was a great deal to be seen, since her white silk shift, held up by two slim straps, ended several inches above her knees. Her creamy shoulders and neck curved expansively. Her long straw-colored hair fell back loosely, except for a few strands that enticingly wound their way forward. If she played with her hair, Clifford decided, he would leave.

"Eggleston tells me you're in Victorian," said Kenners, the second fellow. Paunchy and balding, a wide oval face. "I was just reading *My Secret Life*. What did you think of it?"

"I haven't read it," replied Clifford. He stood with an elbow draped about the mantelpiece of the fireplace.

"Even after Steven Marcus's study?" inquired the string-beanish, horn-rimmed Eggleston.

"Not Marcus either."

"I see."

"What do you do, my dear?" said plumpish Edna Eggleston, turning to Sarah. Mrs. Eggleston taught psychology at B.U.

"Oh, I try to paint," Sarah said ingenuously, "but usually Clifford keeps me busy reading all the criticism."

"Why, what do you mean?"

"I read the critics, that's all. People like Marcus and Trilling and Hillis Miller. Then I tell Clifford what they say." She took an excited gulp and nodded, to confirm the point.

Amused, Clifford looked at the incredulous faces.

"But surely you've read some of the new pornography?" continued Kenners. "Don't you think it opens up an entirely new field for study? It explains so much about Victorian authoritarianism and rigidity, for example. And I agree with Sontag—of course I'm not an expert—there's much to be said for it aesthetically. For example, *The Story of O* . . ."

"I didn't see your name on the anti-war petition," interrupted Clifford. "Did I miss it?"

"My position on the war takes into account certain distinctions . . ." he began.

Leavitt didn't bother to listen and walked away.

At the long hors d'oeuvres table in a corner alcove, he took a small open-faced ham and cheese sandwich, and poured himself more Scotch. He drank it down quickly. For a moment, two of the wooden shelves before him wavered like rubber.

Some woman or other came up and began talking very rapidly to him.

"There you are," Sarah smiled and took his arm. "I must tell my darling something," she said to the bewildered woman. "Would you forgive me?" She took Clifford away.

"You missed a grand conversation, dear. The wife of the fat man, the skinny thing, asked if we had any children. Without waiting for an answer, she began telling me how difficult it was keeping a cleaning woman these days. And if I didn't have a good pediatrician, hers, in Newton, was simply marvelous. Now what do you think of that? You've probably been underestimating that poor woman all this time."

He tried to speak, but she went on.

"And Kenners, after announcing your rudeness, returned to pornography. You know what I did?" She wore a perfect expression of innocence. "As I left, I winked at him. Do you think he'll take me up?"

"Up where?"

She hit him in the ribs. "That wasn't nice. Are you all right?" While he pondered, she said, "Now keep your cool. I'm going to take us to look at our host's new piece of sculpture."

"You look."

"But I promised that I'd bring you. *Promised* him faithfully."

"Tell him you couldn't locate me."

"Don't be silly. It's not exactly Capote's party."

They walked through the vestibule and into a smallish square room, barely furnished. A few people were standing in front of the sculpture, which was lit by two special wall spotlights.

"Ah, Cliff! Come on along. Glad you brought him, Sarah. Come around here. You know the Wachters, don't you? They're in the Art department."

The women exchanged smiles.

The object of the attention was a massive abstract structure, about eight foot by four. The materials were gray steel, iron rods, and interconnecting suspension cables. There were also odd pieces of unpainted wood, twisted out of shape. Clifford read the title at the metal base: "Man, Landscape, and Silence."

"It's a Spitzerberg," said Gerald Sperber, their host, rather too casually.

"Oh," said Clifford, nodding. Sperber was well-meaning. That's why he had come.

"And look here, Bernie," said Sperber, his eyes sparkling, taking Wachter's arm. "You too, Sarah." He led them to the back of the sculpture and waited for everyone to assemble. There, smiling, he proceeded to flick a small switch attached to a metal box, which was held by two crisscrossing cables. Immediately a motor revved into action, setting a complex system of pulleys to moving up and down. Small serrated disks and wheels began rotating and rolling.

"Quick, look around here!" urged the excited Sperber. "Look where it extends to!"

Like a giant mechanical toy, the irregular pieces of metal and wood were moving in and out of various tunnels of space. The burst of unleashed motion lasted five or six minutes, then gradually diminished.

Sarah's attentive look worried Leavitt.

"Marvelous isn't it?" beamed Sperber, his narrow cheeks reddened.

"Yes, most interesting, Gerald," said Wachter, a small stout figure with a neatly trimmed beard. "Most interesting."

"How absolutely divine!" said another guest, who had silently arrived.

"Not quite that," corrected Wachter, smiling quietly. "But Spitzerberg does continue to *mature* in his work. That much is clear enough."

Clifford was about to leave when Sarah spoke up. "That's more than mere ingenuity, Professor Wachter, don't you think?"

"More than ingenuity?" Wachter said, surprised. "I should say so, indeed."

"Oh, of course the totality is," Sarah assured him. "I was referring to the mechanical idea only."

"Ah . . . Well, that is something else. This needs to be determined."

"I still think it's absolutely divine," put in the female admirer. "Where *did* you pick it up, Gerald? I must get Harold to see it."

"What do you think of these lines here?" asked Sarah, pointing to a particularly knotted section.

"Yes," mused Sperber, nodding slowly. "Yes, certainly an area of concentration. Yes . . ."

"But an artificial one, don't you see?" Sarah advanced peremptorily and swiftly. "Look at a similar area just here —look at the fluidity of these lines, and their *contextual* rightness. Nothing arbitrary, nothing preconceived. Rather, functional and organic."

Sperber was trying to follow Sarah's argument.

"Miss, ah, what was your last name again?"

"Sorotkin, Professor, Sarah Sorotkin."

Wachter stroked his beard. "You've had some training, I see. Critical, or, practical?" He emphasized the hardness of the first "c."

Clifford wanted to answer Wachter, but Sarah shrewdly managed to flash him a look.

"Critical mostly." Sarah waited a moment. Then, as Wachter was about to speak, she added, "Not under the name of Sorotkin, of course. Highbottom is my publishing pseudonym. Patricia Louise." She looked both proud and ingenuous.

"Mmmm . . . Highbottom . . ." mused Wachter. "The name does seem to ring some kind of bell. But I really must admit that I can't really place it."

"I'm in some of the old *Art News*. Awful name I got stuck with, though—don't you think?" She blinked innocently.

Wachter continued to adjust his beard.

Sperber expressed surprise, and started speaking to Wachter. Wachter went on with Sarah. "Have you been following Spitzerberg's career closely, young lady?"

"No, in all honesty, I can't say I have."

Wachter nodded professionally. "I know, I know, difficult to keep up with it all," and went on sympathetically. "But your remarks are quite apposite, you know. Look, Sperber," he said, taking the tall man by the arm, and evidently warming up, "it's a *dynamism* that separates one section from the other. That's what Miss . . . ah—"

"Sorotkin."

"Yes, Sorotkin. What Miss Sorotkin is getting at. And such materials can only *become* dynamic through the use of properly related forms. No form unto itself is intrinsically anything, Sperber." He spoke more slowly now. "This much you know, surely. But what you don't realize is the years of experience that are necessary in order to understand what materials are congruent with each other. Years of experience," Wachter's voice took on an edge of harshness to it, "merely to create assurance in craft. Sounds simple, Sperber? No! It is not done overnight. The difference between this first section here and *this* one is all the difference in the world: a difference of years. One is an expression of a style, of a fully developed signature, which has been paid for with years of error and frustration. This . . . this . . . this mishmash here—is pure failure of nerve. That's all. Impatience with searching for the right form. A child's impatience—and the whole is imperfect!" He threw a fist at the sculpture.

The lanky Sperber looked down wide-eyed at the little man's sudden revelation of sheer venom.

There was a moment of pause; then Sarah, gazing fixedly, said, "He is a master of space, isn't he?"

Wachter's tense expression suddenly relaxed. Slowly his face beamed in appreciation.

"Yes, Miss Sorotkin, you have a discerning eye. Space: Spitzerberg's favorite mistress, his favorite material." The professor ran his hand lovingly about the second section. "Ah, space. . . . How he adores it, caresses it, with his cold steel, his wooden chips, his endless engines. How he adores it . . . and adorns it!"

At this moment the female with a hat returned, with a pleasant-looking man at her side.

"There it is, Harold—isn't it . . . stunning?" She smiled respectfully to Wachter and his class. "Wouldn't something like that look just divine in the den?" she said in a low voice to her husband.

Off to the side Wachter made a gesture of hopelessness with his hand. He looked about for Sarah and, catching her attention, muttered, "Culture. There it is!" He sucked at his lips, and proceeded toward the door. He left his wife and Sperber by the door, however, and took a few steps back into the room, where he curled his forefinger at Sarah and bowed slightly.

"Now keep still—he's merely arranging a tryst." She walked toward Wachter.

By now, Harold was being led around the sculpture. He looked uneasy and avoided Clifford's eye. Clifford felt a rush of sympathy for the pale man. Poor Harold probably had an entire household of junk that he didn't want.

Presently Wachter left Sarah and headed out of the room, followed by his wife and Sperber.

Sarah returned. "Some Tuesday or Thursday afternoon . . . A late afternoon drink together?"

"I'll get our coats," said Clifford.

"Good."

"It really moved just like a carnival, Harold," the woman was saying, "and the children can appreciate it too. . . . If only it would turn on again."

"So you're going to turn on with me, huh, Professor?" she said, as they walked up the rickety wooden steps to the fourth floor of the Magazine Street flat.

"Not quite."

"You're just coming to see how the animals live—sort of a Gestalt experiment?"

"Sort of."

"My pudgy Sartre!" She threw her arms about him. "You're so absolutely sweet!" She inundated his face with a flood of small pecks.

"Preparing me for the worst, eh?" he mumbled between kisses.

"Come, innocent, meet the Renaissance. You might even meet some familiar faces."

She knocked at the door. A sentry with a brocaded shirt and striped bell bottoms was posted at the door. "Yeah, what's up?"

"Nick invited us," she answered.

The boy smiled and gestured them in.

"They've been busted once," she explained to Leavitt.

The long vestibule was littered with people standing around or sitting on the floor.

"Morning, baby." A dark Negro grinned widely and reached out his hand for Sarah. She smiled and brushed by, leading Clifford by the wrist.

The crash of electronic music crescendoed as they reached a large loft at the end of the corridor. It was painted a conspicuous white, and from the exposed ceiling beams hung a series of curtained partitions, fashioned from transparent cheesecloth, reaching the floor. They were cleverly constructed to arrange the room into semi-symmetrical squares, divided by Scheherazade veils. A horde of dancers were gyrating to the slow rhythms. Most of the couples wriggled and jerked within the confines of their squares. But there were also single dancers, who floated about from square to square with ethereal smiles and flowery wreaths. They seemed especially fond of intertwining their bodies with the cheesecloth. As the music drummed deafeningly and incessantly, blinding beams of orange, purple, cobalt blue, and yellow rotated wildly from somewhere on the ceiling. They would catch and follow a dancer, exaggerating his already distorted face into a hideous mask of bright, oozing orange.

Through the filmy gauze Clifford could dimly make out the band. A group from Dorchester, someone told him. The five were called The Black Bishops (sequined on the side of the drum). Two singers, wearing berets, screamed into a floor microphone, the words indistinguishable.

Clifford stood transfixed, scared. He heard someone asking Sarah to dance, and nodded absently. . . . The pounding sound of the Bishops distended grotesquely, thrusting upon the walls and ceiling, swelling the space with its exploding vibrations. He imagined at times following the flight of a sound to its point of final descent, as it linked with a strobe beam to shower some human flesh in a flash of blinding color and splitting pitch. Suddenly shaking himself, he had a vision of the dancers lighting on fire, leaping with flames and charring into burnt ash, right there. . . .

"Smokes. Hey!" He was being nudged. "C'mon, light up, baby?" A girl held out a dinner plate with thin brown sticks on it.

Entranced, he took one.

"Do you need a match?"

He nodded.

She produced a flame. "Don't jump, baby, here, c'mere. Here, I'll start it for you." She took the brown stick from his fingers and began inhaling it. Then she handed it back to him. "Go on, try it."

He puffed aimlessly. She smiled and disappeared.

The music tossed itself into new frenzied rhythms. Watching the dancers, Clifford was especially struck by a trim Negro girl. She was wearing a leather mini-dress and high black leather boots that extended beyond her knees. Her blouse was translucent satin, also black. She danced with rigorous authority and style. Her partner, a tall blond youth, tried in vain to follow her steps. Every time he seemed to measure up to her flicking gyrations, she twisted herself into different and more difficult movements. She would twist downward until her backside was grazing the floor, and he would follow, moving clumsily lower; but suddenly the girl, with an artful catapult, was bolt upright again, flinging her hands and hips in demeaning gestures toward his foolishly squatting figure. Or she would draw him into an obscene position and then twirl about behind him, letting her gloved hand dangle mockingly above his wayward head. At one point, she turned toward Clifford and urged her body into a bold bump and grind that was transformed eerily by the spasmodic jerks and stops in her movements. Then the music ceased (an occasional body still thrusting), and she marched imperiously off the floor, leaving the blond boy confused, coughing, and pulling at his collar. As she passed Clifford, she seemed to look up at him, derisively daring him to offer her a challenge. In a moment the blond boy brushed by in feverish pursuit.

His stomach shivered with cold.

"What have you been doing?" asked Sarah, folding some hair back. "Girl-stealing? Opium-eating?"

"Both."

"Let me see." She raised his marijuana hand. "You're about half way there. Any effects?"

"Yeah. I'd like a cigarette. This," indicating the brown stem, "bores me. Not enough taste."

"Aah, you're not letting it penetrate, dear. Too much resistance. Don't worry, I was that way at first."

"I see."

"Don't look now," warned Sarah, "more of your colleagues. And mine."

"Family night out, huh."

"This, approaching, is the good Professor of Sociology who provides me with a little research and much money. Gentle sort."

"Hullo, Sarah, nice to see you." A short bearish man, with a scraggly red beard, leaned over and pecked Sarah (who blinked very innocently and very rapidly at Clifford). "Hello, nice to meet you." He took Clifford's hand firmly. "I've seen you around campus, but I don't think we've ever met."

Clifford shook his head. Lefler was a well-known figure, both for his flashy mass-culture articles in the quarterlies, and for his curiously well-publicized personal life.

"A very swinging pad, don't you think? Some very cool cats, too . . ." His eyes were extremely large and blood-shot. He wore a perpetual smile or leer, and he had a way of boring in on you when he spoke. An academic middle-linebacker, Clifford noted.

"What do you do again, Levin?"

Clifford didn't bother to correct him. "History—"

"Have you made the Testing-Grounds yet?" Lefler said, leaning his body into both of them. "Marvelous name for it, isn't it?" He waited, then added, "Some heads from New York are up—very groovy. A couple of friends of Sandy, in fact."

"I was just going to take Cliff there."

"I'm going there myself now." He locked Sarah's arm and led the way with her.

Clifford followed, the impulse rising to kick the lecherous slob in the ass.

As they negotiated the vestibule bobbing with bodies, a thin young blonde reached out for Lefler, who scooped her in one arm. "Daddy Lefler!" she shrieked joyfully.

"How's my little dove?" he asked, his beard burying itself somewhere in her neck. When he came up, there was a little white flower protruding from his wild hair. "No wonder you never have time to write papers," he said, grabbing Sarah.

"Don't you leave me," she flung back as she was swept along by Lefler. To the end of the corridor, through a bed-room stacked with coats, to a door marked by a lettered sign, embroidered with vines and flowers. It read: Testing-Grounds. And beneath it, in smaller lettering: Forever the Mind.

Lefler knocked, and he and the two girls were welcomed inside. Clifford was stopped until Lefler took over, vouching his kinship, and reaching clumsily for his arm.

As soon as he entered, Clifford was flooded by a warm-sweet aroma, that tickled his throat and set him coughing.

"The incense, man," smiled a heavy-lidded boy sitting on a red cushion. "Sweet, isn't it? Relax . . . let it hit your mind . . . relax."

Still coughing, he looked about. There were posters of Ginsberg, Leary, and D.H. Lawrence, as well as one that advertised genuine Spring Legs of Lamb for 47¢ a pound.

What looked like a Jungian mandala was splashed in bright orange on another wall. Curtains of beads seemed to be everywhere and rattled and wavered as you moved about.

"Sarah, child," said a young man coming up to her.

"This is Sandy Lefler. Our friend's son. My friend Clifford."

"Hi, man." He wore wire-rimmed glasses, was tall and emaciated, and had bleached hair. "Are you all right, Cliff?"

Clifford managed to moderate his choking, while he winced at the presumption.

"It's a great scene, glad you're making it. Both of you."

The sound of a sitar scraped monotonously. Large, multi-colored pillows and cushions lined the walls, with Persian rugs spread in the center. People sat Yoga-like, or lay straight out, legs on cushions. Everyone moved slowly, as if their bodies were accompanying the slow drone of the music.

"Hello," said a young girl in a squaw's dress and head-band. She took Clifford's hand gently. "You're beautiful. Please come with me and let me put my paints on your face."

"Go ahead, Cliff," said Sarah, amused. "Don't spoil her fun."

"No thanks," he said to the girl, taking his hand away.

"Please don't. My mind is so scattered . . . I'm so happy—and this will make me sad." She seemed on the verge of tears.

Bewildered, he said, "I'll sit with you. We can talk about it."

She held his hand and smiled softly back at him, gliding through veils of beaded strings. She led him to her seat, a thick woven Indian blanket.

She sat with her knees bent beneath her, childlike.

"I like you so much," she said, placing her hand on his cheek. "Don't be angry with me for that, you mustn't be."

"All right, I won't be."

Her dark brown eyes stayed fixed on him, large and shining.

"What's your name?" he asked, bored with her silence and stare.

"My name is Blue Flower. I'm Cherokee." She looked around her. "There are hardly any Cherokees here," she said imploringly, "and these people have so much hair on their faces—they could never learn to be Indian. . . . But you could. And I want you to." Again she gazed at him with rapturous concentration, as if they were alone in the night somewhere. "You *will* be my friend, won't you?"

He didn't answer. Then her face moved closer to his. Gently he eased her off, holding her shoulders.

She looked hurt, but then her face changed again. "Please take this gift," she said, raising her necklace of colored beads from around her neck. "I would like you to wear it."

He was being poked in the ribs. "Let her do that, I tell you. She's been withdrawn her entire trip so far." A beaming middle-aged man in a double-breasted blazer was whispering to him.

"Don't listen to him, please."

"See," the man continued, "she's been that way all night. No one can get close to her. Several of us have tried. She's entirely a new piece . . . of data for me."

Clifford looked at him. "What do you do?"

"Social psychiatry. I'm at Harvard. —And you?"

"Engineer."

"Mmmm. Interesting. You're the first I've met at one of these, and I've been to a few. You better watch her—"

He turned back to the girl, who was crying. "You wouldn't wear it because of him," she said.

It was getting too complicated, so he lifted her hand. She brightened, and placed the necklace carefully around his neck. Then she opened two buttons on his shirt and rested the beads on his chest. "I'll get my paints now. You won't leave me now, will you?" She smiled, serene again.

"It's way out, isn't it—the way they carry on. And so many different bags! But the interesting thing is this one's total withdrawal until you came along. Usually we've found that it's connected with some early familial trust crisis, generally occurring at the second growth stage—oh, between seven and ten. You probably resemble her father or some reassuring uncle, appearing at a moment of uncertainty or fear. All internalized of course—and immediately repressed. . . . Sorry, is this all too technical?"

Clifford observed the dew of sweat on the man's forehead, and the puffy boyish cheeks. He should be home with his mother, wearing an apron and drying the dishes, Clifford thought. Psychology by twerps!

The man smiled uneasily. "Something's up? Don't worry," he relaxed, "I'm not *queer*. It's just my job. I'm on an NIH grant—been doing it for two years. Name's Bergstrom, what's yours?"

Just at that moment an older woman in a bright sari leaned over and handed them both small embossed cards. They read: LEGALIZE CUNNILINGUS. Beneath that were initials and a phone number.

"Let me ask you something, Madam, uh . . . I didn't catch the name." Bergstrom rose to his feet to chat with her.

Leavitt looked around for Sarah but didn't see her. The sitar continued to grate. A tall Negro promenaded by with Lefler's undergraduate. Clifford stumbled about, dazed, sickly, and hot.

Turning the corner he caught sight of her sitting with a small group, Lefler among them. As he walked closer, he saw stripes of colored pastel upon her forehead and cheeks. And a white flower in her hair.

"Cliff, sweet, there you are!" She rose to meet him. "Why you've been succumbing!" She smiled and held up his necklace, which he had forgotten about. He made a face, and took it off, tossing it on a pillow.

"Come over, I was waiting for you."

"Why?"

"Don't be difficult. Come on."

She brought him into the small circle.

"Why, hello there," smiled Lefler. "We're just about to embark—coming with us?" His eyes shone as he patted the head of his returned young blond. Next to her sat the Negro, holding her around her waist. Also there was the sari woman, the psychologist, the boy Sandy, and another couple.

Sitting close by were two young men who faced each other as if over a game of chess. Before them on a table sat a single large onion. Transfixed, they stared at it, one mumbling every few minutes, "Too much, man. Like too much."

It was then that Clifford noticed a pitcher and several glasses at Lefler's side.

"C'mon, Levy," said Lefler, lifting the pitcher filled with

what looked like punch and brandishing it, "we're about to take off."

Clifford moved to the edge of the circle and sat on an end of an Oriental rug.

"What is the stuff?" Clifford asked Sarah.

"Acid, dopey," she said kindly.

He looked blank.

"Acid—LSD."

Lefler began to pour out large shot glasses and pass them around.

Bergstrom, the psychologist, his collar open and sporting a bandanna, looked on with greedy curiosity. The woman in the sari sat next to him, the skin on her chest a network of cracks and creases in the light. The young couple looked very much alike: shoulder-flowing hair, dark suede boots, bells tied on strings around their necks. Under heavy lids their eyes looked vacant and distant. The Negro was dressed in a striped African tunic and wore a small red cap on the back of his head. Smiling confidently, he supported a tom-tom between his legs, thumping it with light irregularity. The young blond sat next to him. He had a habit of reaching for her face and turning it with his large hand when he wanted her attention. On her other side sat the wreathed insatiable Lefler, who by now had opened his shirt to bare a soft, tubby chest,

Clifford turned to Sarah. "Well, what do you want to do?"

"What do you mean?"

"All set?" Lefler asked. He raised his glass. "I propose a toast: to our *new selves* about to be liberated!"

Clifford stood.

"What is it, Leavitt? Up-tight suddenly?" Lefler said, his eyes glinting triumphantly.

"It's too bourgeois," Clifford answered calmly. "Like playing bridge. Count me out." He started away.

Sarah caught up with him. "Wait a minute, will you? What the hell are you doing?"

"Leaving. Want to go?"

"But why?"

"You heard me. Bourgeois. Only upside down. Look around you, at the people, the pillows . . . Besides, I'll get my kicks other ways."

She didn't flinch. "Okay, I'll stay."

"Okay."

"Stay with me even if you don't take it."

"I don't like the atmosphere. I don't like those tin cans rubbing together, *amplified*. And I especially don't like your friends."

"Screw you." But she held him. "Suppose I try it, to see what it's like? Suppose I have my own reasons?"

"What are they?"

"I want to see if I can find out new things."

"About what?"

"About me and my past. Me and the kids."

"Go back to a shrink."

"I'll take acid. It's cheaper, nonaddictive, and probably more moral."

"Yeah, it's cheaper."

Her voice changed. "What are you so angry about—these heads? So they're jerky, so what? So I'm jerky, *so what?* Stay and listen, buster. What's really bugging you is me and my *behavior*. You don't like to see me slumming, do you? With people, with acid, with . . ." She poked his shoulder with her forefinger. "Well, I want to get freaked out, see? I want to blow my mind, see? I want to do what's not good for me, see? It's the way things are. And that blimp in there was right about you: you are up-tight. Only not in the way he thought. You play professor too much. Give it up."

Her look was hard and implacable.

He turned away.

Again she caught him. "Stay for my sake . . . I'd like you around when I trip out."

He waited, then said, "Even the lingo is boring." With satisfaction he saw her face change. Then he was sorry. But he turned and left.

In the car he flicked on the radio, found a rock and roll station, and turned it up loud. The incessant pounding eased his nerves as he drove home.

In his apartment, he drank some milk, got undressed, and went to bed.

But he couldn't sleep. The faces and impressions of the tumultuous evening kept pouring in upon him as he twisted and turned. At last he gave up. The clock read two-twenty.

He dressed and left the apartment. He got back into his car, though he had no idea where he wanted to go. But once he was moving, he was drawn to the Charles.

He parked near one of the Harvard houses and crossed Memorial Drive, quiet at this hour. He found himself on the dirt path that ran parallel to the river. A faint drizzle had started up, bathing the scene in a veil of mist. Abruptly, without looking up, he veered from the path and headed down the riverbank. The Weeks footbridge loomed ahead of him, and he realized—with a perverse pleasure in observing the tricks of his will—that he had returned to Sarah's cave. Only just now there was no feeling of her anywhere.

He leaned against the concrete abutment and looked out on the river. The water had lost its sheen, its reflections, and was covered by clouds of gray soot. Thick, heavy, it barely moved.

Thoughts raced through his mind, but in his fatigue and distaste he did not try to separate the strands, to think clearly. He sensed beneath his loneliness and scorn a state of despair that was growing in him. It was a state that he wanted to fight against, to resist. But everything seemed to be such a cheap sham, such mindless, cruel activity, such ugly purpose. Perhaps he was up-tight. But there was something genuinely virulent in society now. Drugs and pornography were merely signs, symptoms. But all that disturbed him less than Sarah did—or rather, disturbed him in relation to her, in the way these things were working upon her.

He had wanted her, badly. That was clear. She had a *quickness* about life, an essential taste for experience that seemed to him rare. It drew him to her. But he had wanted it pure, undefiled, and it didn't come that way. It came with the rest of her—with habits of weakness and failure, with undesirable impulses (toward herself), with a banged-up history, with lousy friends and worse teachers. . . . Then why couldn't he leave her? Fool! he said to himself. Then another part of Leavitt took over and spoke to him—rationally, coolly, with derisive authority. "You're a handsome sight now. Hulking like some derelict or criminal; and moaning over a girl. You're petty, my boy. Petty: face it. Inferior and petty. The deficiencies in the situation are very clear, yet you have 'second thoughts.' You're that enviable product of 'civilization'—some sniveling petty clerk bearing a cross for someone's *feelings*. You weak fool!"

He left the arch and moved on, slowly. He searched for the images of the last time, but the drizzle had dimmed the outlines of the houses and lights and made the river blacker. What looked like a stray piece of wood circled aimlessly where the moonlight had been. From somewhere, he thought he heard a low, irritating drone, but it left. His gaze was caught by a strange object, which seemed to be smiling at him; hesitantly, he stepped closer and saw an old wooden milk box, its wiring torn and mangled, confronting him from a jutting rock. Disoriented, he moved back. The black water seemed immobile, watching, mocking him with its indifference.

He closed his eyes tightly and heard the low suspended drone. He realized that he was near exhaustion and felt helpless before the thoughts and strategies which were struggling in his brain. He swallowed hard and repeatedly, suddenly short of breath. And then, he was looking on unbelievingly as an enlarged Spitzerberg sculpture began moving toward him, Dr. Wachter perched on top with a stethoscope aimed at him. The Negro dancer, swollen into the size of an Amazon, was gyrating obscenely in the water. He saw Sarah for a moment, but she was replaced by the woman in the sari leering and handing him her card . . . The wet spongy bank seemed to suck him downward. An intense burning, beginning in his stomach, surged through him. With a great effort he leaned forward and cupped the thick water in his hands and brought it to his face.

He was crouching forward on his knees, wiping his face with his handkerchief. His head settled somewhat. The images were gone. He breathed more deeply and was refreshed by the rush of air. Suddenly clear-headed again, he stood up. A fresh sense of uncertainty was breaking into his mind and he tried to draw it together.

She was right in a way, wasn't she, about his purity? Bend a little, boy, loosen up, uncork. He recalled a phrase of hers, a self-analysis: a girl of her time. Well, she was. Oh, it was a disastrous, pathological time, a gaudy burst of fragments. Like her. But there was also something else. Something honest, and even—he dreaded the word—free.

And if he was attracted to her—despite his theories—then, after all, he was attracted to certain qualities of the time. It would take a great deal of patience, he knew, to get beyond the psychedelic colors, the rocking senselessness, the mixed-up journeyers, in order to reach that honesty, that little bit of freedom. A great deal of patience. But wasn't that what she was asking him for, in her strange manner, all along?

He knew what he wanted to do now, and began to laugh.

A NEW GUARD was posted at the door, but luckily Clifford remembered the name Nick. It was almost four and the party had reached a more erotic level. Couples—female and male, male and male—seemed to be intertwined wherever there was room, in various stages of undress and sex. The odor of marijuana rose strongly even in the corridor.

The Testing-Ground, however, showed little change. The same heavy-lidded people, the same jangling of beads and bells, the same Ravi Shankar groaning. He made his way carefully, avoiding extended lolling arms and legs. In the L of the room, partitioned by a fence of beads, he came upon a familiar circle. They were broken into two groups. The first included Lefler (now in a brightly striped polo shirt), the Negro, the sari woman, and the blond girl (tapping a tambourine). They were all four dancing together, moving in and around each other, kissing and touching gently and indiscriminately. Just then, Lefler was holding the Negro around the waist, while the sari woman was whispering intimately to the girl. Turning about, Clifford saw that Sarah was standing apart, against the wall, a high stool stationed like a sentry in front of her.

The other group, composed of the young hippie couple, Bergstrom, Sandy, and the two onion-gazers, were on their hands and knees moving like anteaters, or lying flat on their stomachs, peering at the floor. Clifford drew closer, assaulted by a familiar fetid odor. A grease-stained garbage bag lay on its side. The remainder spread out on the rug: chicken and meat bones, empty vegetable tins, eggshells, beer cans and wine bottles, bacon rinds, piles of coffee grounds, bottle caps, indigestible foodstuffs lumped on paper napkins. The bodies peered, smiled, and mumbled to each other. Clifford was suddenly startled by something moving and alive amid this perverse display. A white mouse was darting to and fro maddeningly. He would stop, shoot glances all around, and peck at an eggshell, only to have the enraptured participants reach out and send him scampering again. Periodically he tried to escape, but an extended leg or arm would prevent him. To the left of Bergstrom, Clifford saw a small cage with several more mice in it.

He moved toward Sarah, stopping short a few feet from her. Her arms were crossed, and she looked strangely stiff.

She stared at Clifford in silence for a full minute. Then she said, "Hi Cliff, it's been a bad trip. . . ." She smiled and spoke dreamily as if in a slight shock. "They tell me I've been scared. I even screamed earlier, when Lefler, I think, came near me. I didn't mean to. But he looked so much like Pan—his ears very large and pointed. And then his nose was so wide and flaring. That's why I brought this here, and tucked it into me." She indicated the high drafting stool. "Can you come closer? That's better. Your face is so sweet this way. Gee, it's nice to see you this way . . . I mean like this . . . In this condition. Why do you have this Mac collar up?" She reached across to lower it, and giggled. "Wow, this thick wool. I've never felt it before. Look at the fibers in it, Cliff, will you? There must be thousands of them. I never knew your wool Mac had so many fibers. It used to look so simple. Was it very expensive, Clifford?"

"No. Cheap." The words suddenly hit him. He waited for a response but she was entirely absorbed by the wool.

"It's so much better now that you're here. Honest. I was like a little girl all tensed up . . . How have *you* been?"

"I took a drive. But it wasn't too good."

"I'm so excited now that you're here again. I wasn't this way before." She took his arm, moving out from the wall position. "I just wanted to take it once; and to be with you. But I felt so bad before. So nasty inside . . . and so awfully *helpless*."

Her look was grateful, defenseless, pained. It shook him. It was *he*, he knew, not the acid, that had punished her. Yet here she was, injured, betrayed, overflowing with *gratitude*. Not forgiveness but gratitude! He was defeated.

"It's late. Do you want to go?"

She nodded. "Will you take me for a drive?"

"Okay."

They began to leave.

"Hey, Sarah!" Lefler called. "Come on over here."

She smiled and waved but took Clifford's arm.

Outside it was still drizzling. He helped her into the Ford.

"It's nice to be a patient of yours, Doctor. In fact it's dreamy."

He headed west on Massachusetts Avenue, toward Harvard Square.

"But we're going too fast . . . My head's doing too many things . . . Can we stop, do you think? Anywhere?"

In a minute, he pulled over to the curb and parked in front of the Holyoke building. "It's so nice at this time of evening," she said, as they walked toward Harvard Square.

"Morning, you mean."

He directed her to the concrete island in the middle of the street, housing the subway station and the out-of-town newspaper kiosk.

At the MTA entrance, they stood under the protective arcade, near some tied bundles of newspapers. He looked at her secretly. The white flower was still fresh in her hair, though falling foolishly to the side. Her dark coat, with a button missing, remained open, exposing the funny white shift and her soft neck. Wide-eyed and enrapt, with pastel-smudged cheeks, she was gazing intently at the street. He noticed the soft line of her cheekbone and the slender white hand holding his sleeve . . . a wave of secret pleasure swept through him.

"There's simply so much to take in," she began excitedly, "like the signal lights—small dots at first, then great blobs of yellow, green, and red that keep growing and expanding! Come . . ." She drew him a few steps to the curb and pointed at a wet spot on the black asphalt. "My God, it's breathtaking: the mixture of colors. And they turn, and gather together, and mushroom so! And when you talk to me, the words are so much less important than other things, the nonverbal things. Like the movement of your upper lip, or the curve of your eyelash. I know it must seem trivial to you, all this. In fact, part of me knows that it's trivial too.

It's just that, just now, it's what's happening." And she laughed, appreciating the cliché.

"Did you learn anything about what you wanted to— about the past, or the kids?"

She shook her head. "I was too way down before you came to think of anything."

"And now?"

She shook her head again. "I'm too way up, I guess, too turned on. I can't really think. My mind's just . . . scattered, all over. Racing out there and across there and over here. . . ."

He didn't press it.

After a while they strolled past the kiosk to the far end of the island. An occasional car whisked by. Clifford let his eyes roam. Across the way, by the Harvard houses, three dark green buses, busy, noisy machines during the day, rested peacefully by the curb like immobile caterpillars. On the storefront side, a policeman sauntered easily from one store to another, checking the doors. Thinking himself alone, he played a private game of twirling his nightstick. Massachusetts Avenue and Peabody Street, usually noisy with traffic, were quiet and deserted, extending outward from the square like pieces of dark curving ribbon. And to the left, just before the Commons, stood the First Parish Church, gray and bulky in the distance, its steeple poised skyward and silvery.

"Look!" Sarah exclaimed. "Is that dawn?"

"Almost. And time to go."

They retraced their steps to the Ford. Driving back, he saw the first streaks of light separating the darkness.

"I like morning with you," she murmured, laying her head on his arm.

He drove carefully, not wanting to lose the luxury of these moments. Once he peeked down at her, and was surprised to see her awake and staring at him. He kept her look with him as he followed the road.

"THEY TOLD ME to take two sleeping pills," she said, standing fully dressed by the kitchen sink. "Or I'd never sleep. I'll wait till the kids get up, and then I'll send them down to Ellen's for the morning . . . I never did post that letter for you."

She indicated a letter on the table which was sealed and stamped. "You can take it with you if you want, although I should really throw it out."

"Take the pills now and get to sleep. I'll stay and take care of the kids."

She stared a minute, dumbfounded, and then left the room. He looked over at the frail white envelope . . . *her hand on his sleeve at the kiosk* . . .

When she came back, she was wearing a pair of rumpled blue pajamas. She threw her head back and gulped some water with the pills. She reached her hand out for his and he gave it to her. She walked with him to her bedroom. She got into bed and lay on her back. He leaned over and touched her face. "Good night," she said, and kissed his cheek lightly. "Your beard's grown."

He nodded, and stood up. He walked to the window and lowered the shade. Then he left the room, the fragrance of her skin lingering in his senses . . . slow, precious seconds. . . .

In the kitchen he made himself coffee, then took his mug and the letter into the living room and settled into the armchair by the window. He tore away a corner of the envelope, and slipped out two sheets of thin onionskin paper.

Dear Clifford:

A preface:

I am writing this for you . . . and for me. Tomorrow night, I plan on being a "swinging girl" for a time; and I shall probably turn on for the first time. I don't look forward to it with great eagerness. In part it's simply my well-known eccentric curiosity that is motivating me; in part my irrepressible destructive influences; in part my naïve desire to see if I can get something "educational" from a "mind-drug." (Especially concerning the subject I am going to talk about now to you.) It may be that I will get nothing at all rational or analytic out of it, but rather, an intensification of some deep and lousy emotions that have been with me for a long while. (Emotions: That's a stupid way of putting it. I mean habits of feeling that develop from the cruddy me, that the other me didn't want but could do little about preventing, and that now makes up for the recent past of S.S.) I won't mind the pain if I can get some clarity. Too often I get one without the other.

Letter proper:

As you know, I never wanted to marry K. to begin with. Even if there was a child coming. I didn't *like* him. He was the kind of measly, ambitious grad student with a thoroughly mediocre head and heart that you knew in a few years would be successful and venal. You know, the cheap sort we produce nowadays (they're called in other circles our leaders). But this part, his character is irrelevant (by itself). The point is Joshua, my boy.

Neither of us really wanted him. While I was pregnant I can remember specific moments of hating that unborn thing inside myself. (How the word "fetus" used to send shivers up my spine!) I kept thinking how its growth was at my expense: an affront to my spirit; a negation of my will; a sarcastic control over my future. He was my husband's baby, I thought, not mine. All my frustrated anger against K. was redirected toward that unseen object (its invisibility made it seem much more like some inhuman Fate). Obviously, it was not merely my husband or son who were the objects of my venom: it was also, increasingly, myself. I can't tell you what the world looks like when you're unable to feel anything *good* for anything or anybody. What it's like to wake up mornings and see the sky and feel vile.

Joshua was born under those conditions. I never had a hope that things would be different at his birth. They weren't. I didn't want to keep him. But I did. In spite of myself. I was young, there was enormous pressure from in-laws and parents. Neither K. nor I could do anything about it. What I did do was to attend to Joshua only perfunctorily. I had worked myself into such a state that for the first few years I couldn't stand the touch of his body. Then after the period of intense hatred there was only emptiness. No feeling at all. Joshua was an object, a piece of furniture that needed cleaning regularly. He was not my son. He got very little love from me, or from K., who hung around for a year or so before splitting. Later, he came back and stayed some six months . . . Katie. But I felt different about her. I wanted her. And I loved her.

Joshua's seven now. Only recently in the past several months, has he been doing better. School is manageable now. Having a sister has been the best thing for him. And the shrink he sees now—his third—he likes. He's been seeing him regularly for six months, his longest continuous run.

I think we like each other more now. But it's difficult, especially physical contact. It was a long time before he could tolerate a good night kiss. He still suffers from frequent nightmares. He wakes up screaming in the middle of the night, not knowing where he is, and I can't get through to him. If I try to touch him I can feel his body go suddenly tense. He grows absolutely numb. At first even my *presence* would drive him batty. It's a little better now, but still frightening.

Dot, dot, dot.

(It's hard to say all this.) I've been quiet about it because it's always so dull to parade one's scars. But I would like you to know about it now. Especially since I'm going to be operated on tomorrow night, and you're going to be there; I wouldn't want you to be surprised too much about the organs exposed.

I tried to come out of it as best I could. I saw a couple of psychiatrists, as you know. The first fellow was just too slow in the head, and after the second visit I couldn't go back. (He thought *all* of my humor was symptomatic rather than funny; and since he only caught half the jokes anyway, I felt too many symptoms were passing him by.) The second shrink was okay, I guess. But forty a week was a heavy tax for meeting someone okay. Of course he really wasn't okay. He was an efficient questioning computer—a rather odd host, don't you think, on late Tuesday and Thursday afternoons? I guess I'm antiquarian, and prefer one of those quaint objects: a good friend. Someone involved with me, who gets angry and gets abused and has a hard time with me and gets his emotions ripped up a little once in a while. (The nice ones can listen too.) . . . But there were no good friends. Only friendless lovers and loveless affairs . . . You seem to fit the bill I had forgotten about; a friend I could love.

I suppose I hurt for a while. But it wasn't too bad. I pulled through, didn't I?

Yours—

He raised his head and looked out the window. The gray light of morning had flooded the sky, leaving a few stray smudges of night. Roads of telephone wires, grimy stucco tenements, rusting fields of TV antennas, two bare, bleak trees.

Yet, he thought, there was something about persevering amid grayness and despair and bad times that there was no substitute for. It toughened the spirit, and at times even turned hope into exaltation. For a brief moment he half-expected to see Chagall's violin player descend, splashing the sky and the rooftops with his rich symphony of color. Instead, he watched a few pigeons, gray but flecked with white, as they left their windowsills and flapped into the morning. They looked just fine.

He knew he was filled with her, whether he was near her or away from her. That was a fundamental fact. He also saw clearly that not seeing her again, or her going off with someone else, would be a loss that he didn't want to take anymore. There comes a point, he reasoned, when it was foolish to attempt to correlate strong feelings with rational decisions. That he felt enormously for her, he knew. But that this meant that he should live with or marry her didn't at all follow. There were too many other considerations (her mocking word, "variables"), such as personal ambitions, economic realities, individual habits and temperaments, past history (that she'd been married, for example, and scarred by the experience). And how could he tell what would happen with the children? He could be aware of the problems with them, yes. But that was a long way off from predicting consequences. It seemed so early (Joshua was seven, Kate four) yet it might already be too late. So, you didn't, couldn't, act *rationally* upon such a course. Which meant that you simply acted or didn't, out of other considerations. Mainly, from habit. You got in the habit of being near someone, and away from yourself, and there it was, gripping you; just as, earlier, isolation and solitariness on the one hand, and variety and proliferation (of females, people, possibilities) on the other, gripped you . . . And now, Sarah Sorotkin and Katie and Joshua Sorotkin were a habit.

There was also something else, which he found difficult

to explain. It had to do with terms like responsibility and involvement: he saw that he had been playing games with such words. They weren't a reality, but some protective, abstract formula, nothing more than annoying duties built upon certain clichés (don't hurt others, be a useful citizen, etc.). For any responsibility he had "permitted" himself, he had cautiously set the terms and limits . . . And now, he was coming to believe that the idea meant very little unless it included profound disruption: unless the smooth regularity of your life was jolted from under you; unless you were no longer "permitted" to define the rules of the game but, instead, were shoved violently into position. You had to act, so to speak, from a position of anxiety, from an off-balance rather than an upright stance, for the terms to be meaningful. If there were the comforts of self-aggrandizement, of intellectual vanity, of moral superiority, you were kidding yourself. When you acted from anxiety—and almost pain itself—then you were in that special dark corridor called involvement. If the corridor turned pleasant for a brief time, that was fine. But there was no guarantee or promise of that. All you saw was the strangeness and special discomfort of the corridor . . .

His thoughts struggled and tossed. It was not so much responsibility to a person—to, say, Sarah—that he was grappling with. It was a commitment to that strange corridor itself. The simplicity of the idea perplexed him. The important thing was to enter; yet, paradoxically, you couldn't do this simply by stating your intention, for then you would —being human and preferring illusion to reality—set up your games all over again. All you could do was to bump into it, to bump into the darkness. And the only way you could tell that you were there was empirically—when you looked up and saw yourself bruised and bewildered. Then, you had the choice: to run or to stand. And if you chose to stay, it was not based upon the promise of an imminent reward. You stayed because it was real; because the nature of the real was—generally, essentially strange. And, therefore, difficult to take. It provided this satisfaction: *you knew you were there.* You were reminded of your existence. And of the *life* of existence itself. With Sarah it was like that. . . .

He looked back more closely to the Sorotkin case. Did

bleakness sum it all up? That was foolish. Indulgently morbid. For he knew that Sorotkin was also joy. The kind of intense joy that is best appreciated . . . at a distance: when she was sleeping and you thought about her; or when you were with others, and the contrast was most manifest. Tortured and torturing, casually brutal and savagely serious, and a hundred other mixed ironic bags, still, she *lived* . . . while they, the others, did all the usual ordinary things without quite managing that. Too busy, perhaps about pushing forward. Sarah, in her odd lateral movement, held on to that crucial choice. It moved him, enflamed him, and drew him toward her.

He looked again outside at the creeping dawn. He had soliloquized enough. To live with the woman: there's the involved man's answer to conjecture and contradiction!

He laid Sarah's letter on a hard notebook and wrote at the bottom:

Dear Miss Sorotkin,

I have been checking over your records, and find that you have been spending an exorbitant sum of your monies on postage. This is intolerable. Acting as your financial counselor, as well as the recipient of a large number of your swelling, expensive correspondence, I feel it would best serve your interest if I exchanged my present address for one nearer your vicinity. Such an arrangement will allow you to persist with your present (eccentric) ways, but will save you considerable postage sums, as you will need merely to slip your letters to me, personally, in my mailbox, door jamb, or hand.

Therefore, would you be so good as to inquire if there is a room suitable and available.

Yours,

There was a stirring in the next room and he heard the children talking. Presently Joshua, in flannel pajamas, appeared at the doorway.

"Leavitt! How come you're here?"

"I stayed over."

The small boy walked closer, looking gravely concerned. "Where'd you sleep?"

"In the chair here."

He whispered, "Is Mom here?"

"Yes, but she's sleeping. She's very tired. So how would

it be if I gave you kids breakfast and then spent the morning with you?"

"Gee, Leavitt, that would be *really* great!" He rushed out of the room. Then he rushed back. "Could we go to the playground?"

"Well, I think so."

"Katie, Katie, hurry up! Look who's here!"

In a minute Katie wandered over.

"Guess what, Katie?" Joshua said, putting his arm around his sister's shoulders. "Mom's sleeping this morning, and Leavitt's going to give us breakfast and then take us to the playground—won't that be fun, Katie?"

Katie, now fully awake, placed her hands on her hips petulantly and reflected.

"Well, not *that* much fun."

Whereupon Leavitt raced over and whirled her high in the air, saying, "Oh, yes it will, Kate! Oh, yes it will!" and reveling in her pitched squeals of laughter and anger and gleeful delight. And perching her on his shoulders, he began galloping down the hallway whinnying like an excited pony, trailed by Joshua, who quickly caught the spirit of his gesture and alertly smacked him on the backside and cried out, "Giddyup, giddyup, giddyup!"

from Being Jewish

Edward Field

My MOTHER's family was made up of loving women:
They were, on the whole, bearers,
though Esther, the rich sister, had only one—
she was the exception.

Sarah, the oldest, had five with her first husband,
(that was still in Poland),
was widowed and came here
where she married a man with four of his own,
and together they had another five,
all of whom she raised, feeding them in relays,
except little Tillie who sat in the kitchen
and ate with everyone, meaning all the time,
resulting in a fat figure
that made her despair of ever finding a husband,
but miraculously she did,
for God has decreed there is someone for everyone,
if you're desperate enough
and will take what you can get.

Aunt Rachel had twelve, raising them in a stable.
She was married to a junk dealer
who kept horses to haul the wagons.
He was famous for his stinginess
so they lived in a shack surrounded by baled hay.
That was in America, in a slum called Bronzeville
that the Black people have now inherited from the Jews,
God help them.
Then, as now, plenty of kids turned out bad:
going to work for that Jewish firm, Murder, Inc.,
or becoming junkies like one of my cousins did.

My mother only had six
but that's not counting. . . . I'll say no more
than she was always pregnant

with a fatalistic "what can you do?"
("Plenty," her friend Blanche replied—she was liberated.
"You don't have to breed like a rabbit.")
Like her mother who had a baby a year in Poland
until Grandpa left for America
giving her a rest.
There were women who kept bearing
even then, mysteriously, as from habit.

Women were always tired in those days and no wonder,
with the broken-down bodies they had
and their guts collapsed,
for with every child they got a dragging down.
My mother finally had hers tied back up in the hospital
and at the same time they tied those overfertile tubes
which freed her from "God's terrible curse on women."

And not just the bearing, but the work:
the pots couldn't be large enough for those hungry broods—
Sarah used hospital pots for hers—
and then the problem of filling the pots,
getting up at dawn to go to the fishing boats
for huge fish carcasses cheap,
buying bushels of half-spoiled vegetables for pennies,
begging the butcher for bones,
and then lugging it all home on their bad legs.
They didn't think of their looks for a minute,
and better they didn't, shapeless as that life made them.
(And yet they remained attractive to their men,
by the evidence of their repeated pregnancies.)

They just went around wrecks, always depressed,
unable to cope, or hiding in bed
while the children screamed.
"Escape, escape, there must be escape"
was my mother's theme song, until at last
her children escaped from her and her misery,
having wrecked her life, that endless sacrifice,
for what?

I see the proletarian women like them on the streets,
cows with udders to the waist
lugging black oilcloth shopping bags,

the mamales, the mamacitas, the mammies,
the breeders of the world with loving eyes.
They sit around the kitchen table with full hearts
telling each other their troubles,
never enough money, the beasts their men were to them,
how Leo hit Esther in the face on the street,
the sorrow life was for a woman, a mother,
the children turning out no good,

and fed each other pieces of leftover meat from the icebox
to make up a little for life's pain
and sighing, drank tea
and ate good bread and butter.

CONTRIBUTORS

Russell Banks graduated in 1967 from the University of North Carolina. He is one of the founding editors of *Lillabulero*.

Eric Bentley's most recent book is *The Theatre of Commitment* (Atheneum). Among his other activities, Mr. Bentley is currently co-producer of the DMZ Cabaret in New York.

Allan Block has operated a sandal shop in New York for the past twenty years. His poems have appeared in *Poetry, Prairie Schooner, The Activist,* and other journals.

Marilyn Coffey teaches at Pratt Institute. Along with two other poets, Miss Coffey has created a program of poetry and music, *Sound Forms and Cacaphony,* which has been given in various colleges and coffee houses.

Robert Coover's *The Origins of the Brunists* won the William Faulkner Award for the best first novel of 1966. His second novel, *The Universal Baseball Association: J. Henry Waugh, Prop.,* was published in June by Random House.

Sister Madeline De Frees is a visiting professor at the University of Montana. Her poems have been collected in *From the Darkroom* (Bobbs-Merrill).

Alan Distler has studied at New York University and Yale Drama School. "White and Fast Water" is the first serious fiction he has published.

Leslie Epstein is a lecturer at Queens College in New York. He has previously published fiction in the *Yale Review*.

Irving Feldman is on the faculty of SUNY at Buffalo. His third volume of poetry, *Singing and Dancing,* will be published early next year by Viking.

Edward Field's poems have appeared in the *Paris Review,* the *New Yorker,* the *New York Review of Books,* and various other journals. His most recent book is *Songs and Stories of the Netsilik Eskimoes.*

Richard Gilman is literary editor of the *New Republic.* The present essay has been adapted from a book he is writing on the relation of art to life.

Sidney Goldfarb is an instructor in Humanities at M.I.T. Farrar, Straus and Giroux will publish his first volume of poems in April.

Amy Goldin's essays and reviews appear in *Arts, Art Forum,* and *Art News,* which she also edits.

David Henderson was poet-in-residence with the Free Southern Theatre. He is the editor of *Umbra* and one of the founders of the *East Village Other.*

Richard Howard's "John Ruskin" is one of a series of poems on various British figures of the nineteenth century that will be published by Atheneum. Mr. Howard is also completing a study of American poetry since World War II.

Alan Lelchuk teaches at Brandeis University. Two of his stories have been published in *Transatlantic Review.* He is presently writing a book on George Gissing as well as a novel.

Conor Cruise O'Brien's *Murderous Angels,* a play that deals with the murder of Patrice Lumumba, will be produced by the National Theatre in London late this year.

Mordecai Richler's story "Dinner with Ormsby Fletcher" appeared in *NAR #1. Cocksure,* a novel, was published this past spring by Simon and Schuster.

William Stafford has published three volumes of poetry: *West of Your City* (1960), *Traveling Through the Dark* (1962), and *The Rescued Year* (1966).

Ronald Steel writes regularly for the *New York Review of Books.* His most recent book is *Pax Americana* (Viking).

George Stiles' plays have ben produced by Joan Littlewood's Theatre Workshop in London and by the Theater for Ideas in New York.

Robert Watson teaches at the University of North Carolina at Greensboro. Two volumes of his poetry, *A Paper Horse* and *Advantages of Dark,* have been published by Atheneum.

William Weintraub is a writer and producer of documentary films for the National Film Board of Canada.

James Welch is a Blackfoot Indian who is presently studying for a master's degree at the University of Montana.

Charles David Wright teaches English at the University of North Carolina at Chapel Hill. He is presently collaborating on an anthology of Serbo-Croatian writing as well as compleitng a book on Matthew Arnold.